TAKING SIDES: CLASHING VIEWS ON CONTROVERSIAL BIO-ETHICAL ISSUES

Where there is much desire to learn, there of necessity will be much arguing . . .

John Milton

"The man who pleads his case first seems to be in the right, then his opponent comes and puts him to the test."

Proverbs

STAFF

Jeremy Brenner	Managing Editor
Brenda Filley	Production Manager
Charles Vitelli	Designer
Libra Cusack	Typesetting Coordinator
Jean Bailey	Graphics Coordinator
LuAnn Bishop	Copy Editor

TAKING SIDES: CLASHING VIEWS ON CONTROVERSIAL BIO-ETHICAL ISSUES

Edited, Selected, and with Introductions by
CAROL LEVINE
The Hastings Center

The Dushkin Publishing Group, Inc.
Guilford, Connecticut

Library of Congress Catalog Card Number: 84-072706

Manufactured in the United States of America
First Edition, First Printing

CONTENTS

FOREWORD

These days even our successes cause anxiety. Nowhere is this more true than in the realm of medicine. The last forty years have seen the conversion of medicine from a care-and-comfort profession into a life-saving enterprise. However, the pride in accomplishment seems almost completely submerged in the tragic dilemmas that accompany such awesome power.

If a life can be saved now by an artificial organ, whose life should it be, and on what basis should we decide? If a dying individual can be sustained on a respirator to a point where the distinction between life and death is blurred, how shall we examine when the border of no return has been passed, and by whose criteria and under whose authority will treatment be terminated? When antisepsis permits us to do unheard-of surgery of sweeping and dramatic power to save the life of a cancer patient, how shall we decide if the radical deformity which extends life is worth the extra days of living for the mutilated patient? How are we to equate the *number* of days a patient survives with the *quality* of those days?

These are only some of the tragic dilemmas considered in this book. We are all now—by demand, not choice—philosophers in pursuit of an evasive truth. Medicine has forced a renewed interest in ethics, and all of us—physicians, philosophers, and citizens who inevitably will be caught up in these decisions—are groping for answers.

The answers do not come easily, and each resolution involves a compromise in which something treasured—privacy, autonomy, days of life—may have to be abandoned to preserve something else equally treasured—a sense of justice, human dignity, the common good. I tend to distrust anyone who is comfortable with any decision in these areas. They are hard choices, and most of us come to our conclusions reluctantly, with a sense of anguish and humiliation. And so it should be when one deals with life and death.

The cases offered here are presented in an adversarial way to sharpen your awareness of the dilemmas involved. Every attempt has been made to play with a fair deck, by having the strongest and best case made on each side of the issue. It is hoped that by the time you have finished this book you will be fully aware of the extraordinary extent of the problems that have been created by the Biological Revolution—that you will be informed of the major decisions that you, not some experts, will be called upon to make in the not too distant future, either directly in your personal life or through your legislative representatives. Finally, it is hoped that, as a testament to any good educative effort, on completion of this book you will be left with fewer, rather than more, answers.

Willard Gaylin, M.D.
President, The Hastings Center

PREFACE

This is a book about choices—hard and tragic choices, as Willard Gaylin points out in the Foreword. The choices are hard not only because they often involve life and death but also because there are convincing arguments on both sides of the issues. An ethical dilemma, by definition, is one that poses a conflict not between good and evil but between one good principle and another which is equally as good. The choices are hard because the decisions that are made—by individuals, groups, and public policy makers—will influence the kind of society we have today and the one we will have in the future.

Although the views expressed in the selections in this volume are strong—even passionate—ones, they are also subtle ones, concerned with the nuances of the particular debate. *How* one argues matters in bio-ethics; you will see and have to weigh the significance of varying rhetorical styles and appeals throughout this volume.

Although there are no easy answers to any of the issues in the book, the questions will be answered in some fashion—partly by individual choices and partly by decisions that are made by professionals and government. We must make them the best answers possible, and that can only be done by informed and thoughtful consideration. This book, then, can serve as a beginning for what ideally will become an ongoing process of examination and reflection.

ACKNOWLEDGMENTS

I would like to thank Jeremy Brenner of the Dushkin Publishing Group for his editorial guidance; not only did he provide excellent advice on particular matters but he also knew when to reassure and when to urge onward. All the staff and contributors to The Hastings Center's work have contributed indirectly to this volume, but several people were helpful in specific ways. Eric Feldman provided valuable research assistance, and Marna Howarth and Arthur Caplan read and commented on portions of the manuscript. I would particularly like to thank Daniel Callahan, director of the Center, and Willard Gaylin, its president, not only because they encouraged me to undertake this project but also because they have made The Hastings Center a place where intellectual rigor and a tolerance for clashing points of view—the foundations of this book—are not just an academic ideal but a way of life. Finally, for reasons they alone will understand, I thank my parents, Betty and King Solomon; my husband, Howard Levine; and my children, Jenny, Judy, and Charlie Levine.

Carol Levine
Hastings-on-Hudson, NY
September 1983

INTRODUCTION: MEDICINE AND MORAL ARGUMENTS IN AMERICAN LIFE

Carol Levine

In the fall of 1975, a twenty-one-year-old woman lay in a New Jersey hospital—as she had for months—in a coma, the victim of a toxic combination of barbituates and alcohol. Doctors agreed that her brain was irreversibly damaged and that she would never recover. Her parents, after anguished consultation with their priest, asked the doctors and hospital to disconnect the respirator that was artificially maintaining their daughter's life. When the doctors and hospital refused, the parents petitioned the court to be made her legal guardian so that they could authorize the withdrawal of treatment. After hearing all the arguments, the court sided with the parents, and the respirator was removed. Contrary to everyone's expectations, however, the young woman did not die but began to breathe on her own (perhaps because, in anticipation of the court order, the nursing staff had gradually weaned her from total dependence on the respirator). She is still alive—comatose, and lying in a fetal position—in a New Jersey nursing home. She is visited by her parents regularly but is no closer to consciousness than before.

The young woman's name is Karen Ann Quinlan, and her case brought national attention to the thorny ethical questions raised by modern medical technology: When, if ever, should life-sustaining technology be withdrawn? Is the sanctity of life an absolute value? What kinds of treatment are really beneficial to a patient in a "chronic vegetative state" like Karen's? And (perhaps the most troubling question), who shall decide?

These and similar questions are at the heart of the growing field of "biomedical ethics" or (as it is usually called) "bio-ethics." Other questions have been raised by the development of techniques to screen fetuses for birth defects and, in some cases, to treat them in the womb; the ability to control behavior through psychotropic, or mind-altering, drugs or through psychosurgery; the development of the artificial kidney machine and organ transplants; the possibility of fertilizing human eggs outside a woman's body and implanting them in her (or another woman's) uterus; and the capacity to create new life forms through direct manipulation of DNA, the basic genetic material. All these technological advances have brought enormous promise for improving the health and quality of life for many people, but they have also created problems in deciding when to use these techniques, for whom, and at what cost (both in terms of money and effort and in terms of the other human values that may be compromised in the process).

Ethical dilemmas in medicine are, of course, nothing new. They have been recognized and discussed in Western medicine since a small group of physicians—led by Hippocrates—on the Isle of Cos in Greece around the fourth century B.C., subscribed to a code of practice that newly graduated physicians still swear to uphold today. But unlike earlier times, when physicians and scientists had only limited abilities to change the course of disease, today they can intervene in profound ways in the most fundamental processes of life and death. Moreover, ethical dilemmas in medicine are no longer considered the sole province of professionals. Professional codes of ethics, to be sure, offer some guidance, but they are usually unclear and ambiguous about what to do in specific situations. More important, these codes assume that whatever decision is to be made is up to the professional, not the patient. Today, to an ever-greater degree, lay people—patients, families, lawyers, clergy, and others—want to and have become involved in ethical decision making not only in individual cases, such as the Quinlan case, but also in large societal decisions, such as how to allocate scarce medical resources, including high technology machinery, newborn intensive care units, and the expertise of physicians. While questions of the physician-patient relationship and individual cases are still prominent in bio-ethics (see, for example, Issues 5 on truthtelling and Issue 7 on withholding treatment from newborns with birth defects), today the field covers a broad range of other decisions as well: such as the abolition of the insanity defense (Issue 10), harvesting of organs (Issue 16), and the future of genetic engineering (Issue 17).

This involvement is part of broader social trends: a general disenchantment with the authority of all professionals and, hence, a greater readiness to challenge the traditional belief that "doctor knows best"; the growth of various civil rights movements among women, the aged, and minorities—of which the patients' rights movement is a spinoff; the enormous size and complexity of the health care delivery system, in which patients and families often feel alienated from the professional; the increasing cost of medical care, much of it at public expense; the growth of the "medical model" in which conditions that used to be considered outside the scope of physicians' control, such as alcoholism and behavioral problems, have come to be considered diseases.

Bio-ethics began in the 1950s as an intellectual movement among a small group of physicians and theologians who started to examine the questions raised by the new medical technologies that were starting to emerge as the result of the heavy expenditure of public funds in medical research after World War II. They were soon joined by a number of philosophers who had become disillusioned with what they saw as the arid abstractions of much analytic philosophy at the time, and by lawyers who sought to find principles in the law that would guide ethical decision making or, if such principles were not there, to develop them by case law and legislation or regulation. Although these four disciplines—medicine, theology, philosophy, and law—still dominate the field, today bio-ethics is an interdisciplinary effort, with political scientists, economists, sociologists, anthropologists, nurses, allied health professionals, policy-makers, psychologists, and others contributing their special perspectives to the ongoing debates.

From its modest beginnings bio-ethics has become a major enterprise. Academic departments have been established in many universities and colleges; it is taught as part of science, philosophy, and other courses and has become part of the curriculum of medical schools, nursing schools, and other professional training; scholars devote their careers to it. Regional and national centers have been established—the best known of which are The Hastings Center in Hastings-on-Hudson, New York, and the Kennedy Institute of Ethics, Center for Bio-ethics, which is part of Georgetown University in Washington, D.C. The bio-ethics literature has burgeoned, with encyclopedias, books, periodicals, articles, and newsletters all devoted to the subject matter. Philosophers and other humanists have been invited to join the staffs of medical centers and to participate in discussions about decision making, both at the level of individual cases and institutional policies. Two federal commissions—the National Commission for the Protection of Human Subjects of Biomedical and Behavioral Research (1974-1978) and the President's Commission for the Study of Ethical Problems of Medicine and Biomedical and Behavioral Research (1978-1983)—have contributed major reports and recommendations to federal policy-makers. And the media have discovered in bio-ethics an unending source of stories. Scarcely a day goes by without some bio-ethical dilemma making news: the plight of a family seeking a liver transplant for their baby; a controversial government regulation establishing a "hotline" that people can call when they suspect treatment is being unjustifiably withheld from a baby with a birth defect; a man with leukemia trying to compel a medical center to contact a woman and convince her to donate the bone marrow he hopes will save his life.

The issues discussed in this volume attest to the wide range of bio-ethical dilemmas, their complexity, and the passion they arouse. But if bio-ethics today is at the frontiers of scientific knowledge, it is also a field with ancient roots. It goes back to the most basic questions of human life: What is right? What is wrong? How should people act toward others? And why?

While the "bio" part of "bio-ethics" gives the field its urgency and immediacy, we should not forget that the root word is "ethics."

APPLYING ETHICS TO MEDICAL DILEMMAS

To see where bio-ethics fits into the larger framework of academic inquiry, some definitions are in order. First, *morality* is the general term for an individual's or a society's standards of conduct, both actual and ideal, and of the character traits that determine whether people are considered "good" or "bad." The scientific study of morality is called *descriptive ethics;* a scientist—generally an anthropologist, sociologist, historian, or other social scientist—can describe in empirical terms what the moral beliefs, judgments, or actions of individuals or societies are and what reasons are given for the way they act or believe. The philosophical study of morality, on the other hand, approaches the subject of morality in one of two different ways: either as an analysis of the concepts, terms, and method of reasoning (*metaethics*) or as an analysis of what those standards or moral judgments ought to be (*normative ethics*). Metaethics deals with meanings of moral terms and logic; normative ethics, with which the issues in this volume are concerned, reflects on the kinds of actions and principles that will promote moral behavior.

Because normative ethics accepts the idea that some kinds of acts and character traits are more moral than others (and that some are immoral), it rejects the rather popular idea that ethics is relative. Because different societies have different moral codes and values, ethical relativists, such as the anthropologist Ruth Benedict, have argued that there can be no universal moral judgments: What is right or wrong depends on who does it and where, and whether society approves. Although it is certainly true that moral values are embedded in a social, cultural, and political context, it is also true that certain moral judgments are universal. We think it is wrong, for example, to sell people into slavery—whether or not a certain society approved or even whether or not the person wanted to be a slave. People may not agree about what these universal moral values are or ought to be (those who are opposed to abortion, for instance, see the protection of fetal life as one of them while pro-choice advocates don't) but it is hard to deny that some such values exist.

The other relativistic view rejected by normative ethics is the notion that whatever feels good is good. In this view, ethics is a matter of personal preference, weightier than one's choice of which automobile to buy, but not much different in kind. Different people, having different feelings, can arrive at equally valid moral judgments, according to the relativistic view. Just as we should not disregard cultural factors, we should not overlook the role of emotion and personal experience in arriving at moral judgments. But to give emotion ultimate authority would be to consign reason and rationality—the bases of moral argument—to the ethical trash heap. At the very least, it would be impossible to develop a just policy concerning the care of vulnerable persons, like the mentally retarded or newborns, who depended solely on the vagaries of individual caretakers.

Thus, if normative ethics is one branch of philosophy, bio-ethics is one branch of normative ethics; it is normative ethics applied to the practice of medicine and science. There are other branches—business ethics, legal ethics, journalism ethics, or military ethics. One common term for the entire grouping is *applied and professional ethics,* because these ethics deal with the ethical standards of the members of a particular profession and how they are applied in the professionals' dealings with each other and the rest of society. Bio-ethics is based on the belief that some solutions to the dilemmas that arise in medicine and science are more moral than others and that these solutions can be determined by moral reasoning and reflection.

ETHICAL THEORIES

But if the practitioners of bio-ethics do not rely solely on cultural norms and emotions, what are their sources of determining what is right or wrong? The most comprehensive source is a theory of ethics—a broad set of moral principles (or perhaps just one overriding principle) that is used in measuring human conduct. Divine law is one such source, of course, but even in the Western religious traditions of bio-ethics (both the Jewish and Catholic religions have rich and comprehensive commentaries on ethical issues, and the Protestant religion a less cohesive but still important tradition) the law of God is interpreted in terms of human moral principles. A theory of ethics must be acceptable to many groups, not just the followers of one religious tradition. Most writers outside the religious traditions (and some within them) have looked to one of three major traditions in ethics: teleological theories, deontological theories, and natural law theories.

Teleological theories are based on the idea that the end or purpose (from the Greek *telos* or end) of the action determines its rightness or wrongness. The most prominent teleological theory is *utilitarianism.* In its simplest formulation, an act is moral if it brings more good consequences than bad ones. Utilitarian theories are derived from the works of two English philosophers: Jeremy Bentham (1748-1832) and John Stuart Mill (1806-1873). Rejecting the absolutist religious morality of his time, Bentham proposed that "utility"—the greatest good for the greatest number—should guide the actions of human beings. Invoking the hedonistic philosophy of Epicurean Greeks, Bentham said that pleasure (*hedon* in Greek) is good and pain is bad. Therefore, actions are right if they promote more pleasure than pain and wrong if they promote more pain than pleasure. Mill found the highest utility in "happiness," rather than pleasure. (Mill's philosophy is echoed, you will recall, in the Declaration of Independence's espousal of "life, liberty, and the pursuit of happiness".) Other utilitarians have looked to a range of utilities, or goods (including friendship, love, devotion, and the like) that they believe ought to be weighed in the balance—the utilitarian calculus.

Utilitarianism has a pragmatic appeal. It is flexible, and it seems impartial. However, its critics point out that utilitarianism can be used to justify suppression of individual rights for the good of society ("the ends justify the means") and that it is difficult to quantify and compare "utilities," however they are defined.

Utilitarianism, in its many forms, has had a powerful influence on bio-ethical discussion, partly because it is the closest to the case-by-case risk/benefit ratio that physicians use in clinical decision making. Joseph Fletcher, a Protestant theologian who was one of the pioneers in bio-ethics in the 1950s, developed a utilitarian theory that he called "situation ethics." He argued that a true Christian morality does not blindly follow moral rules but acts from love and sensitivity to the particular situation and the needs of those involved. He has enthusiastically supported most modern technologies on the grounds that they lead to good ends.

Another forceful supporter of utilitarianism is Peter Singer, an Australian philosopher who is represented in this volume in Issue 14. Singer's utilitarian calculus includes not only an assessment of the pain and pleasure a particular act causes humans but also how it affects animals. Other writers in this volume who use a utilitarian theory to arrive at their moral judgments are Joseph Collins (Issue 5), who defends the withholding of the truth from dying patients on the grounds that it leads to better consequences than truth-telling, and Clifford Grobstein (Issue 2), who supports in vitro fertilization.

The second major type of ethical theory is *deontological* (from the Greek *deon* or duty). The rightness or wrongness of an act, these theories hold, should be judged on whether it conforms to a moral principle or rule, not on whether it leads to good or bad consequences. The primary exponent of a deontological theory was Immanuel Kant (1724-1804), a German philosopher. Kant declared that there is an ultimate norm, or supreme duty, which he called the "Moral Law." He held that an act is moral only if it springs from what he called a "good will," the only thing that is good without qualification.

We must do good things, said Kant, because we have a duty to do them, not because they result in good consequences or because they give us pleasure (although that can happen as well). Kant constructed a formal "Categorical Imperative," the ultimate test of morality: "I ought never to act except in such a way that I can also will that my maxim should become a universal law." Recognizing that this formulation was far from clear, Kant said the same thing in three other ways. He explained that a moral rule must be one that can serve as a guide for everyone's conduct; it must be one that permits people to treat each other as ends in themselves, not solely as means to another's ends; and it must be one that each person can impose on himself by his own will, not one that is solely imposed by the state, one's parents, or God. Kant's Categorical Imperative, in the simplest terms, says that all persons have equal moral worth and no rule can be moral unless all people can apply it autonomously to all other human beings. Although on its own, Kant's Categorical Imperative is merely a formal statement with no moral content at all, he gave some examples of what he meant: "Do not commit suicide," and "Help others in distress."

Kantian ethics is criticized by many who note that Kant gives little guidance on what to do when ethical principles conflict, as they often do. Moreover, they say, his emphasis on autonomous decision making and individual will neglects the social and communal context in which people live and make decisions. It leads to isolation and unreality. These criticisms notwithstanding, Kantian ethics has stimulated much current thinking in bio-ethics. The idea that certain actions are in and of themselves wrong underlies, for example, Sissela Bok's appeal to truth-telling (Issue 5) and Thomas Murray's attack on deception in research (Issue 12).

Two modern deontological theorists are the philosophers John Rawls and Robert M. Veatch. In his book *A Theory of Justice* (1971), Rawls places the highest value on equitable distribution of society's resources. He believes that society has a fundamental obligation to correct the inequalities of historical circumstance and natural endowment of its least well-off members. According to this theory, some action is good only if it benefits the least well-off. (It can also benefit others but that is secondary.) His social justice theory has been influential in bio-ethical writings concerning the allocation of scarce resources.

Robert M. Veatch has applied Rawlsian principles to medical ethics. In his book *A Theory of Medical Ethics* (1981), he offers a model of a social contract among professionals, patients, and society that emphasizes mutual respect and responsibilities. This contract model will, he hopes, avoid the narrowness of professional codes of ethics and the generalities and ambiguities of more broadly-based ethical theories.

The third strain of ethical theory that is prominent in bio-ethics is *natural law theory,* first developed by St. Thomas Aquinas (1223-1274). According to this theory, actions are morally right if they accord with our nature as human beings. The attribute that is distinctively human is the ability to reason and to exercise intelligence. Thus, argues this theory, we can know the good, which is objective and can be learned through reason. References to natural law theory are prominent in the works of Catholic theologians and writers; they see natural law as ultimately derived from God, but knowable through the efforts of human beings. The influence of natural law theory can be seen in this volume in John T. Noonan, Jr.'s, attack on abortion (Issue 1) and Hans O. Tiefel's condemnation of in vitro fertilization (Issue 2).

The *theory of virtue,* another ethical theory with deep roots in the Aristotelian tradition, has recently been revived in bio-ethics. This theory stresses not the morality of any particular actions or rules but the disposition of individuals to act morally, to be virtuous. In its modern version its primary exponent is Alasdair MacIntyre, whose book *After Virtue* (1980) urges a return to the Aristotelian model. Gregory Pence has applied the theory of virtues directly to medicine in *Ethical Options in Medicine* (1980); he lists temperance in personal life, compassion for the suffering patient, professional competence, justice, honesty, courage, and practical judgment as the virtues most desirable in physicians. Although this theory has not yet been as fully developed in bio-ethics as the utilitarian or deontological theories, it is likely to have particular appeal for physicians—many of whom have resisted formal ethics education on the grounds that moral character is the critical factor and that one can best learn to be a moral physician by emulating the actions of one's mentors.

Although various authors, in this volume and elsewhere, appeal in rather direct ways to either utilitarian or deontological theories, often the various types are combined. One may argue both that a particular action is immoral in and of itself and that it will have bad consequences (some commentators say even Kant used this argument). In fact, probably no single ethical theory is adequate to deal with all the ramifications of the issues. In that case we can turn to a middle level of ethical discussion. Between the abstractions of ethical theories (Kant's Categorical Imperative) and the specifics of moral judgments (always obtain informed consent from a patient) is a range of concepts—ethical principles—that can be applied to particular cases.

ETHICAL PRINCIPLES

In its four years of deliberation, the National Commission for the Protection of Human Subjects of Biomedical and Behavioral Research grappled with some of the most difficult issues facing researchers and society: When, if ever, is it ethical to do research on the fetus, on prisoners (see Issue 13), or on people in mental institutions. This commission—which was composed of people from various religious backgrounds, professions, and social strata—was finally able to agree on specific recommendations on these questions, but only after they had finished their work did the commissioners try to determine what ethical principles they had used in reaching a consensus. (They did not even try to determine what ethical theory they had used or, indeed, if they had used one.) In their Belmont Report (1978), named after the conference center where they met to discuss this question, the commissioners outlined what they considered to be the three most important ethical principles (respect for persons, beneficence, and justice) that should govern the conduct of research with human beings. These three principles, they believed, are generally accepted in our cultural tradition and can serve as basic justifications for the many particular ethical prescriptions and evaluations of human action. Because of the principles' general acceptance and widespread applicability, they are at the basis of most bio-ethical discussion. Although philosophers argue about whether other principles—confidentiality or truth-telling, for example—ought to be accorded equal weight with these three or should be included under another umbrella, they agree that these principles are fundamental.

Respect for Persons

Respect for persons incorporates at least two basic ethical convictions, according to the Belmont Report. Individuals should be treated as autonomous agents, and persons with diminished autonomy are entitled to protection. The derivation from Kant is clear. Because human beings have the capacity for rational action and moral choice, they have a value independent of anything that they can do or provide to others. Therefore, they should be treated in a way that respects their independent choices and judgments. Respecting autonomy means giving weight to autonomous persons' considered opinions and choices, and refraining from interfering with their choices unless those choices are clearly detrimental to others. However, since the capacity for autonomy varies by age, mental disability, or other circumstances, those people whose autonomy is diminished must be protected—but only in ways that serves their interests and does not interfere with the level of autonomy that they do possess.

Two important moral rules are derived from the ethical principle of respect for persons: informed consent and truth-telling. Persons can exercise autonomy only when they have been fully informed about the range of options open to them, and the process of informed consent is generally considered to include the elements of information, comprehension, and voluntariness. Thus, a person can give informed consent to some medical procedure only if he or she has full information about the risks and benefits, understands them, and agrees voluntarily—that is, without being coerced or pressured into agreement. Although the principle of informed consent has become an accepted moral rule (and a legal one as well), it is difficult—some say impossible—to achieve in a real-world setting. It can easily be turned into a legalistic parody or avoided altogether. But as a moral ideal it serves to balance the unequal power of the physician and patient.

Another important moral ideal derived from the principle of respect for persons is truth-telling. It held a high place in Kant's theory. In his essay "The Supposed Right to Tell Lies from Benevolent Motives," he wrote: "If, then, we define a lie merely as an intentionally false declaration towards another man, we need not add that it must injure another . . . ; for it always injures another; if not another individual, yet mankind generally. . . . To be truthful in all declarations is therefore a sacred and unconditional command of reasons, and not to be limited by any other expediency." (See Issue 5 for a discussion of truth-telling.)

Other important moral rules that are derived from the principle of respect for persons are confidentiality and privacy. (See Issue 9 for a discussion of whether it is justifiable to override the confidentiality that underlies the therapeutic relationship in order to warn a third party about potential violence.)

Beneficence

Most physicians would probably consider beneficence (from the Greek *bene* or good) the most basic ethical principle. In the Hippocratic Oath it is used this way: "I will apply dietetic measures for the benefit of the sick according to my ability and judgment; I will keep them from harm and injustice." And further on, "Whatever houses I may visit, I will comfort and benefit the sick, remaining free of all intentional injustice." The phrase, *Primum non nocere* (First, do no harm), is another well-known version of this idea, but it appears to be a much-later, Latinized version—not from the Hippocratic period.

The philosopher William Frankena has outlined four elements included in the principle of beneficence: (1) one ought not to inflict evil or harm; (2) one ought to prevent evil or harm; (3) one ought to remove evil or harm; and (4) one ought to do or promote good. Frankena arranged these elements in heirarchical order, so that the first takes precedence over the second, and so on. In this scheme, it is more important to avoid doing evil or harm than to do good. But in the Belmont Report, beneficence is understood as an obligation—first to do no harm, and second, to maximize possible benefits and minimize possible harms.

The principle of beneficence is at the basis of the distinction between killing and letting die (see Issue 6); Herbert Hendin's attack on "rational suicide" (see Issue 8); and Robert Neville's defense of involuntary sterilization of the retarded (see Issue 4).

Justice

The third ethical principle that is generally accepted is justice, which means "what is fair" or "what is deserved." An injustice occurs when some benefit to which a person is entitled is denied without good reason or when some burden is imposed unduly, according to the Belmont Report. Another way of interpreting the principle is to say that equals should be treated equally. However, some distinctions—such as age, experience, competence, physical condition, and the like—can justify unequal treatment. Those who appeal to the principle of justice are most concerned about which distinctions can be made legitimately and which ones cannot.

One important derivative of the principle of justice is the recent emphasis on "rights" in bio-ethics. Given the successes in the 1960s and 1970s of civil rights movements in the courts and political arena, it is easy to understand the appeal of "rights talk." An emphasis on individual rights is part of the American tradition, in a way that emphasis on the "common good" is not. The language of rights has been prominent in the abortion debate, for instance, where the "right to life" has been pitted against the "right to privacy" or the "right to control one's body." The "right to health care" is a potent rallying cry, though it is one that is difficult to enforce legally. Although claims to rights may be effective in marshalling political support and in emphasizing moral ideals, those rights may not be the most effective way to solve ethical dilemmas. Our society, as philosopher Ruth Macklin has pointed out, has not yet agreed on a theory of justice in health care that will determine who has what kinds of rights and—the other side of the coin—who has the obligation to fulfill them.

WHEN PRINCIPLES CONFLICT

These three fundamental ethical principles—beneficence, respect for persons, and justice—all carry weight in ethical decision making. But what happens when they conflict? That is what this book is all about.

On each side of the issues included in this volume are writers who appeal, explicitly or implicitly, to one or more of these principles. For example, in Issue 11, Thomas S. Szasz sees respect for persons as paramount: Let people decide autonomously, he argues, whether or not they would wish to be treated in a psychiatric hospital against their will should someone at some later date feel that their behavior warrants it. But Paul Chodoff and Roger Peele look to beneficence as the overriding principle, arguing that it is sometimes necessary to ignore autonomy in order to benefit people—and living a life without psychosis is clearly a benefit. In Issue 1, John T. Noonan, Jr., appeals to justice in establishing his case against abortion: Fetuses are human, he declares, and have been considered so for centuries; therefore it is unfair to treat them differently from the way we treat other humans and to allow their destruction. But Beverly Wildung Harrison sees autonomy as more important: Let the woman decide, she says, whether she is morally capable of assuming the responsibilities of motherhood.

Some of the issues are concerned with how to interpret a particular principle: Whether, for example, it is more beneficent to allow old and sick people to commit suicide or to prevent it (Issue 8), or whether a blood supply for medical purposes is more justly obtained on the basis of a voluntary or commercial system (Issue 15).

Will it ever be possible to resolve such fundamental divisions—those that are not merely matters of procedure or interpretation but of fundamental differences in principle? Lest the situation seem hopeless, consider that some consensus does seem to have been reached on questions that seemed equally tangled a few decades ago. The idea that government should play a role in regulating human subjects research was hotly debated, but it is now generally accepted (at least if the research is medical, not social or behavioral in nature and is federally funded). And the appropriateness of using criteria of brain death for determining the death of a person (and the possibility of subsequent removal of their organs for transplantation) has largely been accepted and written into state laws. The idea that a hopelessly ill patient has the legal and moral right to refuse treatment that will only prolong dying is also well established (though it is often hard to exercise because hospitals and physicians continue to resist it). Finally, nearly everyone now agrees that health care is distributed unjustly in this country—a radical idea only a few years ago. There is of course sharp disagreement about whose responsibility it is to rectify the situation—the government's or the private sector's.

But if there is consensus in some areas, in others there is none. As Daniel Callahan, director of The Hastings Center, has noted in an article in the *New England Journal of Medicine,* it may be harder to deal with the next round of problems precisely because they will confront fundamental issues of principle. Such issues are now being questioned in the arguments over abortion and the future of genetic engineering (see Issue 17). Callahan suggests that no single moral principle may be adequate to resolve the issues and that bio-ethics will have to move into the mainstream of political and social theory—beyond the model of the individual decision maker and into the "thicket of important vested and legitimate private and group interests."

The challenge for bio-ethics in the future is to avoid the extremes of idiosyncratic ethical decision making and what philosopher Stephen Toulmin has called the "tyranny of principle." Robert S. Morison, a physician who has observed the development of bio-ethics for the past two decades, wrote in an article in the *Hastings Center Report:* "Perhaps all general truths or principles are useful over only a limited range. Professional wise men like Emerson and Henry Adams have equated maturity with the ability to tolerate ambiguity; even the physicists have found that there comes a point at which they can no longer explain everything in terms either of particles or of waves." This book will introduce you to the particles and the waves of bio-ethics. Whether we will be able to move beyond them to a realm of moral consensus will depend on society's willingness to struggle with these issues and to make the hard choices that are required.

ISSUE 1

IS ABORTION IMMORAL?

YES: John T. Noonan, Jr., from "An Almost Absolute Value in History," from *The Morality of Abortion: Legal and Historical Perspectives* (Cambridge: Harvard University Press, 1970)

NO: Beverly Wildung Harrison, from *Our Right to Choose: Toward a New Ethics of Abortion* (Boston: Beacon Press, 1983)

ISSUE SUMMARY

YES: Professor of law John T. Noonan, Jr., believes that a fetus is human because it is conceived by human parents and that it is just as wrong to destroy its life as it would be to destroy the life of any human.
NO: Professor of Christian ethics Beverly Wildung Harrison argues that women ought to decide whether or not to bear children on the basis of their own moral preparedness to become responsible mothers.

Abortion is the most divisive bio-ethical issue of our time. The issue has been a persistent one in history, but in the past twenty years or so the debate has polarized. One view—known as "pro-life"—sees abortion as the wanton slaughter of innocent life. The other view—"pro-choice"—considers abortion as an option that must be available to women if they are to control their own reproductive lives. In the pro-life view, women who have access to "abortion on demand" put their own selfish whims ahead of an unborn child's right to life. In the pro-choice view, women have the right to choose to have an abortion—especially if there is some overriding reason, such as preventing the birth of a child with a severe genetic defect or one conceived as a result of rape or incest.

Behind these strongly-held convictions, as political scientist Mary Segers has pointed out, are widely differing views of what determines value (that is, whether value is inherent in a thing or ascribed to it by human beings), the relation between law and morality, and the use and limits of political solutions to social problems, as well as the value of scientific progress. Those who condemn abortion as immoral generally follow a classical tradition in which abortion is a public matter because it involves our conception of how we ought to live together in an ideal society. Those who accept the idea of abortion, on the other hand, generally share the liberal, individualistic ethos of contemporary society. To them, abortion is a private choice, and public policy ought to reflect how citizens actually behave, not some unattainable ideal.

This is what we know about abortion practices in America today: It has been legal since the 1973 Supreme Court decision of *Roe* v. *Wade* declared that a woman has a constitutional right to privacy, which includes an abortion. It is seven times safer than childbirth, although there are some known risks—primarily psychological— and some unknown ones—primarily the effect of repeated abortions on subsequent pregnancies. Abortion is common; in 1980, the last year for which complete figures are available, 1.55 million abortions were performed. That is, one out of four pregnancies (and half of all unintended pregnancies) ended in abortion. About ninety percent of all abortions are performed within the first twelve weeks of pregnancy by a method called suction aspiration. Three-quarters of the women who have abortions are unmarried, and nearly sixty-five percent are between the ages of fifteen and twenty-four. (In comparison, however, in 1965 there were between 200 thousand and 1.2 million illegal abortions, and twenty percent of all deaths from childbirth or pregnancy were caused by botched abortions.)

If abortion today is legal, safe, and common, it undeniably involves the killing of fetal life, and so the question remains: Is it ethical? At the heart of the issue are two complex questions. Does the fetus have a moral status that entitles it to life, liberty, and the pursuit of happiness as guaranteed by the Constitution? And even if it does, does a woman's rights to the same freedoms outweigh those of the fetus?

In the selections that follow, John T. Noonan, Jr., draws on the long history of religious and humanistic thought to support his claim that, from the moment of conception, a fetus is human and entitled to every protection. Beverly Wildung Harrison draws on another strand in ethical thought—concern for the quality of human life—and combines it with a feminist perspective to assert that some abortions, particularly early ones, are moral because they are the result of a woman's careful assessment of her capacities for motherhood.

YES

John T. Noonan, Jr.

AN ALMOST ABSOLUTE VALUE IN HISTORY

. . . The most fundamental question involved in the long history of thought on abortion is: How do you determine the humanity of a being? To phrase the question that way is to put in comprehensive humanistic terms what the theologians either dealt with as an explicitly theological question under the heading of "ensoulment" or dealt with implicitly in their treatment of abortion. The Christian position as it originated did not depend on a narrow theological or philosophical concept. It had no relation to theories of infant baptism.[1] It appealed to no special theory of instantaneous ensoulment. It took the world's view on ensoulment as that view changed from Aristotle to Zacchia. There was, indeed, theological influence affecting the theory of ensoulment finally adopted, and, of course, ensoulment itself was a theological concept, so that the position was always explained in theological terms. But the theological notion of ensoulment could easily be translated into humanistic language by substituting "human" for "rational soul"; the problem of knowing when a man is a man is common to theology and humanism.

If one steps outside the specific categories used by the theologians, the answer they gave can be analyzed as a refusal to discriminate among human beings on the basis of their varying potentialities. Once conceived, the being was recognized as man because he had man's potential. The criterion for humanity, thus, was simple and all-embracing: if you are conceived by human parents, you are human.

The strength of this position may be tested by a review of some of the other distinctions offered in the contemporary controversy over legalizing abortion. Perhaps the most popular distinction is in terms of viability. Before an age of so many months, the fetus is not viable, that is, it cannot be removed from the mother's womb and live apart from her. To that extent, the life of the fetus is absolutely dependent on the life of the mother. This dependence is made the basis of denying recognition to its humanity.

There are difficulties with this distinction. One is that the perfection of artificial incubation may make the fetus viable at any time: it may be removed and artificially sustained. Experiments with animals already show that such a procedure is possible.[2] This hypothetical extreme case relates to an actual difficulty: there is considerable elasticity to the idea of viability. Mere length of life is not an exact measure. The viability of the fetus depends on the extent of its anatomical and functional development.[3] The weight and length of the fetus are better guides to the state of its development than age, but weight and length vary.[4] Moreover, different racial groups have different ages at which their fetuses are viable. Some evidence, for example, suggests that Negro fetuses mature more quickly than white fetuses.[5] If viability is the norm, the standard would vary with race and with many individual circumstances.

The most important objection to this approach is that dependence is not ended by viability. The fetus is still absolutely dependent on someone's care in order to continue existence; indeed a child of one or three or even five years of age is absolutely dependent on another's care for existence; uncared for, the older fetus or the younger child will die as surely as the early fetus detached from the mother. The unsubstantial lessening in dependence at viability does not seem to signify any special acquisition of humanity.

A second distinction has been attempted in terms of experience. A being who has had experience, has lived and suffered, who possesses memories, is more human than one who has not. Humanity depends on formation by experience. The fetus is thus "unformed" in the most basic human sense.[6]

This distinction is not serviceable for the embryo which is already experiencing and reacting. The embryo is responsive to touch after eight weeks[7] and at least at that point is experiencing. At an earlier stage the zygote is certainly alive and responding to its environment.[8] The distinction may also be challenged by the rare case where aphasia has erased adult memory: has it erased humanity? More fundamentally, this distinction leaves even the older fetus or the younger child to be treated as an unformed inhuman thing. Finally, it is not clear why experience as such confers humanity. It could be argued that certain central experiences such as loving or learning are necessary to make a man human. But then human beings who have failed to love or to learn might be excluded from the class called man.

A third distinction is made by appeal to the sentiments of adults. If a fetus dies, the grief of the parents is not the grief they would have for a living child. The fetus is an unnamed "it" till birth, and is not perceived as personality until at least the fourth month of existence when movements in the womb manifest a vigorous presence demanding joyful recognition by the parents.

Yet feeling is notoriously an unsure guide to the humanity of others. Many groups of humans have had difficulty in feeling that persons of another tongue, color, religion, sex, are as human as they. Apart from reactions to alien groups, we mourn the loss of a ten-year-old boy more than the loss of his one-day-old brother or his 90-year-old grandfather. The difference felt and the grief expressed vary with the potentialities extinguished, or the experience wiped out; they do not seem to point to any substantial difference in the humanity of baby, boy, or grandfather.

Distinctions are also made in terms of sensation by the parents. The embryo is felt within the womb only after about the fourth month.[9] The embryo is seen only at birth. What can be neither seen nor felt is different from what is tangible. If the fetus cannot be seen or touched at all, it cannot be perceived as man.

Yet experience shows that sight is even more untrustworthy than feeling in determining humanity. By sight, color became an appropriate index for saying who was a man, and the evil of racial discrimination was given foundation. Nor can touch provide the test; a being confined by sickness, "out of touch" with others, does not thereby seem to lose his humanity. To the extent that touch still has appeal as a criterion, it appears to be a survival of the old English idea of "quickening"—a possible mistranslation of the Latin *animatus* used in the canon law.[10] To that extent touch as a criterion seems to be dependent on the Aristotelian notion of ensoulment, and to fall when this notion is discarded.

Finally, a distinction is sought in social visibility. The fetus is not socially perceived as human. It cannot communicate with others. Thus, both subjectively and objectively, it is not a member of society. As moral rules are rules for the behavior of members of society to each other, they cannot be made for behavior toward what is not yet a member. Excluded from the society of men, the fetus is excluded from the humanity of men.[11]

By force of the argument from the consequences, this distinction is to be rejected. It is more subtle than that founded on an appeal to physical sensation, but it is equally dangerous in its implications. If humanity depends on social recognition, individuals or whole groups may be dehumanized by being denied any status in their society. Such a fate is fictionally portrayed in *1984* and has actually been the lot of many men in many societies. In the Roman empire, for example, condemnation to slavery meant the practical denial of most human rights; in the Chinese Communist world, landlords have been classified as enemies of the people and so treated as nonpersons by the state. Humanity does not depend on social recognition, though often the failure of society to recognize the prisoner, the alien, the heterodox as human has led to the destruction of human beings. Anyone conceived by a man and a woman is human. Recognition of this condition by society follows a real event in the objective order, however imperfect and halting the recognition. Any attempt to limit humanity to exclude some group runs the risk of furnishing authority and precedent for excluding other groups in the name of the consciousness or perception of the controlling group in the society.

A philosopher may reject the appeal to the humanity of the fetus because he views "humanity" as a secular view of the soul and because he doubts the existence of anything real and objective which can be identified as humanity.[12] One answer to such a philosopher is to ask how he reasons about moral questions without supposing that there is a sense in which he and the others of whom he speaks are human. Whatever group is taken as the society which determines who may be killed is thereby taken as human. A second answer is to ask if he does not believe that there is a right and wrong way of deciding moral questions. If there is such a difference, experience may be appealed to: to decide who is human on the basis of the sentiment of a given society has led to consequences which rational men would characterize as monstrous.

The rejection of the attempted distinctions based on viability and visibility, experience and feeling, may be buttressed by the following considerations: Moral judgments often rest on distinctions, but if the distinctions are not to appear arbitrary fiat, they should relate to some real difference in probabilities. There is a kind of continuity in all life, but the earlier stages of the elements of human life possess tiny probabilities of development. Consider for example, the spermatozoa in any normal ejaculate: There are about 200,000,000 in any single ejaculate, of which one has a chance of developing into a zygote.[13] Consider the oocytes which may become ova: there are 100,000 to 1,000,000 oocytes in a female infant, of which a maximum of 390 are ovulated.[14] But once spermatozoon and ovum meet and the conceptus is formed, such studies as have been made show that roughly in only 20 percent of the cases will spontaneous abortion occur.[15] In other words, the chances are about 4 out of 5 that this new being will develop. At this stage in the life of the being there is a sharp shift in probabilities, an immense jump in potentialities. To make a distinction between the rights of spermatozoa and the rights of the fertilized ovum is to respond to an enormous shift in possibilities. For about twenty days after conception the egg may split to form twins or combine with another egg to form a chimera, but the probability of either event happening is very small.

It may be asked. What does a change in biological probabilities have to do with establishing humanity? The argument from probabilities is not aimed at establishing humanity but at establishing an objective discontinuity which may be taken into account in moral discourse. As life itself is a matter of probabilities, as most moral reasoning is an estimate of probabilities, so it seems in accord with the structure of reality and the nature of moral thought to found a moral judgment on the change in probabilities at conception. The appeal to probabilities is the most commonsensical of arguments, to a greater or smaller degree all of us base our actions on probabilities, and in morals, as in law, prudence and negligence are often measured by the account one has taken of the probabilities. If the chance is 200,000,000 to 1 that the movement in the bushes into which you shoot is a man's, I doubt if many persons would hold you careless in shooting; but if the chances are 4 out of 5 that the movement is a human being's, few would acquit you of blame. Would the argument be different if only one out of ten children conceived came to term? Of course this argument would be different. This argument is an appeal to probabilities that actually exist, not to any and all states of affairs which may be imagined.

The probabilities as they do exist do not show the humanity of the embryo in the sense of a demonstration in logic any more than the probabilities of the movement in the bush being a man demonstrate beyond all doubt that the being is a man. The appeal is a "buttressing" consideration, showing the plausibility of the standard adopted. The argument focuses on the decisional factor in any moral judgment and assumes that part of the business of a moralist is drawing lines. One evidence of the nonarbitrary character of the line drawn is the difference of probabilities on either side of it. If a spermatozoon is destroyed, one destroys a being which had a chance of far less than 1 in 200 million of developing into a reasoning being, possessed of the genetic code, a heart and other organs, and capable of pain. If a fetus is destroyed, one destroys a being already possessed of the genetic code, organs, and sensitivity to pain, and one which had an 80 percent chance of developing further into a baby outside the womb who, in time, would reason.

The positive argument for conception as the decisive moment of humanization is that at conception the new being receives the genetic code.[16] It is this genetic information which determines his characteristics, which is the biological carrier of the possibility of human wisdom, which makes him a self-evolving being. A being with a human genetic code is man.

This review of current controversy over the humanity of the fetus emphasizes what a fundamental question the theologians resolved in asserting the inviolability of the fetus. To regard the fetus as possessed of equal rights with other humans was not, however, to decide every case where abortion might be employed. It did decide the case where the argument was that the fetus should be aborted for its own good. To say a being was human was to say it had a destiny to decide for itself which could not be taken from it by another man's decision. But human beings with equal rights often come in conflict with each other, and some decision must be made as whose claims are to prevail. Cases of conflict involving the fetus are different only in two respects: the total inability of the fetus to speak for itself and the fact that the right of the fetus regularly at stake is the right to life itself.

The approach taken by the theologians to these conflicts was articulated in terms of "direct" and "indirect." Again, to look at what they were doing from outside their categories, they may be said to have been drawing lines or "balancing values." "Direct" and "indirect" are spatial metaphors; "line-drawing" is another. "To weigh" or "to balance" values is a metaphor of a more complicated mathematical sort hinting at the process which goes on in moral judgments. All the metaphors suggest that, in the moral judgments made, comparisons were necessary, that no value completely controlled. The principle of double effect was no doctrine fallen from heaven, but a method of analysis appropriate where two relative values were being compared. In Catholic moral theology, as it developed, life even of the innocent was not taken as an absolute. Judgments on acts affecting life issued from a process of weighing. In the weighing, the fetus was always given a value greater than zero, always a value separate and independent from its parents. This valuation was crucial and fundamental in all Christian thought on the subject and marked it off from any approach which considered that only the parents' interests needed to be considered.

Even with the fetus weighed as human, one interest could be weighed as equal or superior: that of the mother in her own life. The casuists between 1450 and 1895 were willing to weigh this interest as superior. Since 1895, that interest was given decisive weight only in the two special cases of the cancerous uterus and the ectopic pregnancy. In both of these cases the fetus itself had little chance of survival even if the abortion were not performed. As the balance was once struck in favor of the mother whenever her life was endangered, it could be so struck again. The balance reached between 1895 and 1930 attempted prudentially and pastorally to forestall a multitude of exceptions for interests less than life.

The perception of the humanity of the fetus and the weighing of fetal rights against other human rights constituted the work of the moral analysts. But what spirit animated their abstract judgments? For the Christian community it was the injunction of Scripture to love your neighbor as yourself. The fetus as human was a neighbor; his life had parity with one's own. The commandment gave life to what otherwise would have been only rational calculation.

The commandment could be put in humanistic as well as theological terms: Do not injure your fellow man without reason. In these terms, once the humanity of the fetus is perceived, abortion is never right except in self-defense. When life must be taken to save life, reason alone cannot say that a mother must prefer a child's life to her own. With this exception, now of great rarity, abortion violates the rational humanist tenet of the equality of human lives. . . .

NOTES

1 According to Glanville Williams (*The Sanctity of Human Life supra* n. 169, at 193), "The historical reason for the Catholic objection to abortion is the same as for the Christian Church's historical opposition to infanticide: the horror of bringing about the death of an unbaptized child." This statement is made without any citation of evidence. As has been seen, desire to administer baptism could, in the Middle Ages, even be urged as a reason for procuring an abortion. It is highly regrettable that the American Law Institute was apparently misled by Williams' account and repeated after him the same baseless statement. See American Law Institute, *Model Penal Code: Tentative Draft No. 9* (1959), p. 148, n. 12.

2 E.g., R.L. Brinster and J.L. Thomson, "Development of Eight-Cell Mouse Embryos in Vitro," 42 *Experimental Cell Research* 308 (1966).

3 J. Edgar Morison, *Fetal and Neonatal Pathology* 99-100 (1963).

4 Peter Gruenwald, "Growth of the Human Fetus," 94 *American Journal of Obstetrics and Gynecology* 1112 (1966).

5 Morison, *Fetal and Neonatal Pathology supra* n. 175, at 101.

6 This line of thought was advanced by some participants at the International Conference on Abortion sponsored by the Harvard Divinity School in cooperation with the Joseph P. Kennedy, Jr., Foundation in Washington, D.C., Sept. 8-10, 1967.

7 Frank D. Allan, *Essentials of Human Embryology* 165 (1960).

8 Frederick J. Gottleib, *Developmental Genetics* 28 (1966).

9 Allan, *Essentials for Human Embryology supra* n. 179, at 165.

10 See David W. Louisell and John T. Noonan, Jr., "Constitutional Balance," *infra*.

11 Another line of thought advanced at the Conference mentioned in n. 178. Thomas Aquinas gave an analogous reason against baptizing a fetus in the womb: "As long as it exists in the womb of the mother, it cannot be subject to the operation of the ministers of the Church as it is not known to men" (*In sententias Petri Lombardi* 4.6 1.1.2).

12 Compare John O'Connor, "Humanity and Abortion," 12 *Natural Law Forum* 128-130 (1968), with John T. Noonan, Jr. "Deciding Who Is Human," 12 *Natural Law Forum* 134-138.

13 J.S. Baxter, *Frazer's Manual of Embryology* 5 (1963).

14 Gregory Pincus, *The Control of Fertility* 197 (1965).

15 *Idem.* Apparently there is some small variation by region.

16 Gottleib, *Developmental Genetics supra* n. 180, at 17.

● ● ●

NO

Beverly Wildung Harrison

OUR RIGHT TO CHOOSE

TOWARD A NEW ETHIC OF ABORTION

. . . With respect to the abortion controversy, it is worth remembering that *any* definition of "a human life" or "person" that neglects the moral reality required to nurture and sustain life after birth is very dangerous to our self-understanding. A "pro-life" movement that invites us to "respect" fetal rights from conception or genetic implantation onward actually undermines us by tempting us to imagine that personal rights inhere in natural processes, apart from any genuine covenant of caring, including the human resolve to create viable conditions of life for all who are born among us. Human rights are qualities that ought to inhere in our social relations. Any use of the concept that neglects this fact invites us to take with less than full seriousness the sort of claim we ought to be making when we say that human beings have "a right to life." Early fetal life does *not* yet possess even the minimal organic requirements for participation in the sphere of human rights. And like Mary Anne Warren, I do not believe that even the highly developed fetus can yet be said to have "an intrinsic right to life." Even so, I recognize that it is morally wise to extend such respect, de facto, to fetuses in late stages of gestation. But to do so is also and simultaneously to insist that rights are moral relations, born of our freedom as mature, other-regarding persons. In extending "a right to life" to fetuses in late stages of development, we are attesting that it is a good use of our freedom as agents, from a moral point of view, to do so.

To argue that we may appropriately predicate to fetuses, in the late stages of gestation, "a right to life" does not mean, however, that the life of a pregnant woman should be overridden in decisions about late-stage pregnancies. Rather, it means that abortions, at least in the second half of gestation, are not to be undertaken without serious justifications. My own belief is that the physical and emotional well-being of the pregnant woman, as a valuable existent person, still outweighs the incremental value of the fetus her life sustains. Of course, it is true that in the later stages of pregnancy, abortions are matters of high risk for pregnant women. But doctors, who under most existing laws have discretion as to whether an abortion is advisable at this stage, are themselves not likely to be "frivolous" about the decisions that confront them given the danger of late abortions.

A more difficult question than the issue of moral "imputation" of rights to late-gestating fetuses is the question of whether such fetuses should be deemed to have *de jure* or legal rights. As I have already observed, moral standards and legal standards are never to be identified. I have also referred to the growing number of cases in which courts, usually at a doctor's behest, have intervened on behalf of the "rights" of the fetus to force pregnant women to submit to cesarean sections when they preferred to deliver their babies by natural childbirth.[1] This type of imputation of "rights" under the law to late-gestating fetuses is new. To be sure, the Anglo-American common law tradition and some legal statutes in the United States confer legal rights on "unborn children," but these are usually "contingent rights,"[2] predicated on eventual birth. To legally invoke "the rights of the fetus" before birth as claims restraining a mother's right to elect the manner in which she wishes to bear her child is a quite different and troubling matter. It is particularly so in light of a growing and, as some believe, a massive legal trend toward ruling against women when any of their rights in relation to childbearing and childrearing are disputed. As one deeply mindful that misogyny is alive and well as a socio-structural reality, I believe it morally unwise to permit extensions of existing laws in the direction of granting *de jure* rights to fetuses, when women's well-being still matters so little before the law and when women's de facto rights are so poorly observed. In legal settings, someone must always "stand in" for the fetus to claim "its" rights. Invariably that person will be the husband, doctor, or lawyer, most frequently powerful men in this society whose judgment will be sustained against the pregnant woman's. One can recognize the great moral ambiguity in such cases and still maintain a principled defense of an existing woman's right, as the most affected party, to be the moral decision maker.

"Hard cases" aside, however, the greater moral respect we are wise to accord fetuses in late stages of gestation has very little bearing on the present abortion controversy. What few people recognize is that the overwhelming number of legal abortions in the United States—very conservatively, over 80 percent—are performed during the first trimester of pregnancy. Equally important is the trend in the United States and elsewhere toward early abortion *wherever abortion is legal.* In Sweden, where there is strong social support for encouraging women to detect, and where need be to terminate, pregnancy early, a norm of very early abortion—well before the third month of pregnancy—has been achieved.[3] In New York State, where numerous outpatient clinics perform legal abortions, the downward trend in the period of gestation during which abortions are performed has been marked since 1973. Furthermore, the availability of safe early abortion in New York has accounted for the large numbers of out-of-state residents seeking abortion there.[4] Women are obviously eager to have abortions as early as possible.

Second-trimester abortions sometimes are elected because it is at this stage of pregnancy that severe physical and mental defects can be detected in the fetus. More and more high-risk pregnancies are being monitored and tested for the presence of fetal abnormalities. Happily, 95 percent of tests conducted for this purpose reveal a healthy, properly developing fetus. The results of 5 percent of these tests, however, confront pregnant women with difficult choices, in which abortion may be the outcome. Nevertheless, abortions after the first three months of pregnancy are most often performed because the pregnant woman or girl is very poor and/or very young. That poverty militates against choosing abortion early is obvious enough, but in the United States it is the very young who have all but a tiny fraction of abortions performed after the fourth month:

> The strong inverse association of period of gestation and woman's age probably reflects the inexperience of the very young in recognizing the symptoms of pregnancy, their unwillingness to accept the reality of their situation, their ignorance about where to seek advice and help, and their hesitation to confide in adults. Economic considerations and, in many places, regulations prohibiting surgery on minors without parental consent also contribute to delays.[5]

Yet few pause to notice these data, while charges of genocide increase without reference to the considerable and mounting evidence that women are, responsibly, seeking early abortions when they have the social supports necessary to make such choices. The "hard cases" involving resort to abortion in the third trimester of pregnancy are, to say the least, rare. The increase in the total number of abortions in the United States can be used, as all data so frequently are used, to mystify the reality of what is going on in women's lives.

As I indicated earlier, abortions will continue to be available whether or not they are legal. Ironically, then, those persons insisting that a human life begins at conception or at an early stage of genetic human development may help to create a situation in which abortions, though they will not cease, will occur at a later stage of gestation. If we are forced to "honor" the sort of reasoning that predicates full humanity to early fetal life, we can safely predict that the trend toward early abortion will be reversed and that women who want to terminate their pregnancies early will find it more difficult to do so. A "life begins at conception" mentality constructs a social reality that requires us to accept not merely moral judgments about fetal life with which we disagree but life conditions that decrease the possibility of our terminating developing fetal life when it ought to be terminated—in the early stage of gestation. For any of us to celebrate the potentiality of a life we do not intend to care for concretely, as free moral agents, signifies not moral maturity but childish moral irresponsibility. To maintain that "society" (an abstract, not a concrete term) should welcome every conceptus simply because it has been conceived is to play fast and loose with the real character of our moral relations as persons.

Women, as childbearers, and all men as well need to understand that the quality of all our lives depends not on blindly embracing an automatic organic process but on the texture of concern and our very human, very moral readiness to provide for the children we choose to bring into the world. That the availability of safe surgical abortion in the early period of gestation, as a means of birth control, enhances our ability to make childbearing a moral choice is, I believe, an incontrovertible fact. If we turn back the clock, in the interest of early fetal "rights to life," we simultaneously will obstruct women in making the moral choices many of them have resolved to make in any case. We will undermine women who want to approach motherhood in a responsible way, aware of what they are undertaking and determining when they are prepared to provide the moral environment of caring imperative for the development of genuine personal existence. The "principled righteousness" of those who are determined to champion "the rights" of the embryo or fetus, treating women who have early abortions as criminals guilty of infanticide, is taking a heavy toll on the very social group that has made the greatest progress in recent decades toward assuming their full standing as moral persons—that is, women who have come to perceive that motherhood is no "natural condition" but, rather, a creative moral action to be undertaken in freedom, intelligently and with forethought.

Those who recognize that the processes of fetal development should be terminated early, precisely to avoid the "hard cases" where a woman's rights as a moral agent come to loggerheads with the value she imputes to the individuated human life form in her womb, need also recognize that only social conditions that make early abortions feasible are those that also make it *both* legal and, at least in the early stages of abortion, elective. To guarantee the feasibility of early abortion in any society, abortion must be decriminalized and pregnant women granted early discretion to choose it, medical reasons aside. When safe, legal, elective abortion is available, women experience strong social pressure for detecting an unwanted pregnancy early and terminating it with dispatch. Where abortion is illegal or discretion in the early stages of pregnancy is restricted to the medical profession, even before medical complications are detectable, social pressure operates in a different fashion. When the authority to make fundamental moral choices over one's own life is denied and placed at someone else's discretion, procrastination in confronting one's own reality, particularly if it means confronting another's power over you, is bound to ensue. Elective abortion is a precondition for early abortion.

The moral meaning of the act of abortion shifts, then, depending on the extent of the actual development of fetal life. Until the complexity of the fetal organism enables at least clear-cut potential, differentiated survival as a human body, recognizing the fetus as a human life should be viewed as an arbitrary classification. As the gestating fetus matures biologically, moving toward the point of functional maturation, the pregnant woman has good reason to impute claims to the fetus, grounded in intrinsic value, that weigh against her own. But from a moral point of view, there can be no "demand" that she take her own moral claim to life and well-being less seriously or as something readily to be discarded. What she—and the rest of us—need to understand is that it is best, when possible, to avoid living [in a] situation where such conflicting claims arise. If a pregnancy is unwanted, a woman's moral obligation is best expressed by early recognition and termination of fetal life. That many women have yet to deliberate these matters seriously or to recognize that there is an obligation to intentionality in childbearing has much to do with female socialization and the objective disadvantage females incur in any society. The condemnatory ethos prevailing around the abortion debate in the United States is itself a force in delaying this "coming of age"[6] for many women. A society that does not extend genuine respect to women is also one that fails to recognize the moral issue at stake in whether women are helped or hindered in integrating decisions about abortion into their life plans. Without social support for women in making decisions about pregnancy and abortion, childbearing cannot be a humane and life-enhancing option.

If those who condemn all acts of abortion are successful, women's lives will be drastically altered for the worse. However, as I indicated much earlier, there are reasons for wishing that women were not forced to elect abortions, particularly second-trimester abortions, so often. It is incumbent that we, not our opponents, take seriously the question of how resort to abortion could be minimized. From a moral point of view, the proper way to frame this question is to ask what sort of society we would have to be in order to reduce resort to abortion, especially late abortion, *and* simultaneously enhance the quality and range of choice in most women's lives. . . .

NOTES

1 Janet Gallagher, *Ms.*, April 1983.
2 *The Problem of Abortion,* Joel Feinberg ed. (Belmont, Calif.: Wadsworth, 1973), pp. 33-51.
3 See Christopher Tietze, *Induced Abortion: A World Review* (New York: Population Council, 1981). In Sweden, the mean duration of pregnancies before abortion dropped from 14.1 weeks in 1968 to 9.9 in 1979 (p. 66).
4 Ibid., pp. 66-67. New York's permissive law and the availability of many clinics that perform abortions mean that numerous abortions are performed on nonresidents there. Tietze notes the trend toward earlier abortions among New York State residents. On the effects of legalization on early abortion in New York State from 1970 onward, see Alan F. Guttmacher, M.D., "The Genesis of Liberalized Abortion in New York: A Personal Insight," in David F. Wahlbert and J. Douglas Butler, eds., *Abortion, Society and Law* (Cleveland: Press of Case Western Reserve, 1973), pp. 63-87.
5 Tietze, pp. 66-67.
6 This phrase is from Dietrich Bonhoeffer's *Letters and Papers from Prison* (London: SCM Press, Fontana Books, 1953), pp. 106-110.

● ● ●

POSTSCRIPT

IS ABORTION IMMORAL?

In June 1983, in a series of cases, the Supreme Court reaffirmed its support of the legality of abortion. In the most important case, it ruled six to three that ordinances passed by the city of Akron, Ohio requiring an "informed consent" procedure before an abortion could be performed were designed to deter the woman from the procedure and hence were unconstitutional. The Supreme Court's decision will probably mean that anti-abortion political forces will shift their focus to the passage of a Human Life Amendment to the Constitution.

The literature on abortion is large and often impassioned. Noonan's view, expressed in the preceding selection, is amplified in his book *A Private Choice: Abortion in America in the Seventies* (The Free Press, 1979). Paul Ramsey's *Ethics at the Edges of Life* (Yale, 1978) is another eloquent statement of the pro-life stance.

Judith Jarvis Thomson's article, "A Defense of Abortion" (*Philosophy and Public Affairs,* Fall 1971), is a classic philosophical defense of the feminist argument that a woman has the right to control her own body. In her article, "On the Moral and Legal Status of Abortion" (*The Monist,* January 1973), Mary Anne Warren goes even further, asserting that the fetus is not a person and that abortion is always permissible.

Other volumes that present a range of viewpoints on abortion are: *The Rights and Wrongs of Abortion* edited by M. Cohen, T. Nagel, and T. Scanlon (Princeton, 1973); and *Abortion: Pro and Con,* edited by Robert Perkins (Schenckman, 1974).

ISSUE 2

IS IT WRONG TO CREATE TEST-TUBE BABIES?

YES: Hans O. Tiefel, from "Human In Vitro Fertilization: A Conservative View," *Journal of the American Medical Association* 247:23, June 18, 1982

NO: Clifford Grobstein, from "Coming to Terms with Test-Tube Babies," *New Scientist* 96, October 7, 1982

ISSUE SUMMARY

YES: Professor of religion Hans O. Tiefel opposes the new technology of in vitro fertilization on the grounds that it may cause harm to both mother and embryos, which ought to be protected because they are part of humanity.
NO: Biologist Clifford Grobstein argues that this technology is a useful therapy for infertile couples and that we can avoid the "slippery slope" of potential moral problems by developing sound principles.

Few babies have been born to such instant celebrity as Louise Joy Brown. When she was born in Manchester, England, on July 25, 1978, she was the world's first documented "test-tube" baby. Robert G. Edwards, a physiologist and Patrick C. Steptoe, an obstetrician, had perfected the technique called "in vitro" or, more properly, "external" fertilization. ("In vitro" literally means "in glass"; the fertilization did not take place in a test-tube but in a petri dish.)

Simply put, this is the way the procedure works: A ripe egg is removed through surgery from the mother's ovary, then mixed in a special solution with the male sperm. If fertilization occurs, the resulting embryo is implanted after two or three days in the mother's uterine wall, where it develops to term—that is, if all goes well. Like normal fertilization, external fertilization is subject to the vagaries of nature. Like many scientific achievements, Louise Brown's birth was the culmination of many years of experimentation, beginning with tests on animals in the late nineteenth century. Today about 150 to 200 babies, including several sets of twins, have been born as a result of this technique, primarily in England, Australia, and the United States.

External fertilization offers some hope—perhaps the only one—of alleviating infertility in women whose fallopian tubes are blocked. External fertilization might eventually be used to treat more of the nearly 1.5 million American women who are infertile. Thousands of women have applied to the more than forty American clinics that offer this therapy, even though it is painful, expensive ($3,000 to $4,000 per try, with three to four tries not uncommon), and successful only a third of the time. (This is a relatively recent improvement over the original success rates.)

In the five years since Louise Brown was born, the technology has advanced even further. Scientists in England and Australia have succeeded in freezing externally-fertilized embryos in liquid nitrogen and storing them for future use. These "spare" embryos can also be implanted in another woman—one who cannot produce fertilizable eggs, or who agrees to carry the fetus of another couple to delivery, for instance. In this country all "spare" embryos are implanted and none are destroyed or otherwise manipulated, say the clinic directors.

But if Louise Brown's birth and the subsequent events answered one question—can it be done?—it raised another, more troubling one—ought it be done? In 1979 an Ethics Advisory Board convened by the then-Department of Health, Education, and Welfare (now Health and Human Services) recommended, after a year and a half of hearings and study, that research on in vitro fertilization was "ethically acceptable" under specific conditions. This included a provision that the fertilized embryo not be maintained outside the mother's body beyond fourteen days, or the stage normally associated with implantation. However, the board did not recommend what level of federal funding, if any, ought to be given to such research. While the board's work represented the most exhaustive examination of the subject to date, it by no means quieted all fears.

In the following selection, Hans O. Tiefel takes the view that in vitro fertilization is at best a "mixed blessing" and that human embryos ought to be considered as persons and protected from unjustifiable research. Clifford Grobstein, while not denying the existence of ethical problems, believes that external fertilization is beneficial and that calling a halt to the practice is unjustifiable because ethical problems can be overcome by sound guidelines and policies.

YES

Hans O. Tiefel

HUMAN IN VITRO FERTILIZATION: A CONSERVATIVE VIEW

The extracorporeal engendering of human life that led to the birth of Louise Brown in 1978 struck the world as an awesome medical achievement. Even 3½ years later, the 15th—but this nation's first—child so conceived was fittingly welcomed as the "miracle in Norfolk" (*Washington Post,* Dec 31, 1981, p A-14).

This striking accomplishment offers hope to many of the circa half-million American women whose obstructed or missing Fallopian tubes had seemingly ruled out any chance of having children of their own. Relatively few of the more than 6,000 couples who have applied at the Eastern Virginia Medical School, however, can be helped there or at the other three American clinics.

Two authorities on issues of in vitro fertilization and embryo transfer, LeRoy Walters, PhD, director of the Kennedy Institute's Center for Bioethics, and John D. Biggers, DSc, PhD, the Harvard specialist in human reproductive biology, therefore called for federal support for test-tube conceptions a week after the birth of Elizabeth Carr (*Washington Post,* Jan 4, 1982, p A-3). The national government should stop turning its back on childless couples who want babies, according to Dr Walters, particularly since the US Department of Health, Education, and Welfare Ethics Advisory Board had concluded in June 1979 that such funding is "acceptable from an ethical standpoint." The nationwide hearings on whether to lift a 1974 moratorium on such funding, held by the Ethics Advisory Board in 1978 and 1979, elicited similar recommendations. Particularly, medical professionals hope "to break the log jam of prejudice and law, at both state and federal levels, that at present denies infertile couples the blessing of a child by this remarkable method."

This article opposes such recommendations on moral grounds by arguing that this new technology may be a mixed blessing, that federal funding may be blocked not by prejudice but by moral doubts, and that a more cautious or conservative position is justified by valid objections to both means and ends of test-tube babies. . . .

From "Human In Vitro Fertilization: A Conservative View," by Hans O. Tiefel, *Journal of the American Medical Association,* 247:23, June 18, 1982, pp. 3235-3242.

The [most significant moral] meaning of the charge that this new technology is unnatural refers not to means but to ends, namely, to the fear that this innovation may prove harmful. Such harm would be widely conceived: mental or physical, emotional or social, possible or actual, detracting from health or worth of any or all parties. That, in my judgment, is the crucial issue, especially as it pertains to the offspring. But that problem is more familiar under the rubric of risk or harm.

RISK TO THE WOULD-BE MOTHER

LeRoy Walters succinctly describes the kinds of risks to the woman in in vitro fertilization and embryo transfer:

> (1) pretreatment of the woman with hormones to induce superovulation, a therapy which occasionally produces ovarian cysts; (2) removal of oocytes by means of laparoscopy, a surgical procedure which requires general anesthesia; (3) potential damage to the uterus during embryo transfer . . . (4) the risks which accompany careful monitoring of the pregnancy, for example, the risks of amniocentesis . . . (5) the risk of ectopic pregnancy.

The second of these seems to be the most important. But to assess that risk, one needs statistics of normal impregnation. Biggers concludes that, normally, one can expect between 69% and 78% embryonic loss, which is consistent with data showing that it takes an average of four months of regular inseminations to achieve pregnancy by artificial insemination or four months of sexual activity to achieve normal pregnancy. Thus even under normal conditions, the required number of embryo transfers will, on average, be four times as great as the number of births one can expect.

The success rate for laparoscopies and embryo transfer have been much lower. In their early work, Edwards and Steptoe claimed two births out of 68 laparoscopies. Biggers concluded in February 1981 that when an ovum is discovered, the probability of obtaining a live birth by the Steptoe-Edwards method was about 0.044. That appears to have been the method that yielded 30 failures to impregnate 30 patients in 1980 for Drs Howard and Georgeanna Jones in Norfolk.

With fertility-inducing drugs, however, the odds apparently improve. More than one ovum can be obtained, which allows more than one embryonic implant. In 1981 the Norfolk clinic reported six pregnancies in some 50 tries. Australian results have similarly improved. Steptoe claimed that as of Oct 31, 1981, out of 436 laparoscopies, 337 implantations, and 74 pregnancies, eight babies had been born and 48 women were still pregnant (*Washington Post*, Dec 23, 1981, p A-24).

Despite such improvements and the prospects of better odds in the future, the success rate still resembles lottery statistics more than promising therapy. Infertile couples, perhaps misled by their own desperation and unqualified news stories, present themselves as patients when their role is more that of subjects in clinical trials.

Even if the meager success rate is explained to couples and they consent to the odds, there are moral limits to surgical risk, time, resources, and stress on human relationships. The fact that prospective parents say that they will do anything to have a baby of their own is not necessarily a moral justification. "Doing anything" may not only be inimical to oneself but neglects ties and duties to others. To use an odd example, one research team supports the claim that a pregnancy actually resulted from their transplant by stating that "the subject abstained from intercourse during the entire treatment as a result of her own firm and deliberate decision." There is no word whether the husband shared in that decision, which seemed to benefit only the researchers. Similarly, one wonders if the delivery of these babies by cesarean section is always necessary and should be one of the risks of this procedure.

Low success rates, repeated risks, disruption of lives, unneeded impositions, and financial and emotional costs to would-be parents as well as to those supporting them are serious moral problems. But all such liabilities are voluntarily assumed by those who hope to benefit from this technology. That is not true for the would-be child.

RISK TO THE WOULD-BE CHILD

Is there risk to a child conceived in vitro and transferred in embryo form into the uterus? It seems that nobody knows for sure. A recent review of the probability of producing a congenitally abnormal baby is offered by Biggers. His conclusion, that the danger of increased congenital defects is not high, seems to be based on the spontaneous elimination of most abnormalities before birth rather than on assurance of no increase in abnormal embryos. But there is no guarantee that this would happen, assuming that such loss is reassuring and of little moral relevance.

When the count of children so conceived was 21, only one was reported to have been born with a serious defect, which will be repaired by cardiac surgery, according to the *Washington Post* (Jan 4, 1982, p A-3). But Walters' conclusion that the procedures do not pose "unreasonable risk" is both sanguine and premature.

Not only are there insufficient data about the effects on humans, but the relevance of in vitro studies on animals is in doubt. Thus, some researchers (Mastroianni, Brackett, Gould) call for more animal studies, while others (Soupart, Biggers) dismiss that as irrelevant. The Ethics Advisory Board found a golden mean by giving its imprimatur to both animal and human studies.

In any case, knowledge about risk requires long-range human studies, decades in which to follow up children so conceived into reproductive age and through a normal life span. Not only time but sufficient numbers are required. Schlesselman, in a careful statistical study, concludes that 99.3% to 99.5% of chromosomal abnormalities are eliminated in vivo through spontaneous abortion or fetal death. Such low survival rates of abnormal fetuses imply that even a doubling of abnormalities of in vitro implantations would result in only two or three additional abnormalities per 1,000 live births. Thus, "a large number of births would be required to provide definitive assessment of risk. The morally crucial answer to the question of risk to the would-be child thus requires a great number of births and much time. The answers seem a long way off, and we must make moral judgments without the benefit of knowing all the facts.

Several responses to this factual uncertainty of risk are troubling. Ethicists have stated repeatedly that risk to the child conceived in vitro would be acceptable if it is no greater than risk to children conceived in vivo. But it is not helpful to say that when no one knows the actual risk. Here ethicists avoid the dilemma.

Others recommend that if couples with recessive defects decide to have children, then the assumed lower risk of in vitro fertilization must be acceptable. Or, since "it is not general practice in this country to interfere with reproductive options facing couples who may be at increased risk for having abnormal offspring, it is held to be right to inform and to accede to a couple's decision here as well.

This acceding role of medical conscience is the opposite extreme of paternalism. Implementing the couple's choice unavoidably makes the physician a part of that decision. But surely the physician should be neither father nor slave, but a responsible participant. If medical judgment anticipates harm, he is obligated to keep patients "from harm and injustice" by virtue of the Hippocratic oath.

Medical proponents of extracorporeal fertilization also offer ethical relativism as a way of overcoming the problem of risk. Individual wishes become king. The fact that a couple wants this procedure is held to make it morally right. For example, one researcher claims that "childless couples' rights to utilize whatever methods and techniques are available to produce wanted offspring far exceeds and surpasses the rights and privileges of the critics who would condemn and suppress scientific work directed toward helping them to accomplish this aim."

Disregarding the lese majesty against science, this is ethical relativism, where individual choice or preference settles moral issues. Medicine should avoid such quicksand, for shifting individual preferences offer no solid support for the objective values undergirding medicine and research. If one lets go of objective and universal values to defer to dubious patient choice, one also relinquishes the heart of medicine, whose life is the objective value of healing and of doing no harm.

A PROPOSAL FOR THE ETHICS OF RISK

How, then, is one to assess the moral issue of unknown risk to the would-be child? The subject, the would-be child, must first be clearly defined lest we confuse our responsibilities to existing and to future children. For offspring who are actually on the way, we must allow great risk when that is the only option for their continued existence. To the would-be child that is not yet conceived, we have no such obligation. Our responsibilities to living offspring, before and after birth, should not be undercut by the risks they face. But offspring who are concepts rather than conceptions may not claim that immunity. We literally do not owe them a living.

Though no one knows for sure, there is some justification for deeming in vitro fertilization to be harmful to offspring thus conceived. The great embryonic and fetal loss, compared with natural pregnancies, is good reason for saying that this mode of begetting is more dangerous. Moreover, the dimensions of risk may not even be known. To a layman there are repeated surprises in the way in which risk studies appear about therapies that were long thought to be safe. Even medical professionals seem surprised by the latent effort of thalidomide or diethylstilbestrol. To create an artificial environment, to handle, stimulate, and disturb human life at its very beginning when its building blocks are being laid, is to risk damage to the finished construct, even for those few structures that survive spontaneous collapse and demolition.

As best we can, we owe every child a fair

chance at physical and mental health. This principle, which is so often misused to justify the destruction of seriously ill fetuses or newborns, is fittingly applied to the would-be child. We must weigh the chances for the well-being of the child while we yet have a choice about initiating this life. Would-be parents have moral obligations to a would-be child. The resolve to have a child of one's own must be tied to a love that seeks the best for that child. To be sure, no parents can guarantee health to future offspring. Nor can they secure safety from nuclear war, a harmful environment, or other dangers over which they have little or no control. But every parent owes every child-to-be reasonable care not to take chances with its health, as every obstetrician explains to every mother-to-be. And the uncertain risks inherent in in vitro fertilization are definitely avoidable by abstinence from this particular technology.

It makes good moral sense never to beget offspring when would-be-parents cannot reasonably ensure a future child a fair chance at health. When there are untried risks and even indications of greater than normal risk, "one cannot ethically choose for a child the unknown hazards that he must face, and simultaneously choose to give him life in which to face them." For would-be mothers to undertake risks and burdens for themselves and for consenting partners is one thing. For them knowingly to place future children at risk is quite another. No one has the moral right to endanger a child while there is yet the option of whether the child shall come into existence. That is the crucial and decisive ethical argument against the clinical use of in vitro fertilization. That also makes this procedure unnatural in the sense of being possibly harmful to human beings.

It is misleading and flippant to object that we should ask the children so conceived what they thought of the risks as objections to their being conceived. For if they turn out to be healthy, they are lucky winners in this technological gamble. If handicapped, they would only have the choice between their burdened life or no existence at all. Whether they say yes or no, the moral choice for actually existing children should generally be for life. That is why the choice exists only for would-be children. The dilemma of risk before conception cannot be resolved after the fact.

Ramsey made the crucial moral point about risk to the future child a decade ago. That seems to have made little impact. A survey of the literature yields no medical researcher who thinks that this is one procedure that should not be used. None of the medical experts rejects this risky technology that is being tested even as it is used on women and their babies.

One subtle but significant threat to children so conceived has not yet been mentioned because it is one of the certain rather than likely problems. The suspicion—and guilt on the part of parents—will be unavoidable that whatever health problems develop are the result of this unique genesis. And uncertainty about the future is apt to create anxiety. The possibility of unknown problems yet to come will overshadow the lives of these children, of their parents, and surely also of their medical "creators" and monitors. . . .

FREEZING HUMAN EMBRYOS

Superovulation yields more ova, more implants, and reduces the need for repeated laparoscopies. But what should be done with "surplus" embryos? Both Australian and British centers have temporarily resolved the problem by "putting it on ice." Freezing was the alternative to discarding the embryos, which could be sustained in no other way.

Freezing also makes sense in another way. The hormones used to induce superovulation may have a detrimental effect on implantation and on early embryonic development. Freezing oocytes or embryos would allow implantation in the subsequent cycle when the woman no longer suffers aftereffects from hormones or from surgery and anesthesia.

A third proposed benefit, recommended by Steptoe and Edwards, lies in banks of frozen embryos for donation to other women, permitting "prenatal adoption" by infertile couples (*New York Times,* Feb 11, 1982, p A-26).

How is one to evaluate this morally? Freezing embryos is particularly unnerving to persons who think that even the earliest forms of human life are special. Here human life is put on hold, as it were. Even if one wants to avoid the judgment that this is unnatural, prolonged freezing may rob a thawed and growing life of its genetic progenitors, of its roots and support. Such a Buck Rogers of the 21st century would lack memories of lost ties, but genuine bonds might well be lost. It is also not too farfetched to think that once the progenitors are forgotten or gone, these suspended beings may lose their natural protectors to become interesting research material, as may already be happening with embryos incidentally recovered during hysterectomies.

Freezing even for long periods seems to damage only the quantity but not the quality of animal embryos, but whether this is true for humans is again unknown. Therefore, the same worries about risk of in vitro fertilization apply here. It would be preferable to freeze ova rather than embryos, since the former are not yet genetically unique lives. And—assuming that the earlier moral arguments against extracorporeal conception will not dissuade anyone—it would be the lesser evil to freeze surplus embryos. The only other practical option, once they have been conjured into existence, is to discard them, a practice that has been described as "a matter solely between a doctor and his plumber." Even if freezing were to entail additional risks, including those of experimentation, it would at least give embryos a chance to live.

As to prenatal adoption, the legal unclarities of who belongs to whom and who owes what to whom would be legion. But again, an acknowledgment of the intrinsic value of the human embryo might also see this mode of life as better than none....

THE STATUS OF THE EMBRYO

The ethics of nonclinical in vitro fertilization hangs on the decision about status. The Ethics Advisory Board agreed "that the human embryo is entitled to profound respect: but this respect does not necessarily encompass the full legal and moral rights attributed to persons." That amounts to a polite bow in the direction of the embryo before dispatching it for tissue cultures. The key question is whether one may use the embryo in nontherapeutic experiments, whether one may use it up. The board said that, at least for 14 days, one may do so. How much profound respect the embryo enjoys as it is being fixed in slides remains in doubt. In any case, the respect due falls short of never using such human life as a means only.

This peculiar use of "respect" also explains the board's strange conclusion that research on human in vitro fertilization was "ethically acceptable" in the sense of still being legitimately controverted. That controversy hinges on embryonic status.

Neither the board nor I can prove our beliefs about embryonic status, but I shall nevertheless offer reasons for a more inclusive vision of humanity.

The problem with embryonic status lies partly in our inconsistency. On the one hand, we know that we, at least our bodily selves, began as embryos. If we are special, embryos are special. Even Mr Edwards is reported to have said at the birth of Louise Brown, "The last time I saw the baby it was just eight cells in a test tube. It was beautiful then, and it's still beautiful now" (*Newsweek*, Aug 7, 1978, p 69). That may have been poetic license, but it shows that the value of human beings is linked to our embryonic origin. We also assent to a practical wisdom in the law that allows offspring to bring suit for malpractice against researchers for harm to themselves as embryos.

On the other hand, we acknowledge the value of increased knowledge about earliest human development, such as chromosome constitution of gametes and human infertility. The simplest and most useful way to find out is to experiment, to look through the window that has been opened on early development by in vitro fertilization. Only in this case, our seeing fatally affects the embryo. Such looking may not be done with human beings. We are therefore inclined to exclude the embryo from human status.

This ambiguity growing out of opposing motives was offered to the Ethics Advisory Board by a philosopher who proposed that the status of this being may be judged only in retrospect. If it should be damaged as an embryo and be malformed later, it is fitting to say that the initial harm was an "injury to someone." But if the embryo does not live to term, we may not say that. That ascribes status ("someone") according to what we want to do with the embryo.

Such flexibility is convenient. But historical instances of ascribing human status selectively have not turned out to be our better moments. It is also true that one of the rules of ethics is consistency. If any embryos count as human beings, all do.

It may be a sign of ferment or of poverty in contemporary philosophy, but there is less and less consensus about who counts and why. Handicapped newborns are pushed into the limbo of deferred personhood until we can decide whether they should live. Fetuses are said to have value only when their potentiality is wanted by their progenitors. And a chimpanzee is held to be of more value than a human zygote.

The general trend to restrict humanity to rational and volitional beings may solve a host of medical problems. It cuts the Gordian knot of whether to treat or to protect human beings at the borders of life with a definitional sword that strikes off all who cannot reason. But our medical, humanistic, and religious traditions have been less fierce. We have held and should continue to hold that every human life counts, regardless of capacity. In this more compassionate vision it is fitting to include even the earliest versions of ourselves within the human community. . . .

• • •

NO

Clifford Grobstein

COMING TO TERMS WITH TEST-TUBE BABIES

The first baby that was conceived by external (*in vitro*) fertilisation was born in England in 1978. The event created much excitement and some controversy. First reactions died down as additional technology-assisted babies were born, not only in England but in Australia and the US. More than three years later, however, controversy in England is stirring anew—as though people are suddenly seeing the matter in a new light. This "double-take", sometimes exploited by comedians to get a laugh, in this instance has serious significance.

Earlier misgivings in the US were effectively summarised in the hearings and deliberations of the Ethics Advisory Board, charged in 1978 by Joseph Califano, then Secretary of the Department of Health, Education and Welfare, to evaluate external human fertilisation. Central in the board's consideration were questions of the safety and efficacy of the procedure—designed to relieve female infertility due to blockage or loss of the fallopian tubes. Safety referred largely to possible harmful effects on the offspring, efficacy largely to the percentage of attempts that would yield viable offspring. Three years later, with about a score of babies born, all but one appear to have been normal at birth and the several clinics with greatest experience are projecting a one in five chance of success for each attempt. The trend of the growing clinical experience is, therefore, toward safety and success rates close to those for the natural internal process.

While external fertilisation cannot yet be regarded as an established medical procedure, its trials so far suggest that it will prove reasonably safe and efficacious. The new wave of concern, in fact, centres on broader issues—the "open window" on early human development afforded by the procedure and conceivable procedures that can be visualised as ranging along a "slippery slope" toward applications that are unpalatable to many people. The "open window", of course, is the accessibility external fertilisation provides for observation or manipulation of early human developmental stages, previously rarely obtainable and never before able to be maintained alive while undergoing

From "Coming to Terms with Test-Tube Babies," by Clifford Grobstein, *New Scientist*, October 7, 1982.

development. The Cambridge physiologist Robert Edwards and obstetrician Patrick Steptoe and their colleagues, whose arduous and dedicated efforts brought the procedure to realisation, have recently reported on the growth of externally cultured human embryos from fertilisation to the blastocyst ("ball of cells") stage, at which time the embryos normally would be implanting in the wall of the uterus. The objective of these observations is to improve further the safety and efficacy of the procedure. However, such entirely reasonable efforts are further widening the open window and heightening concern in some quarters about the presumed slippery slope. This much more consequential matter undoubtedly is providing the major impetus to calls for a second look, and even a moratorium, on continued research to improve and expand the use of the procedure. The concern stems from the fact that manipulations of fertilisation and early stages in development, comparable with those now accessible in humans, are being practised increasingly widely on other mammalian species, both in the laboratory and in commercial animal production. Two objectives of these practices are to gain greater knowledge of hereditary and developmental processes on one hand and to apply this knowledge to achieve economic benefits on the other. The concern is that the very same manipulations, if applied to human eggs or embryos, raise unprecedented moral issues and, in some minds, the possibility of unanticipated or frankly undesirable social impacts.

The possibility of entering upon a slippery slope has come more sharply into focus largely because of two technical innovations in external fertilisation, one already in effect and the other under consideration. The first is the use of hormonal stimulation to increase the number of mature eggs that can be obtained from a given donor. In humans, of course, only a single egg usually matures in each menstrual cycle. Having several eggs mature clearly might increase the success rate for a given procedure for recovering eggs. Edwards and Steptoe in early efforts, however, had poorer success when they obtained multiple eggs by hormonal stimulation than they had with single eggs obtained from a natural cycle. Their first births, in fact, were from eggs obtained in natural cycles. Subsequently, however, other groups using slightly different methods, notably Carl Wood at the Monash University in Australia, have had greater success with multiple eggs hormonally induced from a single donor and are achieving overall improved success rates. The reinsertion of more than one egg has given rise to a few twin pregnancies, and, because up to six mature eggs can be produced hormonally, donors may be stimulated to produce more than the optimal number of eggs for a given cycle.

There are several options for the further fate of such surplus eggs. They might be killed and discarded. They might be used, as the Edwards and Steptoe group has done, to gain more knowledge about these early human stages, in turn perhaps contributing to the safety and efficacy of the procedure. Or they might be frozen and stored for other, later use. Each of the options is controversial, for each raises the knotty issue of the legal and social status of the early human embryo. If one holds, as legislation pending in the US Congress does, that a person exists from conception, then any option other than immediate return to a receptive uterus (and possibly even that) is excluded. If, however, one holds that the early embryo is something other than a person, then the options are admissible, but with a degree of restriction depending upon how close to a person the early embryo is defined to be.

VALUABLE BY-PRODUCTS

Setting aside this question of status for the moment, what do the options offer technically? The first obviously offers nothing other than avoiding the necessity to face the other two. Surplus embryos would be treated as unwanted by-products of the procedure and would be dispatched without further consideration or concern. The second option would assign special value to the early embryos as a source of additional knowledge, not for the benefit of the embryos themselves but possibly to benefit other embryos and humanity in general. The third option is the most complex because it puts the embryos in temporary stasis for purposes that have not been specified. What might some of these purposes be?

The most immediate purpose and the closest to the original rationale of the basic procedure of external fertilisation would be to provide embryos for insertion into the uterus of the donor in later menstrual cycles. One of the concerns about the hormonal induction of multiple eggs is that the hormonal stimulation may not only affect the ovary but might also disturb the cycle of the uterus. Having obtained the embryos it might be advantageous not to return them immediately to the uterus but to wait for a subsequent cycle uncomplicated by the administration of hormones. At the very least, this would allow successive attempts at reinsertion after only a single extraction of eggs. Obtaining the egg is the most uncomfortable step for the patient, involving a small incision through the abdominal wall under light anaesthesia. Moreover, the reinsertion step also has, at the moment, the lowest success rate. If multiple eggs were obtained by a single extraction from the ovary and if all that were not immediately reinserted were frozen, the thawed embryos could later be inserted in successive cycles until success were achieved. This might enhance the success rate while adding as little as possible to the patient's discomfort.

The pertinent question, of course, is the possible harm done to the embryo by freezing and thawing. Here it is important to note that the freezing and thawing of embryos stems from extensive studies over several decades in what is called cryobiology. It is now possible, as the result of research on the processes of freezing and thawing of living tissues in various media and at different temperatures, to freeze and thaw many microbial, plant and animal cells with minimal damage. In the frozen state metabolism is suspended and even genetic change is slowed down to insignificant levels. Mammalian embryos, including those of mice and cattle, have been kept in frozen storage and shown to continue normal development with high frequency on thawing. Scientifically valuable strains of mice are now being stored in frozen embryo banks to eliminate the effort and cost of constant breeding.

The application of the procedure to human embryos would not, therefore, be a shot in the dark. On the other hand, its application to humans is not the same as its application to mice or cattle. Ninety per cent success rates, for example, may be acceptable for laboratory and domestic animals. In humans it is the 10 per cent failure rate that is of concern—particularly if these are partial failures, not detectable until after birth or even later in life. Clearly these are matters for most careful consideration before frozen-thawed human embryos are reinserted for continued development.

If the safety issue were favourably resolved, we can envisage further technical possibilities. Eggs surplus for the original donor might also be inserted into the receptive uterus of a non-donor. Such embryo transfers are commonly done with high rates of success in laboratory animals and cattle. They are done most effectively with frozen-thawed embryos because these can be held until the uterus of the recipient is in the most receptive stage of the cycle. We can imagine two circumstances in which this might be attempted in humans. The first is based upon the original rationale for external human fertilisation; that is, to relieve infertility. The recipient would be a woman whose ovaries do not produce mature and normal eggs but whose uterus is normal. The insertion of an embryo into her uterus would be comparable with an early adoption. She would have the full experience of pregnancy but with an offspring to which she had made no genetic contribution. If, incidentally, she were to receive a surplus egg fertilised by her husband's sperm the offspring would have genetic kinship at least with the father, a situation exactly the converse of artificial insemination by donor to cope with male infertility.

The slippery slope would begin to steepen if the same technical procedure were to be applied to a non-donor who was not sterile but who acted as a surrogate ("foster mother") for the donor. This might still be a measure to overcome sterility if the donor were without a uterus due to an earlier hysterectomy. It might, however, also be done because the donor might expect a pregnancy to be dangerous to her health or merely inconvenient. In the last instance the original motivation to relieve sterility would have been diluted to the vanishing point, replaced by considerations of maternal preference and convenience.

Having reached this point, further options might be seen that would still employ the same basic techniques. For example, there is a trend in the US for women to postpone pregnancy to avoid interrupting their careers. In addition, the incidence of Down's syndrome in offspring rises sharply as maternal age moves into the last decade of fecundity, between 35 and 45. Suppose a young woman were to have eggs removed from her ovaries to be fertilised externally by sperm from her husband (or other male), and the resulting embryos were to be frozen. These embryos could then be inserted into her uterus at convenient times that fit her career needs, and possibly reduce the risk of developmental defect. Incidentally, with a secure supply in the frozen-embryo bank, a couple could submit to sterilisation procedures without losing the capacity to have a family. This comes close to the ultimate in family planning.

This is but one chain of options along an imaginable and not wildly speculative slippery slope. It is the kind of thing that arouses uneasiness and causes many people to say, "Now wait! What are we rushing into? Let's take another look." A prudent position, but what comes next? Do we attempt to prohibit a procedure that is on the way to being safe and efficacious, and able to bring satisfaction to many people? Could or should such a procedure be effectively prohibited? Would it not simply become covert, more expensive and perhaps less well managed? Should we attempt instead to cut off all further advance by limiting research on reproduction, endocrinology and genetics? If this were seriously to be considered could such a draconian measure be enforced worldwide? Can we, should we, cut off the progress of human knowledge?

Better, it would seem, to examine more carefully the kinds of slippery slopes that can reasonably be anticipated to appear on the rising peak of external human fertilisation. All slopes, after all, do not end in precipices and not all are slippery. We live most of our lives on slopes of one kind or another, sometimes using them to advantage, sometimes by exercise of will moving up them instead of down, sometimes enjoying the very slipperiness of slopes or the challenge to overcome them. We do not invariably forgo something that is basically beneficial because it may be abused or may lead toward something malignant. Rather we move to establish sound guidelines and policies that set appropriate boundaries, limits to rates of progression, or otherwise reassure against over-enthusiasm or irresponsibility.

For example, another identifiable slope is arising in the possible combination of external human fertilisation with molecular genetics. Some human genes have been chemically characterised, can be reproduced in bacteria and can be manipulated to yield their normal product. Human insulin has been produced in this way. Moreover, normal genetic material has been inserted into cultured human cells to correct genetic defect in those cells. This is but one step—though possibly a long one—from gene therapy to correct defects in precursor human red cells that give rise to sickle-cell anaemia and B-thalassaemia. Gene transfers also have been made into mouse embryos, leading to genetic modification not only of the resulting adult but of offspring in the next generation. The embryonic stages used in the mouse experiments are precisely the ones in the open window provided by external human fertilisation. The slope thus points toward a distant capability to influence human evolution in limited ways.

We cannot avoid considering the implications of such slopes, even though they may not have to be faced with full responsibility for a generation or two. We cannot avoid this consideration because anxiety over the possibilities produces the reaction mentioned earlier; stop moving ahead until we know where we are going. A reasonable response is to start thinking ahead even as we move ahead, so as to proceed under agreed consensus as to purposes and precautions. The agreed consensus, if it is to be achieved and effective, must be formulated on a broad social base. It must have the character of a future-sensitive tradition that will soundly guide our growing powers to intervene in human reproduction, heredity and development.

IMPROVING THE SPECIES

This is not a task that will be completed in any definable period while all progress is stopped. It is a task to begin now and to intensify as wider options evolve. It might be started by attempting to formulate principles that allow near-term progress but emphasise awareness on the part of all involved that existing concerns and long-term consequences must be carefully considered. For example, many would be reassured to know that the intent of any intervention in human reproduction would be to benefit individuals and not to "improve" the species as a whole. Though these two are linked, in contemporary thinking the first is generally understood and accepted, the second is burdened by suspicion and fraught with uncertainties as to how "improvement" will be defined—and by whom.

It would also be reassuring to know that

defects that *limit* self-realisation and self-satisfaction are the legitimate target; that conservation and fuller fruition of humanity as we know it is the goal, not the "engineering" of new forms of human life. It should be specified most compellingly that no intervention will be countenanced that reduces or limits human potential, regardless of assumed benefits to particular societies, groups or ideologies. On the other hand, interventions to gratify individual desires (for example, to provide offspring of a particular sex) will not be practised without full evaluation of collective consequences (such as distorted sex ratios).

Can such policies be formulated, elevated to the status of social guidelines and implemented? An affirmative answer can be given only if the procedures for establishing such guidelines are soundly formulated. Formulation would have to be by a deliberative body of appropriate integrity, stature and authority. The deliberations must be sufficiently accessible to incorporate all relevant opinion, and yet secluded enough to be free of excessive immediate pressures. The principles must be formulated cogently and emotively, yet simply, so that they can easily gain currency in broad communities. They should not be entangled in statutory legalities but should become matters of individual conscience, of professional ethics and of common law.

This is but a sketch to indicate the nature of the task ahead. The inventiveness of human mind has vastly extended the powers of the human hand; now we are challenged to display equivalent innovativeness in defining human purpose. It is a time for prudence but it is also a time for vision. We must not freeze into immobility but we must step carefully as we move upward to new uncharted ground. At this new level our future will be brought in greater degree into the orbit of our deliberate choice. This will, indeed, take our measure as we move into a new millenium.

• • •

POSTSCRIPT

IS IT WRONG TO CREATE TEST-TUBE BABIES?

In July 1983 a team of California scientists announced that they had performed two apparently successful embryo transfers in humans. In each case one woman was artificially inseminated with the sperm of another woman's husband, and the fertilized egg that resulted was flushed from her body and implanted in the uterus of the sperm donor's wife. This latest variation on reproductive technology might, the scientists say, benefit women whose fallopian tubes are blocked but whose eggs cannot be removed for external fertilization. It might also be used when the woman does not wish to pass on her own genes to her offspring, perhaps because she carries a genetic defect.

In 1982 both the British and Australian medical associations issued guidelines for the ethical practice of in vitro fertilization; they permit it under controlled circumstances but require informed consent and other protections for the research subjects involved. In America the Ethics Advisory Board's recommendations have never received an official response from any secretary of the department on whether to implement them, modify them, or reject them. And while the clinical practice of in vitro fertilization continues to expand, so too does the opposition.

Clifford Grobstein's views in favor of this technology are amplified in his book *From Chance to Purpose* (Addison-Wesley, 1981), which also contains the text of the Ethics Advisory Board's recommendations. A comprehensive review of varying ethical views is LeRoy Walter's "Human In Vitro Fertilization: A Review of the Ethical Literature" (*Hastings Center Report*, August 1979).

Two classic articles opposing in vitro fertilization, and other forms of reproductive technology, are: " 'Making Babies' Revisited" by Leon Kass (*The Public Interest*, Winter 1979); and "Shall We 'Reproduce'?" a two-part series by Paul Ramsey (*Journal of the American Medical Association*, June 5 and June 12, 1972).

ISSUE 3

SHOULD WOMEN BE ALLOWED TO BEAR BABIES FOR A FEE?

YES: John A. Robertson, from "Surrogate Mothers: Not So Novel After All," *Hastings Center Report* 13:5, October 1983

NO: Herbert F. Krimmel, from "The Case Against Surrogate Parenting," *Hastings Center Report* 13:5, October 1983

ISSUE SUMMARY

YES: Professor of law John A. Robertson maintains that infertile couples have a right to arrange for a surrogate mother to bear the husband's child and that the ethical and legal problems that might result are not very different from those that already exist in adoption and artificial insemination by donor.

NO: Professor of law Herbert F. Krimmel takes the position that it is immoral to bear a child for the purpose of giving it up and that surrogate mother arrangements will put additional stress on our society's shared moral values.

The desire to bear a child is a deep and natural one, and for the 3.5 million infertile American couples their inability to reproduce is often a source of sorrow and pain. But adoption is not an easy alternative today. Because of the availability of legal abortion and because an increasing number of unwed teenage mothers are choosing to keep their babies, there are fewer babies available through adoption agencies—particularly the healthy, white newborns that are most in demand. The new reproductive technologies of external fertilization and embryo transfer are available only to a few women who meet the rigid medical and other criteria.

Under these circumstances, it is not surprising that when the wife is infertile, some couples are turning to "surrogate mothers"—women who will bear the husband's baby for a fee and give it up for legal adoption. This is the way it works: A broker (usually a lawyer) puts an infertile couple in contact with potential surrogates who have been recruited (usually through newspaper advertisements) and screened for medical and psychological characteristics. If the couple and the surrogate agree, they sign a contract specifying in detail the fee (usually $10,000), the surrogate's responsibilities to care for her health during pregnancy, the conditions under which she will have an abortion, the transfer of legal custody, and the like. The price tag is high: In addition to the surrogate's fee, the couple will have to pay the broker ($5,000 to $10,000), the doctor who performs the insemination and the one who delivers the baby, and the other medical costs. The total costs can run to $30,000 or more.

In the past such arrangements were almost certainly carried out in secret, and probably without any money changing hands, between friends and relatives. But in 1980 "Elizabeth Kane" (a pseudonym), a married woman with three children, announced publicly that she had borne a baby for a fee. "It's the father's child," she is reported to have said. "I'm only growing it for him." Since then there have been an estimated two hundred to three hundred babies born by contract, and about twenty firms are now engaged in matching would-be adoptive parents and willing surrogates.

Are these contracts legal? Most states have laws prohibiting "baby-selling": the offering, giving, or receiving anything of value for placing a child for adoption. But whether surrogate mother contracts are "baby-selling" or just another form of private adoption has still to be settled in the courts. At present several states—among them South Carolina, Michigan, California, Maryland, and Alaska—are considering whether to ban, or at least to regulate, the practice. Even if the contracts are proven to be legal, serious questions remain about whether they are enforceable—whether, for instance, a mother who decides to keep the baby when it is born can be forced to give it up (in the few cases that have come to court, the mothers have won).

When any unusual social arrangement is introduced, people tend to see it either as a continuation of already existing patterns or as something completely novel, and therefore suspect. Those who support the idea of surrogate mothers see it as similar to other practices in which a child is reared by someone other than its genetic parents. As long as the child is wanted and cared for, they believe, the practice is acceptable—even desirable. That position is expressed in the selection by John Robertson that follows.

Those who oppose the practice point not only to the legal uncertainties but also the psychological and family stresses that will face the children, the surrogate, and the adoptive family. It is unethical, according to the view expressed in the selection by Herbert F. Krimmel, to produce children in order to give them up and to encourage the view of children as commodities.

YES

John A. Robertson

SURROGATE MOTHERS: NOT SO NOVEL AFTER ALL

All reproduction is collaborative, for no man or woman reproduces alone. Yet the provision of sperm, egg, or uterus through artificial insemination, embryo transfer, and surrogate mothers makes reproduction collaborative in another way. A third person provides a genetic or gestational factor not present in ordinary paired reproduction. As these practices grow, we must confront the ethical issues raised and their implications for public policy.

Collaborative reproduction allows some persons who otherwise might remain childless to produce healthy children. However, its deliberate separation of genetic, gestational, and social parentage is troublesome. The offspring and participants may be harmed, and there is a risk of confusing family lineage and personal identity. In addition, the techniques intentionally manipulate a natural process that many persons want free of technical intervention. Yet many well-accepted practices, including adoption, artificial insemination by donor (AID), and blended families (families where children of different marriages are raised together) intentionally separate biologic and social parenting, and have become an accepted thread in the social fabric. Should all collaborative techniques be similarly treated? When, if ever, are they ethical? Should the law prohibit, encourage, or regulate them, or should the practice be left to private actors? Surrogate motherhood—the controversial practice by which a woman agrees to bear a child conceived by artificial insemination and to relinquish it at birth to others for rearing—illustrates the legal and ethical issues arising in collaborative reproduction generally.

AN ALTERNATIVE TO AGENCY ADOPTIONS

Infertile couples who are seeking surrogates hire attorneys and sign contracts with women recruited through newspaper ads. The practice at present probably involves at most a few hundred persons. But repeated

Reprinted by permission from the *Hastings Center Report*, 13:5, October 1983.

attention on *Sixty Minutes* and the *Phil Donahue Show,* and in the popular press is likely to engender more demand, for thousands of infertile couples might find surrogate mothers the answer to their reproductive needs. What began as an enterprise involving a few lawyers and doctors in Michigan, Kentucky, and California is now a national phenomenon. There are surrogate mother centers in Maryland, Arizona, and several other states, and even a surrogate mother newsletter.

Surrogate mother arrangements occur within a tradition of family law that gives the gestational mother (and her spouse, if one exists) rearing rights and obligations. (However, the presumption that the husband is the father can be challenged, and a husband's obligations to his wife's child by AID will usually require his consent.)[1] Although no state has legislation directly on the subject of surrogate motherhood, independently arranged adoptions are lawful in most states. It is no crime to agree to bear a child for another, and then relinquish it for adoption. However, paying the mother a fee for adoption beyond medical expenses is a crime in some states, and in others will prevent the adoption from being approved.[2] Whether termination and transfer of parenting rights will be legally recognized depends on the state. Some states, like Hawaii and Florida, ask few questions and approve independent adoptions very quickly. Others, like Michigan and Kentucky, won't allow surrogate mothers to terminate and assign rearing rights to another if a fee has been paid, or even allow a paternity determination in favor of the sperm donor. The enforcibility of surrogate contracts has also not been tested, and it is safe to assume that some jurisdictions will not enforce them. Legislation clarifying many of these questions has been proposed in several states, but has not yet been enacted.

Even this brief discussion highlights an important fact about surrogate motherhood and other collaborative reproductive techniques. They operate as an alternative to the non-market, agency system of allocating children for adoption, which has contributed to long queues for distributing healthy white babies. This form of independent adoption is controlled by the parties and planned before conception, and enables both the father and mother of the adopted child to be selected in advance.

Understood in these terms, the term "surrogate mother," which means substitute mother, is a misnomer. The natural mother, who contributes egg and uterus, is not so much a substitute mother as a substitute spouse who carries a child for a man whose wife is infertile. Indeed, it is the adoptive mother who is the surrogate mother for the child, since she parents a child borne by another. What, if anything, is wrong with this arrangement? Let us look more closely at its benefits and harms before discussing public policy.

ALL THE PARTIES CAN BENEFIT

Reproduction through surrogate mothering is a deviation from our cultural norms of reproduction, and to many persons it seems immoral or wrong. But surrogate mothering may be a good for the parties involved.

Surrogate contracts meet the desire of a husband and wife to rear a healthy child, and more particularly, a child with one partner's genes. The need could arise because the wife has an autosomal dominant or sex-linked genetic disorder, such as hemophilia. More likely, she is infertile and the couple feels a strong need to have children. For many infertile couples the inability to conceive is a major personal problem causing marital conflict and filling both partners with anquish and self-doubt. It may also involve multiple medical workups and possibly even surgery. If the husband and wife have sought to adopt a child, they may have been told either that they do not qualify or to join the queue of couples waiting several years for agency adoptions (the wait has grown longer due to birth control, abortion, and the greater willingness of illegitimate mothers to keep their children[3]). For couples exhausted and frustrated by these efforts, the surrogate arrangement seems a Godsend. While the intense desire to have a child often appears selfish, we must not lose sight of the deep-seated psychosocial and biological roots of the desire to generate children.[4]

The arrangement may also benefit the surrogate. Usually women undergo pregnancy and childbirth because they want to rear children. But some women want to have the experience of bearing and birthing a child without the obligation to rear. Phillip Parker, a Michigan psychiatrist who has interviewed over 275 surrogate applicants, finds that the decision to be a surrogate springs from several motives.[5] Most women willing to be surrogates have already had children, and many are married. They choose the surrogate role primarily because the fee provides a better economic opportunity than alternative occupations, but also because they enjoy being pregnant and the respect and attention it draws. The surrogate experience may also be a way to master, through reliving, guilt they feel from past pregnancies that ended in abortion or adoption. Some surrogates may also feel pleased or satisfied, as organ donors do, that they have given the "gift of life" to another couple.[6]

The child born of a surrogate arrangement also benefits. Indeed, but for the surrogate contract, this child would not have been born at all. Unlike the ordinary agency or independent adoption, where a child is already conceived or brought to term, the conception of this child occurs solely as a result of the surrogate agreement. Thus even if the child does suffer identity problems, as adopted children often do, because they are not able to know their mother, this child has benefited, or at least has not been wronged, for without the surrogate arrangement, she would not have been born at all.[7]

BUT PROBLEMS EXIST TOO

Surrogate mothering is also troublesome. Many people think that it is wrong for a woman to conceive and bear a child that she does not intend to raise, particularly if she receives a fee for her services. There are potential costs to the surrogate and her family, the adoptive couple, the child, and even society at large from satisfying the generative needs of infertile couples in this way.

The couple must be willing to spend about $20,000-25,000, depending on lawyers' fees and the supply of and demand for surrogate mothers. (While this price tag makes the surrogate contract a consumption item for the middle classes, it is not unjust to poor couples, for it does not leave them worse off than they were.) The couple must also be prepared to experience, along with the adjustment and demands of becoming parents, the stress and anxiety of participating in a novel social relationship that many still consider immoral or deviant. What do they tell their friends or family? What do they tell the child? Will the child have contact with the mother? What is the couple's relationship with the surrogate and her family during the pregnancy and after? Without established patterns for handling these questions, the parties may experience confusion, frustration, and embarrassment.

A major source of uncertainty and stress is likely to be the surrogate herself. In most cases she will be a stranger, and may never even meet the couple. The lack of a preexisting relation between the couple and surrogate and the possibility that they live far apart enhance the possibility of mistrust. Is the surrogate taking care of herself? Is she having sex with others during her fertile period? Will she contact the child afterwards? What if she demands more money to relinquish the child? To allay these anxieties, the couple could try to establish a relationship of trust with the surrogate, yet such a relationship creates reciprocal rights and duties and might create demands for an undesired relationship after the birth. Even good lawyering that specifies every contingency in the contract is unlikely to allay uncertainty and anxiety about the surrogate's trustworthiness.

The surrogate may also find the experience less satisfying than she envisioned. Conceiving the child may require insemination efforts over several months at inconvenient locations. The pregnancy and birth may entail more pain, unpleasant side effects, and disruption than she expected. The couple may be more intrusive or more aloof than she wishes. As the pregnancy advances and the birth nears, the surrogate may find it increasingly difficult to remain detached by thinking of the child as "theirs" rather than "hers." Relinquishing the baby after birth may be considerably more disheartening and disappointing than she anticipated. Even if informed of this possibility in advance, she may be distressed for several weeks with feelings of loss, depression, and sleep disturbance.[8] She may feel angry at the couple for cutting off all contact with her once the baby is delivered, and guilty at giving up her child. Finally, she will have to face the loss of all contact with "her" child. As the reality of her situation dawns, she may regret not having bargained harder for access to "her baby."

As with the couple, the surrogate's experience will vary with the expectations, needs, and personalities of the parties, the course of the pregnancy, and an advance understanding of the problems that can arise. The surrogate should have a lawyer to protect her interests. Often, however, the couple's lawyer will end up advising the surrogate. Although he has recruited the surrogate, he is paid by and represents the couple. By disclosing his conflicting interest, he satisfies legal ethics, but he may not serve the interests of the surrogate as well as independent counsel.

HARMS TO THE CHILD

Unlike embryo transfer, gene therapy, and other manipulative techniques (some of which are collaborative), surrogate arrangements do not pose the risk of physical harm to the offspring. But there is the risk of psychosocial harm. Surrogate mothering, like adoption and artificial insemination by donor (AID), deliberately separates genetic and gestational from social parentage. The mother who begets, bears, and births does not parent. This separation can pose a problem for the child who discovers it. Like adopted and AID children, the child may be strongly motivated to learn the absent parent's identity and to establish a relationship, in this case with the mother and her family. Inability to make that connection, especially inability to learn who the mother is, may affect the child's self-esteem, create feelings of rootlessness, and leave the child thinking that she had been rejected due to some personal fault.[9] While this is a serious concern, the situation is tolerated when it arises with AID and adoptive children. Intentional conception for adoption—the essence of surrogate mothering—poses no different issue.

The child can also be harmed if the adoptive couple are not fit parents. After all, a willingness to spend substantial money to fulfill a desire to rear children is no guarantee of good parenting. But then neither is reproduction by paired mates who wish intensely to have a child. The nonbiologic parent may resent or reject the child, but the same possibility exists with adoption, AID, or ordinary reproduction.

There is also the fear, articulated by such commentators as Leon Kass and Paul Ramsey,[10] that collaborative reproduction confuses the lineage of children and destroys the meaning of family as we know it. In surrogate mothering, as with sperm or ovum or womb donors, the genetic and gestational mother does not rear the child, though the biologic father does. What implications does this hold for the family and the child's lineage?

The separation of the child from the genetic or biologic parent in surrogate mothering is hardly unique. It arises with adoption, but surrogate arrangments are more closely akin to AID or blended families, where at least one parent has a bloodtie to the child and the child will know at least one genetic parent. He may, as adopted children often do, have intense desires to learn his biologic mother's identity and seek contact with her and her family. Failure to connect with biologic roots may cause suffering. But the fact that adoption through surrogate mother contracts is planned before conception does not increase the chance of identity confusion, lowered self esteem, or the blurring of lineage that occurs with adoption or AID.

The greatest chance of confusing family lines arises if the child and couple establish relations with the surrogate and the surrogate's family. If that unlikely event occurs, questions about the child's relations with the surrogate's spouse, parents, and other children can arise. But these issues are not unique. Indeed, they are increasingly common with the growth of blended families. Surrogate mothering in a few instances may lead to a new variation on blended families, but its threat to the family is trivial compared to the rapid changes in family structure now occurring for social, economic, and demographic reasons.

In many cases surrogate motherhood and other forms of collaborative reproduction may shore up, rather than undermine, the traditional family by enabling couples who would otherwise be childless to have children. The practice of employing others to assist in child rearing—including wetnurses, neonatal ICU nurses, day-care workers, and babysitters—is widely accepted. We also tolerate assistance in the form of sperm sales and donation of egg and gestation (adoption). Surrogate mothering is another method of assisting people to undertake childrearing, and thus serves the purposes of the marital union. It is hard to see how its planned nature obstructs that contribution.

USING BIRTH FOR SELFISH ENDS

A basic fear about the new reproductive technologies is that they manipulate a natural physiologic process involved in the creation of human life. When one considers the potential power that resides in our ability to manipulate the genes of embryos, the charges of playing God or arrogantly tampering with nature, and the dark Huxleyian vision of genetically engineered babies decanted from bottles are not surprising. While *Brave New World* is the standard text for this fear, the 1982 film *Bladerunner* also evokes it. Trycorp., a genetic engineering corporation, manufactures "replicants," who resemble human beings in most respects, including their ability to remember their childhoods, but who are programmed to die in four years. In portraying the replicants' struggle for a long life and full human status, the film raises a host of ethical issues relevant to the issue of gene manipulation, from the meaning of personhood to the duties we have in "fabricating" people to make them as whole and healthy as possible.

Such fears, however, are not a sufficient reason to stop splicing genes or relieving infertility through external fertilization.[11] In any event they have no application to surrogate mothering, which does not alter genes or even manipulate the embryo. The only technological aid is a syringe to inseminate and a thermometer to determine when ovulation occurs. Although embryo manipulation would occur if the surrogate received the fertilized egg of another woman, the qualms about surrogate mothering stem less from its potential for technical manipulation, and more from the attitude that it reflects toward the body and mother-child relations. Mothers bear and give up children for adoption rather frequently when the conception is unplanned. But here the mother conceives the child for that purpose, deliberately using her body for a fee to serve the needs of others. It is the cold willingness to use her body as a baby-making machine and deny the mother-child gestational bond that bothers. (Ironically, the natural bond may turn out to be deeper and stronger than the surrogate imagined.)

Since the transfer of rearing duties from the natural gestational mother to others is widely accepted, the unwillingness of the surrogate mother to rear her child cannot in itself be wrong. As long as she transfers rearing responsibility to capable parents, she is not acting irresponsibly. Still, some persons take a deontological position that it is wrong to use the reproductive process for ends other than the good of the child.[12] But the mere presence of selfish motives does not render reproduction immoral, as long as it is carried out in a way that respects the child's interests. Otherwise most pregnancies and births would be immoral, for people have children to serve individual ends as well as the good of the child. In terms of instrumentalism, surrogate mothering cannot be distinguished from most other reproductive situations, whether AID, adoption, or simply planning a child to experience the pleasures of parenthood.

In this vein the problems that can arise when a defective child is born are cited as proof of the immorality of surrogate mothering. The fear is that neither the contracting couple nor the surrogate will want the defective child. In one recent case (*New York Times*, January 28, 1983, p. 18) a dispute arose when none of the parties wanted to take a child born with microcephaly, a condition related to mental retardation. The contracting man claimed on the basis of blood typing that the baby was not his, and thus was not obligated under the contract to take it, or to pay the surrogate's fee. It turned out that surrogate had borne her husband's child, for she had unwittingly become pregnant by him before being artificially inseminated by the contracting man. The surrogate and her husband eventually assumed responsibility for the child.

An excessively instrumental and callous approach to reproduction when a less than perfect baby is born is not unique to surrogate mothering. Similar reactions can occur whenever married couples have a defective child, as the Baby Doe controversy, which involved the passive euthanasia of a child with Down syndrome, indicates. All surrogate mothering is not wrong because in some instances a defective newborn will be rejected. Nor is it clear that this reaction is more likely in surrogate mothering than in conventional births for it reflects common attitudes toward handicapped newborns more than alienation inherent in the surrogate arrangement.

As with most situations, "how" something is done is more important than the mere fact of doing it. The morality of surrogate mothering thus depends on how the duties and responsibilities of the role are carried out, rather than on the mere fact that a couple produces a child with the aid of a collaborator....

NOTES

The author gratefully acknowledges the comments of Rebecca Dresser, Mark Frankel, Inga Markovits, Phillip Parker, Bruce Russell, John Sampson, and Ted Schneyer on earlier drafts.

1 People v. Sorenson, 68 Cal. 2d 280, 437 P.2d 495; Walter Wadlington. "Artificial Insemination: The Dangers of a Poorly Kept Secret," *Northwestern Law Review* 64 (1970), 777.

2 See, for example, Michigan Statutes Annotated, 27.3178 (555.54)(555.69).

3 William Landes and Eleanor Posner, "The Economics of the Baby Shortage," *Journal of Legal Studies* 7 (1978), 323.

4 See Erik Erikson, *The Life Cycle Completed* (New York: Norton, 1980), pp. 122-124.

5 Phillip Parker, "Surrogate Mother's Motivations: Initial Findings," *American Journal of Psychiatry* 140:1 (January 1983), 117-118; Phillip Parker, "The Psychology of Surrogate Motherhood: A Preliminary Report of a Longitudinal Pilot Study" (unpublished). See also Dava Sobel, "Surrogate Mothers: Why Women Volunteer," *New York Times*, June 25, 1981, p. 18.

6 Mark Frankel, "Surrogate Motherhood: An Ethical Perspective," pp. 1-2. (Paper presented at Wayne State Symposium on Surrogate Motherhood, Nov. 20, 1982.)

7 See John Robertson, "In Vitro Conception and Harm to the Unborn," 8 *Hastings Center Report* 8 (October 1978), 13-14; Michael Bayles, "Harm to the Unconceived," *Philosophy and Public Affairs* 5 (1976), 295.

8 A small, uncontrolled study found these effects to last some 4-6 weeks. Statement of Nancy Reame, R.N. at Wayne State University, Symposium on Surrogate Motherhood, Nov. 20, 1982.

9 Betty Jane Lifton, *Twice Born: Memoirs of an Adopted Daughter* (New York: Penguin, 1977); L. Dusky, "Brave New Babies," *Newsweek*, Dec. 6, 1982, p. 30.

10 Leon Kass, "Making Babies—the New Biology and the Old Morality," *The Public Interest* 26 (1972), 18; "Making Babies Revisited," *The Public Interest* 54 (1979), 32; Paul Ramsey, *Fabricated Man: The Ethics of Genetic Control* (New Haven: Yale University Press, 1970).

11 The President's Commission for the Study of Ethical Problems in Medicine and Biomedical and Behavioral Research, *Splicing Life: The Social and Ethical Issues of Genetic Engineering with Human Beings* (Washington, D.C., 1982), pp. 53-60.

12 Herbert Krimmel, Testimony before California Assembly Committee on Judiciary, Surrogate Parenting Contracts (November 14, 1982), pp. 89-96.

• • •

NO

Herbert T. Krimmel

THE CASE AGAINST SURROGATE PARENTING

Is it ethical for someone to create a human life with the intention of giving it up? This seems to be the primary question for both surrogate mother arrangements and artificial insemination by donor (AID), since in both situations a person who is providing germinal material does so only upon the assurance that someone else will assume full responsibility for the child they help to create.

THE ETHICAL ISSUE

In analyzing the ethics of surrogate mother arrangements, it is helpful to begin by examining the roles the surrogate mother performs. First, she acts as a procreator in providing an ovum to be fertilized. Second, after her ovum has been fertilized by the sperm of the man who wishes to parent the child, she acts as host to the fetus, providing nurture and protection while the newly conceived individual develops.

In this second role as host I see no insurmountable moral objections to the functions she performs. Her actions are analogous to those of a foster mother or of a wet-nurse who cares for a child when the natural mother cannot or does not do so. Using a surrogate mother as a host for the fetus when the biological mother cannot bear the child is no more morally objectionable than employing others to help educate, train or otherwise care for a child. Except in extremes, where the parent abdicates or delegates responsibilities for a child for trivial reasons, the practice would not seem to raise a serious moral issue.

I would argue, however that the first role that the surrogate mother performs—providing germinal material to be fertilized—does pose a major ethical problem. The surrogate mother provides her ovum, and enters into a surrogate mother arrangement, with the clear understanding that she is to avoid responsibility for the life she creates. Surrogate mother arrangements are designed to separate in the mind of the surrogate mother the decision to have and raise that child. The cause of this disassociation is some other benefit she will receive, most often money.[1] In other words, her desire to create a child is born of some motive other than the desire to be a parent. This separation of the decision to create a child from the decision to parent it is ethically suspect. The child is conceived not because he is wanted by his biological mother, but because he can be useful to someone else. He is conceived in order to be given away.

At their deepest level, surrogate mother arrangements involve a change in motive for creating children: from a desire to have them for their own sake, to a desire to have them because they can provide her some other benefit. The surrogate mother creates a child with the intention to abdicate parental responsibilities. Can we view this as ethical? My answer is no. I will try to explain why by analyzing various situations in which surrogate mother arrangements might be used.

WHY MOTIVE MATTERS

Let's begin with the single parent. A single woman might use AID, or a single man might use a surrogate mother arrangement, if she or he wanted a child but did not want to be burdened with a spouse.[2] Either practice would intentionally deprive the child of a mother or a father. This, I assert, is fundamentally unfair to the child.

Those who disagree might point to divorce or to the death of a parent as situations in which a child is deprived of one parent and must rely solely or primarily upon the other. The comparison, however, is inapt. After divorce or the death of a parent, a child may find herself with a single parent due to circumstances that were unfortunate, unintended, and undesired. But when surrogate mother arrangements are used by a single parent, depriving the child of a second parent is one of the intended and desired effects. It is one thing to ask how to make the best of a bad situation when it is thrust upon a person. It is different altogether to ask whether one may intentionally set out to achieve the same result. The morality of identical results (for example, killings) will often times differ depending upon whether the situation is invited by, or involuntarily thrust upon, the actor. Legal distinctions following and based upon this ethical distinction are abundant. The law of self-defense provides a notable example.[3]

Since a woman can get pregnant if she wishes whether or not she is married, and since there is little that society can do to prevent women from creating children even if their intention is to deprive them of a father, why should we be so concerned with single men using surrogate mother arrangements if they too want a child but not a spouse? To say that women can intentionally plan to be unwed mothers is not to condone the practice. Besides, society will hold the father liable in a paternity action if he can be found and identified, which indicates some social concern that people should not be able to abdicate the responsibilities that they incur in generating children. Otherwise, why do we condemn the proverbial sailor with a pregnant girl in every port?

In many surrogate mother arrangements, of course, the surrogate mother will not be transferring custody of the child to a single man, but to a couple: the child's biological father and a stepmother, his wife. What are the ethics of surrogate mother arrangements when the child is taken into a two-parent family? Again, surrogate mother arrangements and AID pose similar ethical questions: The surrogate mother transfers her parental responsibilities to the wife of the biological father, while with AID the sperm donor relinquishes his interest in the child to the husband of the biological mother. In both cases the child is created with the intention of transferring the responsibility for its care to a new set of parents. The surrogate mother situation is more dramatic than AID since the transfer occurs after the child is born, while in the case of AID the transfer takes place at the time of the insemination even before the child is yet in being. Nevertheless, the ethical point is the same: creating children for the purpose of transferring them. For a surrogate mother the question remains: is it ethical to create a child for the purpose of transferring it to the wife of the biological father?

At first blush this looks to be little different from the typical adoption, for what is an adoption other than a transfer of responsibility from one set of parents to another? The analogy is misleading, however, for two reasons. First, it is difficult to imagine anyone conceiving children for the purpose of putting them up for adoption. And, if such a bizarre event were to occur, I doubt if we would look upon it with moral approval. Most adoptions arise either because an undesired conception is brought to term, or because the parents wanted to have the child, but find that they are unable to provide for it because of some unfortunate circumstances that develop after conception.

Second, even if surrogate mother arrangements were to be classified as a type of adoption, not all offerings of children for adoption are necessarily moral. For example, would it be moral for parents to offer their three-year old for adoption because they are bored with the child? Would it be moral for a couple to offer for adoption their newborn female baby because they wanted a boy?

Therefore, even though surrogate mother arrangements may in some superficial ways be likened to adoption, one must still ask whether it is ethical to separate the decision to create children from the desire to have them. I would answer no. The procreator should desire the child for its own sake, and not as a means of attaining some other end. Even though one of the ends may be stated altruistically as an attempt to bring happiness to an infertile couple, the child is still being used by the surrogate. She creates it not because she desires it, but because she desires to get something from it.

To sanction the use and treatment of human beings as means to the achievement of other goals instead of as ends in themselves is to accept an ethic with a tragic past, and to establish a precedent with a dangerous future. Already the press has reported the decision of one couple to conceive a child for the purpose of using it as a bone marrow donor for its sibling (*Los Angeles Times,* April 17, 1979, p. 1-2). And the bioethics literature contains articles seriously considering whether we should clone human beings to serve as an inventory of spare parts for organ transplants[4] and articles that foresee the use of comatose human beings as self-replenishing blood banks and manufacturing plants for human hormones.[5] How far our society is willing to proceed down this road is uncertain, but it is clear that the first step to all these practices is the acceptance of the same principle that the Nazis attempted to use to justify their medical experiments at the Nuremberg War Crimes Trials: that human beings may be used as means to the achievement of other worthy goals, and need not be treated solely as ends in themselves.[6]

But why, it might be asked, is it so terrible if the surrogate mother does not desire the child for its own sake, when under the proposed surrogate mother arrangements there will be a couple eagerly desiring to have the child and to be its parents? That this argument may not be entirely accurate will be illustrated in the following section, but the basic reply is that creating a child without desiring it fundamentally changes the way we look at children—instead of viewing them as unique individual personalities to be desired in their own right, we may come to view them as commodities or items of manufacture to be desired because of their utility. A recent newspaper account describes the business of an agency that matches surrogate mothers with barren couples as follows:

> Its first product is due for delivery today. Twelve others are on the way and an additional 20 have been ordered. The "company" is Surrogate Mothering Ltd. and the "product" is babies.[7]

The dangers of this view are best illustrated by examining what might go wrong in a surrogate mother arrangement, and most important, by viewing how the various parties to the contract may react to the disappointment of their expectations.

WHAT MIGHT GO WRONG

Ninety-nine percent of the surrogate mother arrangements may work out just fine; the child will be born normal, and the adopting parents (that is, the biological father and his wife) will want it. But, what happens when, unforeseeably, the child is born deformed? Since many defects cannot be discovered prenatally by amniocentesis or other means, the situation is bound to arise.[8] Similarly, consider what would happen if the biological father were to die before the birth of the child. Or if the "child" turns out to be twins or triplets. Each of these instances poses an inevitable situation where the adopting parents may be unhappy with the prospect of getting the child or children. Although legislation can mandate that the adopting parents take the child or children in whatever condition they come or whatever the situation, provided the surrogate mother has abided by all the contractual provisions of the surrogate mother arrangement, the important point for our discussion is the attitude that the surrogate mother or the adopting parent might have. Consider the example of the deformed child.

When I participated in the Surrogate Parent Foundation's inaugural symposium in November 1981, I was struck by the attitude of both the surrogate mothers and the adopting parents to these problems. The adopting parents worried, "Do we have to take such a child?" and the surrogate mothers said in response, "Well, we don't want to be stuck with it." Clearly, both groups were anxious not to be responsible for the "undesirable child" born of the surrogate mother arrangement. What does this portend?

It is human nature that when one pays money, one expects value. Things that one pays for have a way of becoming viewed as commodities. Unavoidable in surrogate mother arrangements are questions such as: "Did I get a good one?" We see similar behavior with respect to the adoption of children: comparatively speaking, there is no shortage of black, Mexican-American, mentally retarded, or older children seeking homes; the shortage is in attractive, intelligent-looking Caucasian babies.[9] Similarly, surrogate mother arrangements involve more than just the desire to have a child. The desire is for a certain type of child.

But, it may be objected, don't all parents voice these same concerns in the normal course of having children? Not exactly. No one doubts or minimizes the pain and disappointment parents feel when they learn that their child is born with some genetic or congenital birth defect. But this is different from the surrogate mother situation, where neither the surrogate mother nor the adopting parents may feel responsible, and both sides may feel that they have a legitimate excuse not to assume responsibility for the child. The surrogate mother might blame the biological father for having "defective sperm," as the adopting parents might blame the surrogate mother for a "defective ovum" or for improper care of the fetus during pregnancy. The point is that the adopting parents desire a normal child, not *this* child in any condition, and the surrogate mother doesn't want it in any event. So both sides will feel threatened by the birth of an "undesirable child." Like bruised fruit in the produce bin of a supermarket, this child is more likely to become an object of avoidance than one of desire.

Certainly, in the natural course of having children a mother may doubt whether she wants a child if the father has died before its birth; parents may shy away from a defective infant, or be distressed at the thought of multiple births. Nevertheless, I believe they are more likely to accept these contingencies as a matter of fate. I do not think this is the case with surrogate mother arrangements. After all, in the surrogate mother arrangement the adopting parents can blame someone outside the marital relationship. The surrogate mother has been hosting this child all along, and she is delivering it. It certainly *looks* far more like a commodity than the child which arrives in the natural course within the family unit.

A DANGEROUS AGENDA

Another social problem, which arises out of the first, is the fear that surrogate mother arrangements will fall prey to eugenic concerns.[10] Surrogate mother contracts typically have clauses requiring genetic tests of the fetus and stating that the surrogate mother must have an abortion (or keep the child herself) if the child does not meet these tests.[11]

In the last decade we have witnessed a renaissance of interest in eugenics. This, coupled with advances in biomedical technology, has created a host of abuses and new moral problems. For example, genetic counseling clinics now face a dilemma: amniocentesis, the same procedure that identifies whether a fetus suffers from certain genetic defects, also discloses the sex of a fetus. Genetic counseling clinics have reported that even when the fetus is normal, a disproportionate number of mothers abort female children.[12] Aborting normal fetuses simply because the prospective parents desire children of a certain sex is one result of viewing children as commodities. The recent scandal at the Repository for Germinal Choice, the so called "Nobel Sperm Bank," provides another chilling example. Their first "customer" was, inbeknownest to them, a woman who "had lost custody of two other children because they were abused in an effort to 'make them smart.' "[13] Of course, these and similar evils may occur whether or not surrogate mother arrangements are allowed by law. But to the extent that these arrangements are part of the milieu that promotes the view of children as commodities, they contribute to these problems. There is nothing wrong with striving for betterment, as long as it does not result in intolerance to that which is not perfect. But I fear that the latter attitude will become prevalent.

Sanctioning surrogate mother arrangements can also exert pressures upon the family structure. First, as was noted earlier, there is nothing technically to prevent the use of surrogate mother arrangements by single males desiring to become parents and, indeed, single females can already do this with AID or even without it. But even if legislation were to limit the use of the surrogate mother arrangement to infertile couples, other pressures would make themselves felt: namely the intrusion of a third adult into the marital community.[14] I do not think that society is ready to accept either single parenting or quasi-adulterous arrangements as normal.

Another stress on the family structure arises within the family of the surrogate mother. When the child is surrendered to the adopting parents it is removed not only from the surrogate mother, but also from her family. They too have interests to be considered. Do not the siblings of that child have an interest in the fact that their little baby brother has been "given" away?[15] One woman, the mother of a medical student who had often donated sperm for artificial insemination, expressed her feelings to me eloquently. She asked, "I wonder how many grandchildren I have that I have never seen and never been able to hold or cuddle."

Intrafamily tensions can also be expected to result in the family of the adopting parents due to the asymmetry of relationship the adopting parents will have toward the child. The adopting mother has no biological relationship to the child, whereas the adopting father is also the child's biological father. Won't this unequal biological claim on the child be used as a wedge in child-rearing arguments? Can't we imagine the father saying, "Well, he is my son, not yours"? What if the couple eventually gets divorced? Should custody in a subsequent divorce between the adopting mother and the biological father be treated simply as a normal child custody dispute in any other divorce? Or should the biological relationship between father and child weigh more heavily? These questions do not arise in typical adoption situations since both parents are equally unrelated biologically to the child. Indeed, in adoption there is symmetry. The surrogate mother situation is more analogous to second marriages, where the children of one party by a prior marriage are adopted by the new spouse. Since asymmetry in second marriage situations causes problems, we can anticipate similar difficulties arising from surrogate mother arrangements.

There is also the worry the offspring of a surrogate mother arrangement will be deprived of important information about his or her heritage. This also happens with adopted children or children conceived by AID,[16] who lack information about their biological parents, which could be important to them medically. Another less popularly recognized problem is the danger of half-sibling marriages,[17] where the child of the surrogate mother unwittingly falls in love with a half sister or brother. The only way to avoid these problems is to dispense with the confidentiality of parental records; however, the natural parents may not always want their identity disclosed.

The legalization of surrogate mother arrangements may also put undue pressure upon poor women to use their bodies in this way to support themselves and their families. Analogous problems have arisen in the past with the use of paid blood donors.[18] And occasionally the press reports someone desperate enough to offer to sell an eye or some other organ.[19] I believe that certain things should be viewed as too important to be sold as commodities, and I hope that we have advanced from the time when parents raised children for profitable labor, or found themselves forced to sell their children.

While many of the social problems I have outlined here have their analogies in other present-day occurrences such as divorced families or in adoption, every addition is hurtful. Legalizing surrogate mother arrangements will increase the frequency of these problems, and due to its dramatic nature is more likely to put stress on our society's shared moral values.[20]. . .

NOTES

1 Phillip J. Parker, "Motivation of Surrogate Mothers: Initial Findings," *American Journal of Psychiatry* 140:1 (January 1983), 117-18; see also Doe v. Kelley, Circuit Court of Wayne County Michigan (1980) reported in 1980 Rep. on Human Reproduction and Law II-A-1.

2 See. e.g., C.M. v. C.C., 152 N.J. Supp. 160, 377 A.2d 821 (1977); "Why She Went to 'Nobel Sperm Bank' for Child," *Los Angeles Herald Examiner,* Aug. 6, 1982, p. A9; "Womb for Rent," *Los Angeles Herald Examiner,* Sept. 21, 1981, p. A3.

3 See also Richard McCormick, "Reproductive Technologies: Ethical Issues" in *Encyclopedia of Bioethics*, edited by Walter Reich, Vol. 4 (New York: The Free Press, 1978) pp. 1454, 1459; Robert Snowden and G.D. Mitchell, *The Artificial Family* (London: George Allen & Unwin, 1981), p. 71.

4 See, e.g., Alexander Peters, "The Brave New World: Can the Law Bring Order Within Traditional Concepts of Due Process?" *Suffolk Law Review* 4 (1970), 894. 901-02; Roderic Gorney, "The New Biology and the Future of Man," *UCLA Law Review* 15 (1968), 273, 302; J.G. Castel, "Legal Implications of Biomedical Science and Technology in the Twenty-First Century," *Canadian Bar Review* 51 (1973), 119, 127.

5 See Harry Nelson, "Maintaining Dead to Serve as Blood Makers Proposed: Logical, Sociologist Says," *Los Angeles Times*, February 26, 1974; Hans Jonas, "Against the Stream: Comments on the Definition and Redefinition of Death," in *Philosophical Essays: From Ancient Creed to Technological Man* (Chicago: University of Chicago Press, 1974), pp. 132-40.

6 See Leo Alexander, "Medical Science under Dictatorship," *New England Journal of Medicine* 241:2 (1949), 39; United States v. Brandt, Trial of the Major War Criminals, International Military Tribunal: Nuremberg, 14 November 1945-1 October 1946.

7 Bob Dvorchak, "Surrogate Mothers: Pregnant Idea Now a Pregnant Business," *Los Angeles Herald Examiner,* December 27, 1983, p. A1.

8 "Surrogate's Baby Born with Deformities Rejected by All," *Los Angeles Times,* January 22, 1983, p. 1-17; "Man Who Hired Surrogate Did Not Father Ailing Baby," *Los Angeles Herald Examiner,* February 3, 1983, p. A-6.

9 See, e.g., Adoption in America, Hearing before the Subcommittee on Aging, Family and Human Services of the Senate Committee on Labor and Human Resources, 97th Congress. 1st Session (1981), p. 3 (comments of Senator Jeremiah Denton and p. 3 (statement of Warren Master, Acting Commissioner of Administration for Children, Youth and Families, HHS.

10 Cf. "Discussion: Moral, Social and Ethical Issues," in *Law and Ethics of A.I.D. and Embryo Transfer* (1973) (comments of Himmelweit); reprinted in Michael Shapiro and Roy Spece, *Bioethics and Law* (St. Paul: West Publishing Company, 1981), p. 548.

11 See, e.g., Lane (Newsday), "Womb for Rent," *Tucson Citizen* (Weekender), June 7, 1980, p. 3; Susan Lewis, "Baby Bartering? Surrogate Mothers Pose Issues for Lawyers, Courts," *The Los Angeles Daily Journal,* April 20, 1981; see also Elaine Markoutsas, "Women Who Have Babies for Other Women," *Good Housekeeping* 96 (April 1981), 104.

12 See Morton A. Stenchever, "An Abuse of Prenatal Diagnosis," *Journal of the American Medical Association* 221 (1972), 408; Charles Westoff and Ronald R. Rindfus, "Sex Preselection in the United States: Some Implications," *Science* 184 (1974), 633, 636; see also Phyllis Battelle, "Is It a Boy or a Girl"? *Los Angeles Herald Examiner,* Oct. 8, 1981, p. A17.

13 "2 Children Taken from Sperm Bank Mother," *Los Angeles Times,* July 14, 1982; p. I-3; "The Sperm-Bank Scandal," *Newsweek* 24 (July 26, 1982).

14 See Helmut Thielicke, *The Ethics of Sex,* John W. Doberstein, trans. (New York: Harper & Row, 1964).

15 According to one newspaper account, when a surrogate mother informed her nine-year-old daughter that the new baby would be given away, the daughter replied: "Oh, good. If it's a girl we can keep it and give Jeffrey [her two-year-old half brother] away." "Womb for Rent," *Los Angeles Herald Examiner,* Sept. 21, 1981, p. A3.

16 See, e.g., Lorraine Dusky, "Brave New Babies"? *Newsweek* 30 (December 6, 1982). Also testimony of Suzanne Rubin before the California Assembly Committee on Judiciary, Surrogate Parenting Contracts, Assembly Publication No. 962, pp. 72-75 (November 19, 1982).

17 Regarding how this has posed an accelerating problem for children conceived through AID, see, e.g., Martin Curie-Cohen, et al., "Current Practice of Artificial Insemination by Donor in the United States," *New England Journal of Medicine* 300 (1979), 585-89.

18 See Richard M. Titmuss, *The Gift Relationship: From Human Blood to Social Policy* (New York: Random House, 1971).

19 See, e.g., "Man Desperate for Funds: Eye for Sale at $35,000," *Los Angeles Times,* February 1, 1975; "100 Answer Man's Ad for New Kidney," *Los Angeles Times,* September 12, 1974.

20 See generally Guido Calabresi, "Reflections on Medical Experimentation in Humans," *Daedalus* 98 (1969), 387-93; also see Michael Shapiro and Roy Spece, "On Being 'Unprincipled on Principle': The Limits of Decision Making 'On the Merits,'" in *Bioethics and Law,* pp. 67-71.

● ● ●

POSTSCRIPT

SHOULD WOMEN BE ALLOWED TO BEAR BABIES FOR A FEE?

None of the legal difficulties or adverse publicity about surrogate mothers that surrounded the case of the Michigan baby who was born defective and turned out to have been fathered by the surrogate's husband have deterred some infertile couples from seeking the services of surrogates. Harriett Blankfeld of the National Center for Surrogate Parenting in Chevy Chase, Maryland, says, "Surrogate parenting is a concept whose time has come."

Concerned by the growth of the practice, the American College of Obstetricians and Gynecologists has issued the first ethical guidelines for its members. The organization cautions physicians to avoid any surrogate mother arrangement that is likely to lead to any financial exploitation of any of the parties and acknowledges that many physicians may not wish to take part in such arrangements. One particularly troubling issue for physicians is: Who shall give the consent for treatment: the surrogate or the adoptive parents who are going to be responsible for the baby?

A persuasive argument for surrogate mothering contracts is *The Surrogate Mother* (Everest House, 1981), by Noel P. Keane with Dennis L. Breo. Keane is a lawyer who handled the first surrogate mother cases. A journalistic account is Elaine Markoutsas, "Women Who Have Babies for Other Women," *Good Housekeeping* (April 1981).

A number of articles have appeared in law journals, including Cynthia A. Rushevsky's "Legal Recognition of Surrogate Gestation," *Women's Rights Law Reporter* (Winter 1982) and M. Louise Graham's "Surrogate Gestation and the Protection of Choice," *Santa Clara Law Review* (Spring 1982). While these articles focus on the legal difficulties, they also bring up many ethical problems. George J. Annas, in his article "Contracts to Bear a Child: Compassion or Commercialism," (*Hastings Center Report,* April 1981) stresses that the best interests of the children ought to be the uppermost concern but are often ignored by the parties.

ISSUE 4

IS IT ETHICAL TO STERILIZE THE RETARDED WITHOUT CONSENT?

YES: Robert Neville, from "Sterilization of the Retarded: In Whose Interest? The Philosophical Arguments," *Hastings Center Report* 9:5, June 1978

NO: Rosalind Pollack Petchesky, from "Reproduction, Ethics, and Public Policy: The Federal Sterilization Regulations," *Hastings Center Report* 9:5, October 1979

ISSUE SUMMARY

YES: Philosopher Robert Neville argues that involuntary sterilization is in the best interests of some mildly mentally retarded people and can foster, rather than deny, them membership in the moral community.
NO: Political scientist and feminist writer Rosalind Pollack Petchesky counters with the view that involuntary sterilization denies the retarded the fundamental human right of reproduction and is often used to avoid providing adequate services and protection.

In 1927 the Supreme Court upheld a Virginia court decision permitting the involuntary sterilization of Carrie Buck, a seventeen-year-old woman who was described as the retarded daughter of a resident of Virginia's State Colony for Epileptics and Feebleminded Persons. Carrie Buck had recently given birth to an illegitimate child, who was also described as retarded. In his ruling in the case of *Buck v. Bell*, Justice Oliver Wendell Holmes said: "In order to prevent our being swamped with incompetents, it is better for all the world if instead of waiting to execute degenerate offspring for crime or to let them starve for their imbecility, society can prevent those who are manifestly unfit from continuing their kind. The principle that sustains compulsory vaccination is broad enough to cover cutting the fallopian tubes: 'Three generations of imbeciles are enough.' "

Justice Holmes' words sound archaic and callous today. The ideas of eugenics—improving the human race through selective breeding—that dominated the thinking of his day are no longer scientifically credible. Since more than eighty percent of retarded people are born to normal parents, sterilization of the retarded will not eliminate retardation. Moreover, the various civil rights movements of the 1960s and 1970s have raised public consciousness about discrimination against minorities, including the retarded. Psychological and behavioral studies have demonstrated that among people labeled as "retarded" there are a very wide range of abilities and competencies. According to recent research, Carrie Buck was probably not retarded, and her daughter was a brighter than average second-grader when she died of smallpox.

But if *Buck* v. *Bell* seems hopelessly out of date in terms of its rationale for involuntary sterilization, it has never been overturned. Although state laws vary, the justification behind the court decisions permitting sterilization without consent has increasingly emphasized that the procedure will be in the best interests of the individual who cannot choose for herself (most of the cases involve women) and will serve society's interests by preventing the birth of children to parents who cannot care for them. Procedural safeguards are often established, the most far-reaching of which were those issued by the federal Department of Health, Education, and Welfare in 1979. These regulations, which concerned the sterilizations that were to be paid for with federal money, were intended to protect the types of vulnerable women—the poor, minorities, and the retarded—who had commonly been sterilized without their consent and often without their knowledge.

Although the legal situation is murky, the ethical arguments are sharply drawn. On one side are those who, though sympathetic to the rights of the mentally retarded, see them as undeniably different from other citizens and in need of protection. In this view, which Robert Neville takes in the following selection, sterilization can be justified because it promotes the best interests of retarded individuals and encourages them to exercise their capacity for moral behavior.

On the other side are those, like Rosalind Pollack Petchesky, who stress the similarities of the retarded with other people. They see sterilization as a barely disguised way to deprive the retarded of the basic human right to reproduce, as an infringement of their dignity, and as a denial of their sexuality.

YES

Robert Neville

STERILIZATION OF THE RETARDED: IN WHOSE INTEREST?

Under certain specific circumstances it is morally permissible to sterilize some mildly mentally retarded people without their consent. At the outset of my argument I want to acknowledge that there is a grave difficulty, conceptually and empirically, in identifying which individuals belong to the relevant class of the mentally retarded. If that class is either conceptually so vague or empirically so confused that individuals who do not belong in it are inadvertently placed there, then it would be ethically impermissible to subject the class to involuntary sterilization. But let me put that difficulty aside until the end, and proceed with the argument as if we knew with acceptable exactness who the mildly mentally retarded are and which of them meet the specified requirements for sterilization.

THE HUMBLE ARGUMENT

My argument is really two arguments, one nested in the other. The first can be called the "humble argument" for involuntary sterilization, and it attempts to make the case that involuntary sterilization is in the best interest of certain mildly mentally retarded people. The second can be called the "philosophical argument," and it interprets the "humble argument" as a problem of rights and responsibilities, and attempts to show that involuntary sterilization in the right cases fosters rather than denies the membership of the mildly retarded in the moral community.

The humble argument begins with certain observations. First, at least some mildly mentally retarded people are capable of engaging in and taking pleasure in heterosexual intercourse. My following remarks concern only this group; presumably those incapable of such intercourse would not need sterilization; those who, because of inexperience, do not know their capacities for pleasure should be viewed as capable of engaging in and taking pleasure from sexual activity until proved otherwise.

Second, for some mildly retarded people sexual activity is capable of being integrated into emotional aspects of affection and this in turn can contribute to positive, rewarding fulfillments of personal and social life. Freed from pregnancy, childbearing, and childrearing, an active heterosexual life can enrich the existence of some mildly mentally retarded people in much the way it can that of so-called "normals." Other things being equal, mildly mentally retarded people can benefit from and have a right to sexual activity and the social forms sexual relationships can involve, such as marriage. Capacities for marriage and long-lasting affection do not have to be clearly present, however, for the retarded to have a claim on sexual activity for pleasure purposes alone.

Third, what begins to make the situation for the retarded "not equal" to that for "normals"? For mildly mentally retarded women the physiological and emotional changes that take place during pregnancy, and the violence of childbirth, are often experienced as disorienting and terrifying traumas. To the extent that a retarded man participates in the process, he too can be disoriented and lose his personal equilibrium.

Fourth, childrearing is sometimes beyond the capacities of mildly mentally retarded people precisely because of the characteristics of their retardation. The fact that childrearing is in practice also beyond the emotional capacities of many normal people should not obscure the overwhelming difficulty this often poses for the retarded. Now it seems a *prima facie* argument that children ought not be conceived if there is not some reasonable expectation that they will receive minimal care. (Note that this is not an argument that conceived children should be aborted, which is more difficult to sustain.)

Fifth, mildly mentally retarded people have very great difficulty in managing impermanent forms of contraception. I am assuming that sterilization is the only permanent contraceptive; at least it cannot be reversed without medical help. Therefore, if these mildly mentally retarded people are to engage in sexual intercourse, which is otherwise desirable, without fear of the woman becoming pregnant, sterilization seems the only responsible contraceptive choice.

The humble argument, then, puts together these observations and says that the mildly mentally retarded people to whom these conditions apply should be sterilized so that they may enjoy heterosexual activity if they are so inclined. If they were not sterilized they would have to be prevented from engaging in sexual activity, or conditioned to homosexual or autoerotic sexual activity exclusively, which would be hard to guarantee. If their sex lives were not so controlled, they would run the risk of pregnancy with likely trauma for themselves and improper care for their child. If the retarded people do not or cannot give consent, then someone should have the standing to insist that the retarded be sterilized involuntarily.

An added consideration may be raised at the level of the "humble argument." Who is to be sterilized, men or women or both? The answer to that question clearly depends on the circumstances, whether the candidates are living in an institution, whether that institution is highly regulated or more informal in its management of personal associations, or if the candidates are living outside institutions, in what kinds of settings. But generally the point of sterilization is to maximize the freedom of the mildly mentally retarded in sexual matters, and it is relevant to administer the procedure to any candidate meeting the conditions who stands to suffer harm or loss of freedom without it.

THE PHILOSOPHICAL ARGUMENT

The humble argument is a fairly straightforward prudential argument operating within the limits and categories generally taken for granted when dealing with the mildly mentally retarded. The philosophical argument differs by calling into question the limits and categories otherwise taken for granted.

My philosophic argument consists of two main parts. The first considers the objection that sterilization of the mildly mentally retarded is wrong if done involuntarily because it would thereby deny the subjects their proper place in the moral community, treating them as means only and not ends in themselves. I shall argue on the contrary that the procedure enhances the dignity of their position in the moral community. The second part raises the very large problem of who decides about sterilization in the context of the mildly mentally retarded. Whereas some people might argue that because no third party has sufficient standing in the matter to warrant doing violence to the candidate, I shall argue that it is the responsibility (a) of the moral community to establish policy warranting that, and (b) of its properly delegated representatives to carry it out, subject to a variety of checks.

Membership in the Moral Community

In that tradition of Western theory which takes most seriously the dignity of the human individual, the Kantian, one of the central concepts is that of the moral community. The dignity that should be accorded to each person as a human being consists in being regarded as a member of the moral community. Membership in that community means that a person is held to be morally responsible for his or her actions and life, and is to be held responsible by the rest of the community for assuming that responsibility.

With respect to human dignity, the grave danger is that a person will be treated as a thing rather than a responsible agent. This may happen when someone or some group treats a person merely as a means toward their own ends; this was Immanuel Kant's particular worry. It may also happen when the community simply fails to recognize the person as a moral agent, which happens most often when people's behavior is explained in such a way as to shift responsibility onto causes other than themselves. This objectification or alienation has been a primary worry of existentialists and many other social critics. In a strict philosophical sense (deriving from Aristotle) violence is done to people when they are prevented by external forces from fulfilling their basic or natural goals; one form of violence is to prevent someone from exercising membership in the moral community.

The mildly retarded suffer enough from their incapacities that special care should be taken to ensure them as full a membership in the moral community as possible. To sterilize them involuntarily, some people argue, is to do them unnecessary and dehumanizing violence. It is to regard them first of all as incapable of making a responsible decision about sterilization, thus ruling them out of membership in this respect; no defender of involuntary sterilization could deny this. It is, second, to regard their sex lives and childbearing and childrearing lives as so controlled by irresponsible impulses that the people may just as well be managed like objects in those areas of life. Third, it is quite possible and indeed likely, according to this position, that sterilization is sought for the mildly mentally retarded in order to make their custody easier, in which cases the people are treated in that respect as means only, not as ends in themselves.

In answer to these arguments let me point out three characteristics of the moral community. First, membership in the moral community is relative to the capacity for taking moral responsibility; there is no membership in the moral community under ordinary circumstances in the respects in which there is no capacity for taking responsibility. Second, most capacities for taking moral responsibility need to be developed; ordinary socialization develops most of them. The state of moral adulthood can be defined as being in possession of the capacity to take responsibility for developing the other capacities for responsible action that might be called upon. Third, a general moral imperative for any community is that its structures and practices foster the development of the capacities for responsible behavior wherever possible, and avoid hindering that development.

The idea of a moral community is an ideal that exists in pure form only in the imagination. When the ideal is applied to actual communities, it must be tailored to the fact that some people can have only partial memberships because of limited capacity for morally responsible behavior. Children for example only slowly take on the capacities for full membership in the moral community, and come to be treated as full members by degrees. Ordinarily we think of young children as full human beings because of their potential to develop into adults with full capacity for responsible action; when the coherence of their lives is extended over a reasonable life span, they can be expected to have moral capacities in due season.

Other people have other sorts of limited capacities for responsible behavior, such as those resulting from mental illness or senility, in which certain areas of life may involve severe incapacities for responsible behavior whereas others do not. In these cases, we usually regard people as fully human members of the moral community by according them the rights of responsibility where they do in fact have the capacity and by assigning to other people the responsibilities of proxy in areas of incapacity. The concept of a proxy, in the restrictive use of my distinction, is that of an agent who fits into the patient's overall moral responsibility as a substitute in a certain area or under certain circumstances; the concept of proxy is used to maintain and support the notion that a person is a member of the moral community in circumstances where the direct capacity for that is lacking.

The case of the mildly mentally retarded is somewhat different from that of children and from the limited capacity of the mentally ill or senile. Like children, their capacities develop; with promising advances in behavioral techniques their capacities for development may be far greater than would have been imagined a few years ago. But unlike children, the pacing and sequencing of their development does not lead to emotional maturity at the same time they reach bodily maturity. For instance, the emotional and intellectual capacities to manage conventional birth control methods, or to take pregnancy in stride or to raise children, do not develop by the time their physical development and their social peers among nonretarded people are ready for sexual activity.

Neither, sometimes, does the capacity to make informed decisions about sterilization. Indeed, if one were to say that heterosexual activity should be prevented among certain mildly mentally retarded people until such time as they developed the capacities for responsible behavior regarding pregnancy, or for consenting to surgical sterilization, the result is very likely to be the prevention of heterosexual activity completely. As the "humble argument" says, this would amount to preventing the development of an important capacity for responsible behavior in areas that would be possible if an active sex life were possible, and therefore contrary to the imperative that the moral community foster such capacities.

Mildly mentally retarded people are like certain kinds of mentally ill people in that from the adult perspective, there are certain areas of life in which they may lack capacities for responsible behavior and other areas where they may have them. But they are unlike mentally ill people in an important respect. A mentally ill person is conceived to be a member of the moral community because even though a proxy might exercise some of his or her responsibilities, he or she is believed to have the structure of a person who possesses the capacities for those responsibilities.

This belief is based on the fact, for instance, that the person once exercised those responsibilities before becoming ill. With the help of a proxy, almost as a prosthetic device, a mentally ill person can be presented to the moral community as a fully responsible moral agent. A mildly mentally retarded person, however, lacks the full personality structure that would come from having had the capacities for morally responsible behavior in the past. Although another person might make decisions in areas in which the retarded person is incapacitated, that would not strictly speaking be a case of proxy because the retarded person does not have a personality structured around the capacity for which a proxy might have to substitute.

Paternalism and proxy are models for enabling persons, children and the mentally ill respectively, to enjoy membership in the moral community when they themselves have capacities for only partial membership. Another model is needed for the limited capacity of mildly mentally retarded people, one which I propose to call the model of "involuntary restrictive conditions." The model depicts mildly mentally retarded people as members of the moral community on the condition that they meet certain restrictions. Just as people with bad eyesight may be licensed to drive with the restriction that they wear glasses, so mildly mentally retarded people may be required to meet certain restrictions in order to be members of the moral community.

The analogy with drivers' licenses is imperfect, however, because a person with bad eyesight can always choose to not drive and thereby not to need to wear glasses. But a person cannot choose to be in or out of the moral community; one is either in the position to be held responsible or one is not. Mildly mentally retarded people, and perhaps other groups, must meet the restrictions as conditions for being in the community. Therefore, from the standpoint of the mildly mentally retarded people, the restrictive conditions are involuntary.

In a moment I shall urge that sterilization may be a proper involuntary restrictive condition for membership in the moral community for mildly mentally retarded people, subject to the limitations mentioned in connection with the "humble argument." Before that, however, I want to address the question of who decides about "involuntary restrictive conditions."

Who Should Decide?

Whether a certain restrictive condition does indeed foster the capacity for responsible moral behavior is an empirical question. The suggestion has been made that, with sterilization, mildly mentally retarded people will be able to engage in the kind of sex life that can develop their capacities for responsible behavior in various human relationships. Without sterilization they either would be prevented from having sex, and therefore would not develop those capacities for sexual affection and comradeship, or they would have sex and land themselves in such trouble that sexual affection and companionship would again be beyond them.

Furthermore, this empirical argument suggests that behavior having to do with sexual affection and companionship is more important than what mildly mentally retarded people might get out of opportunities for pregnancy, childbirth, and childrearing. The first "who decides" question is: who decides whether that empirical argument is right? I suggest that this decision is a broad social one, which should be as informed as possible by experts in all the relevant fields, including both mental retardation and ethics. Clearly that argument will always be under redefinition and refinement.

But the next "who decides" question is: who sets the policies regarding the treatment of the mildly mentally retarded? The answer is that the decision must come from the political process (again informed by relevant experts, and formulated by broad intellectual dialogue). The reason for locating the decision in the political process is that this is the only legitimate way by which individuals can be dealt with against their wills by due process. But there are two normative factors within the political process. One is that the process should conform to whatever political norm structures it, for instance, that of a representative democracy. According to this factor, what the political process decides about mildly mentally retarded people is *legitimate* if due political procedures have been followed. The other normative factor, however, is the demands of being a moral community, since the political process is the vehicle for actualizing those demands. A political decision is moral if it accords with what is required as a minimum for a moral community.

If the sterilization of mildly mentally retarded people, subject to appropriate limitations, does indeed foster important capacities for morally responsible behavior, and if a moral community ought to foster such capacities where possible, the warrant for politically deciding to sterilize certain mildly mentally retarded people is a moral one, not merely one of political legitimacy. There is a *prima facie* obligation to foster people's capacity for responsibility, since this is the basis of their membership in the moral community. Paradoxically, to refrain from sterilization is to do them the violence of preventing them from participating in the moral community in one of the important respects of which they are capable.

Assuming that the political process results in a sterilization policy, by what procedures and what officers should decisions be made about particular candidates? That is a prudential political question that I shall not attempt to address. It is necessary at this point, however, to refer to what Hastings Center lore calls the "klutz factor," namely, that translating a theoretical moral argument into a public policy with significant effects is likely to lead to blunders and abuse. Because of the klutz factor, prudence may very well dictate that policies should be far more conservative than morality otherwise would dictate.

For instance, as I stated [in] the "humble argument," the candidates for involuntary sterilization should include those who are capable of engaging in and taking pleasure in heterosexual activity, and yet who are incapable of taking responsibility for this activity in regards to pregnancy and the rest. This is a positive argument for sterilizing a class of people. In light of the klutz factor, according to which the wrong people might be sent to the surgeon, perhaps it would be a prudent extra restriction to insist that candidates have demonstrated their need for sterilization by having already gotten into trouble by their sexual activity. I am not sure how to prevent such a restriction from being turned into a punitive measure against the retarded, however.

In general, with regard to all the "who decides" questions, it is important to make sure that the process of decision is self-critical and that opposition to any point of view is always funded as a corrective support.

UNIFYING THE ARGUMENTS

The philosophical side of the argument has intended to show that, contrary to the beliefs of some, involuntary sterilization does not involve treating the mildly mentally retarded as if they were not members of the moral community; rather, it acknowledges real incapacities and neutralizes their effects, thereby enabling other capacities to be realized. Furthermore, if sterilization does in some important ways lead to the development of greater capacities for responsibility, then it is part of the obligation a society owes to its potential members to provide it, subject to appropriate protections against abuse. If a mildly mentally retarded person lacks the capacity to give or withhold informed consent because he or she does not understand the subtle issues involved, then having the decision made by the society's agents is one of the "involuntary restrictive conditions" that might help place the person in the community. The society has the *prima facie* obligation to make that decision and should do so unless other considerations override.

The basic philosophical principle involved in this argument is that a moral community has the social responsibility to foster capacities for morally responsible behavior. It should do so paternalistically in the case of children; it should do so with appropriate proxies in the case of impaired capacities; and it should do so through the institution of involuntary restrictive conditions in the case of basic human capacities that are undevelopable or developable only in a future too late for other valuable capacities to be developed that otherwise would be possible.

This brings us back to the "humble argument." From a philosophical point of view, the humble argument might well be valid. At least it is not wrong by virtue of violating the canons of membership in the moral community; it does not deny human dignity. Indeed, the form of the humble argument is to provide for the dignity of humane heterosexual relations by removing the unbearable complications of potential pregnancy. Whether its premises are valid is an empirical matter.

Let me close by dealing with the question of adequate diagnosis of the appropriate conditions for involuntary sterilization. Some structure must be worked out to determine appropriate subjects. This we have seen to require two sorts of determination. First, whether informed and emotionally balanced decisions regarding sterilization are within the capacities of the candidates; if they are, then the candidates' word should be decisive, and if they prefer nonsterilization then society should respect that, whatever other compensatory restrictions it requires (such as no sexual activity). Second, whether the candidates are capable of heterosexual intercourse but not capable of coping adequately with pregnancy, childbirth, and childrearing. Not all mentally retarded people would fall into this category, and specific empirical criteria would have to be developed before a program of involuntary sterilization should be instituted.

If no mildly mentally retarded people can be found who fall into this category, then none of them should be involuntarily sterilized. The consequence of this requirement is that the validity of involuntary sterilization programs depends upon the development of criteria and diagnostic skills sufficient to discriminate the proper category of people. There have been disagreements concerning whether the definitions of relevant characteristics, and diagnostic skills at discerning them, are sufficiently developed to provide a capacity for responsible programs. In the face of excessive modesty and caution it should be pointed out that people are now classified as mildly mentally retarded and subjected to programs intended to help them.

One final point. It is sometimes believed that there is a totalitarian impetus lurking in any social policy that might require people to be good, in this case to submit to involuntary restrictive conditions in order to develop the amiable responsibilities of a decent sex life. I admit that this is a danger, but urge that it be guarded against by specific safeguards and internal critical mechanisms rather than by a blanket rejection. If people could be whole and fully responsible by themselves, society would have no positive responsibilities, only negative peacekeeping ones. But because people become responsible through the grace of social life, and because some people need special help in exercising responsibility, society does have positive duties in developing the capacity for responsible moral behavior.

• • •

NO

Rosalind Pollack Petchesky

REPRODUCTION, ETHICS, AND PUBLIC POLICY

On March 8, 1979, the Department of Health, Education, and Welfare's rules governing federal financial participation in sterilization programs went into effect.[1]... The regulations attempt to formulate a government policy for some difficult ethical questions: the meaning of "voluntary consent," the boundary between justifiable protection from abuse and unjustifiable paternalism, and the rights of those judged "incompetent to decide."...

Surgical sterilization is a procedure that renders a person permanently unable to bear children. While the ethics of a biomedical procedure are never determined by technology alone, the virtually irreversible nature of surgical sterilization makes the choice a more drastic one than it might be otherwise. The question of "voluntariness" becomes more problematic and the conditions under which the decision is made—including the social, economic, institutional, and sexual conditions—require critical scrutiny.

WHAT IS REPRODUCTIVE FREEDOM?

Whether sterilization is moral or immoral in itself may be debated among theologians and ethicists. For the purposes of public policy and of this article, however, it is the *social arrangements* in which the procedure is embedded—the degree to which those arrangements allow for full participation and consciousness of the person being sterilized, and respond to that person's concrete social and biological needs—that are critical. The value of any method of contraception must be determined not only with regard to effectiveness and safety for the user (risks), but also with regard to *reproductive freedom* (autonomy). This means the degree to which the form and the social relations implied by a particular birth control method allow the user fully to understand its medical consequences, actively to control its use and nonuse, and consciously to integrate its use with thoughtful decisions about the meaning of sexuality and childbearing in her or his own life and in society. In this view, *sterilization abuse* (or any form of involuntary sterilization) is wrong because it subverts the need of a person to control her or his own body and to decide, in a fully informed and conscious way, what sorts of interventions may be made into bodily processes, including the biological capacity to procreate. . . .

Involuntary sterilization is an invasion of a woman's bodily integrity and identity for ends that usually accommodate the needs of others in disregard of her own needs, and that pre-empt her bodily self-determination. This is not to say that the need for control over one's body and reproductive capacities is absolute or exists in isolation from one's connections to other people. Individuals exist as social beings whose needs are defined by family, class, and racial as well as gender identities. Individual women exercise, limit, or lose their capacity to bear children in relation to others to whom they are responsible and who are responsible for them—sexual partners, parents, children; and wider communities beyond the family. But in the last analysis these social connections and responsibilities do not abrogate the necessity, in any morally acceptable system of "fertility control," to maximize the consciousness and participation of the individuals whose fertility is directly involved. . . .

UNDER WHAT CONDITIONS IS VOLUNTARY CONSENT UNOBTAINABLE?

The DHEW has continued its moratorium on sterilizations of certain groups for whom voluntary consent may be problematic. These include minors (under age twenty-one), institutionalized persons, and persons declared mentally incompetent. . . .

The moratorium on the mentally incompetent is based on two considerations. As with the moratorium on minors, the intention is to avoid *prima facie* judgments about the inherent capacities of mentally incompetent persons as a category and instead to assess the concrete conditions under which such persons live either in existing institutional or "deinstitutionalized" settings. First, the comments oppose sterilization of mentally incompetent persons on the ground that such persons may be "only temporarily incompetent," and that medical and legal judgments about the permanence of incompetence are susceptible to error and difficult to monitor. The "normalization," or "developmental," view of retardation as an often changeable, ameliorable, rather than a fixed, condition is implicit in this view. Second, and most important, the Department recognizes the danger that caretakers, including parents, may "be tempted to consent to sterilization" as a way of avoiding the more difficult responsibilities of sex education, training in other forms of birth control, or alternatives to sterilization, "irrespective of the 'best interests' of the individual," and that this "could lead to abuse." While parents have tended to consider this conclusion a dismissal of their needs and concerns, it could be seen as an acknowledgment of existing social realities—for example, the lack of sufficient training and community support services for mentally incompetent individuals, which increases the burden on parents and pressures them to seek sterilization for their retarded child. . . .

"PATERNALISM" AND THE LIMITS OF PROTECTION

Laws intended to protect the "vulnerable" and the "weak" from harm have no doubt been used as a pretext to exclude certain persons from full membership in society; many instances of protective labor legislation for "women only" are a case in point. It would appear that the only way to distinguish justifiable from unjustifiable "protective" laws and rules—that is, those that provide the necessary preconditions for moral and social autonomy from those that paternalistically deny such autonomy—is to look concretely at who is being protected and from what. (Another clue is to ask who is demanding protection, and on whose behalf—a political question.) In the case of sterilization regulations, opponents argue that the thirty-day waiting period and other procedural requirements attached to informed consent provisions are "paternalistic" and "discriminatory" because they "deny poor people's right to decide for themselves" and they "limit access to services." Whether these charges are true can best be determined by looking at what happens when no such protections exist.

. The critical thing about sterilization, as DHEW recognizes, is its irreversibility. While those seeking sterilization may be inconvenienced by having to wait thirty days or fill out a rather long consent form, such inconvenience is hardly of the same magnitude as the experience of Norma Jean Serrena, a Native American woman, or the ten Chicana women who have sued the Los Angeles Medical Center, or the Relf sisters, or others who have been permanently sterilized without knowing or understanding and who regret it deeply. . . .

In contrast, we might look at the reasoning of those who oppose the federal regulations on benevolent-protective grounds. Whose interests are they protecting, and from what sorts of harm? Recent statements in favor of loosening the moratorium on sterilization of the mentally incompetent argue that sterilization is necessary—is, in fact, the most efficient means to protect retarded persons from sexual exploitation and abuse. Indeed, many parents of the retarded who are deeply concerned with their disabled children's well-being and ability to function outside of institutions look to sterilization as an answer. But the problem with this approach is that, while mentally retarded women are frequently the victims of rape and sexual abuse, sterilization is no remedy against it whatsoever; all that sterilization protects against is pregnancy, but a sterile woman can still be raped. Indeed, it could be argued that sterilization may make retarded women, particularly those in institutions or exposed to assault from male relatives, more vulnerable to sexual abuse, insofar as it eliminates the most visible evidence of such abuse, that which caretakers are most worried about, and provides an excuse for failure to offer real forms of protection (such as better counseling and management).

The same is true with regard to the concerns of parents of retarded young men, who are vulnerable to sexual stereotyping and suspicion. Sterilization will provide no guarantee against malicious accusations of sexual perversion or molestation, for the very simple reason that sexuality and fertility are not the same thing. But the fact that this obvious reality is ignored says something about the real fears of parents. Behind the argument about "protection from sexual abuse" is often the concern of caretakers—parents as well as institutions—to protect themselves from the burdens of a retarded woman's pregnancy or from being involved in a paternity suit. While such burdens are real, do they justify the severe "protective" measure involved in involuntary sterilization? If protection from sexual abuse is really an aim, would not more adequate staffing, training in self-defense measures, better supervision and safer transportation be more relevant? It would seem that "protection" here is a gloss for other concerns to which sterilization may be an efficient but inappropriate response.

Another "benevolent" pretext for sterilization of the retarded, with or without their consent (usually the unstated assumption of such proposals is that consent will be given by guardians or third parties), is that, "freed from pregnancy, childbearing, and childrearing," they may thereby enjoy "an active heterosexual life." Again, however, this assumption rests on a deep-seated fallacy, one which equates sterility with sexual pleasure (not so different from the equation of sterility with sexual safety). There is no evidence to suggest that sterilization is a necessary or a sufficient condition for sexual enjoyment, for the retarded any more than for anyone else. The only sense in which this might be true is the extrinsic one imposed by the perceptions and requirements of caretakers (if you become sterilized, then you will be allowed sexual privileges). A genuine concern for the sexual expression of retarded persons ought to focus, not on sterilization, but on the institutional and social conditions that most retarded persons experience, except those lucky enough to be in the most privileged families or the most progressive, experimental programs. More pertinent to "an active heterosexual life" for such persons would be commitment to programs involving sex counseling, body awareness, sex-integrated activities, private bedrooms, and many other basic conditions that are presently inaccessible to many retarded people (and many teenagers as well).

It would seem that the sexuality of retarded persons becomes real for parents and guardians only when it becomes visible, that is, if pregnancy occurs; conversely, if pregnancy can be avoided, it also becomes possible to avoid the conflicts and issues involved in teenage sexuality, to pretend they do not exist. The tendency to use sterilization to dispose of all the complex problems regarding sexuality, sex education, and birth control among the retarded would seem to be a form of denial. Its implications for the retarded themselves are potentially dangerous, not so much because it deprives them of their "childbearing rights," but insofar as it rationalizes the neglect of basic needs and services necessary for their full sexual expression. In this context, the federal moratorium offers a measure of protection that may open the way to more socially useful changes.

CAPACITIES AND THE LIMITS OF VOLUNTARISM

Proposals for involuntary sterilization, particularly of the mentally incompetent, rest on the premise that such persons lack a capacity to exercise voluntary consent. For those who oppose the federal regulations, especially the moratorium, claims on behalf of the mentally incompetent have tended to dominate those on behalf of interested others, such as parents and potential children of the retarded. Clearly, the courts have been more favorably disposed to benevolent-protective arguments than to utilitarian ones where involuntary sterilization is concerned. In both cases, however, the claims are supported by assumptions or assertions about the inherent characteristics of mentally incompetent persons as a group—their capacity to use alternative forms of birth control and to exercise consent, as well as their capacity to bear and raise children (these issues are often and unjustly conflated).

What are the real limits on the capacity of retarded persons to participate in their own reproductive and sexual decisions, and how should these limits be determined?

4. IS IT ETHICAL TO STERILIZE THE RETARDED?

A full discussion of this question lies outside the bounds of this article, but certain general issues may be considered without venturing into debates about the etiology of retardation. Two main points, widely accepted by specialists in developmental disabilities, need emphasis: first, the tremendous range in both functional and cognitive abilities represented by different degrees of retardation, and particularly within the largest classification, the "mildly retarded"; and, second, the necessity of taking "each case on its own merits rather than on generalized emotion or blanket legal solution." While the American Association on Mental Deficiency's classifications of mental retardation into "mild," "moderate," "severe," and "profound" are based primarily on IQ levels, it is important to remember that IQ—for "retarded" as for "normal" persons—is only a crude measure at best; that the functional capacities of persons with similar IQ levels may differ greatly depending on the quality of training, services, and care to which they have had access; and that IQ levels themselves may be increased through environmental ameliorations. Indeed, as one geneticist of retardation points out, the retarded are in fact "simply those individuals at the tail end of the normal distribution of intelligence and differ quantitatively rather than qualitatively from the remainder of the population." Functional variation is particularly broad among those approximately 5.25 million persons classified as "mildly retarded" (including an IQ range of 68 to 52 on the Stanford-Binet Scale), who in fact represent well over three-fourths of all the retarded. But even among those whose disabilities place them in the "moderate" or "severe" category, counselors working in the field attest that there are some who develop an ability not only to function sexually and to use contraceptives but to understand what they are doing.

In contrast, state involuntary sterilization laws and opponents of the moratorium rely on a set of assumptions about the origins of retardation and the inherent incapacities of retarded persons as an abstract category. These assumptions commonly include the following: (1) that retardation is in most cases genetically determined; (2) that most *mildly* retarded persons are "incapable of managing temporary forms of birth control"; (3) that most mildly retarded persons are incapable of raising children, although they may be capable of marrying or otherwise engaging in sexual activity; and (4) that the capacity of retarded persons to understand and consent freely to contraceptive planning, including sterilization, is negligible or nonexistent. The logical conclusion to such views was unceremoniously drawn in a recent newspaper column by George Will: "It is arguable that the right of the retarded to procreate . . . is problematic. And it is arguable that the state should—let us speak bluntly—license procreation."

Leaving aside for a moment the issue of parenting capacity (and Will's "blunt" proposal), all of these assumptions are highly questionable, particularly when applied to the mildly retarded. First, there is little scientific basis for assuming a strict genetic determinism in most cases of mental disability, or that its incidence in the population could be "significantly" affected by preventing the retarded themselves from propagating. There are a few disorders that are known to be genetically transmitted, such as Down Syndrome and Tay-Sachs disease. In such cases, it is possible to use genetic counseling and diagnosis to prevent unwanted births. For the most part, however, it would seem truer to view mental disability as simply one tail of a bell-shaped curve. Like all variations in intelligence, its sources represent a complex set of interactions between genetic and environmental determinants; the genetic determinants of intellectual abilities cannot be isolated, since these are themselves affected by environmental conditions. The evidence suggests, moreover, that a large proportion of mental deficiencies are associated with environmental conditions such as poverty, malnutrition, low birth weight, poor health care, or exposure to toxic substances such as lead or radiation, usually experienced prenatally and leading to permanent brain or central nervous system damage. And these are the conditions, of course, that characterize the lives of lower-class and minority people, and many people working in hazardous occupations. Clearly it is cheaper and more politically expedient—particularly in a period of economic crisis and neoconservatism—to sterilize retarded persons rather than dealing with the economic, nutritional, medical, and environmental conditions that are known threats to healthy mental development. But such eugenics programs, based on totally faulty scientific premises, can never work even on their own terms; and their "blame-the-victim" connotations are morally obnoxious.

While little is known about the ability of mildly retarded persons to use alternative forms of birth control, much is taken for granted rather than empirically verified. As one rather cautious authority points out, in this as in any other area of functional behavior, the "capacity" of mildly retarded persons will vary greatly depending on the individual user's level of cognitive and functional ability; the presence of necessary counseling and education programs, including clinicians, parents, and personnel trained and sensitive in this particular area; and a cooperative state social service agency. In the absence of such clinical and social conditions, we have little basis for assuming anything about the potential capacity of "many" or "most" retarded persons to adjust to temporary forms of birth control. On the other hand, there are reports of experimental programs that are attempting to provide retarded persons in group homes with sexual counseling services, birth control counseling and methods, and regular opportunities for a variety of sexual experiences (homosexual and autoerotic as well as heterosexual). These pilot projects indicate that such programs, when offered seriously and with sensitivity and follow-up, may be quite successful (result in a high degree of self-regulation, low pregnancy rates, and satisfying social and sexual lives). Retarded persons involved in such programs, when given the necessary training and supervision, have been able to manage nonpermanent forms of birth control. The point is not that other forms of birth control are always "better" for retarded persons than is sterilization (the pill, for example, has been associated with far more serious risks to health), or that they will always work. Rather, it is that access to a variety of options and services to enhance their reproductive and sexual experience is a necessary condition for retarded persons (or any persons) to develop the capacity to engage actively and voluntarily in such experience. Until programs of this kind are widely available and taken seriously, we will not really know much about the potential capacity of the mildly retarded either for sexuality or for self-administered birth control.

The assumption that many mildly retarded persons will be incapable of exercising sufficient foresight and responsibility to raise children independently may well be valid under existing social conditions. Yet even here it is important to point out the absence of empirical data. There are no studies reported that compare the behavior and effectiveness of retarded and nonretarded parents. Moreover, the argument voiced by advocates of the retarded is persuasive: that summary denial of the childbearing rights of retarded persons is discriminatory. What about other categories of "social deviants" whose behavior or condition may be detrimental to their children but whose legal right to raise their children is not challenged *a priori* (alcoholics, neurotics, emotionally disturbed persons)? Why are the issues any different in these cases? Again, it would seem necessary to deal with the question of childbearing capacity in terms of an individual situation rather than on a wholesale basis through procedures that provide adequate guarantees of due process and effective advocacy.

This discussion might be clarified if we could separate the issue of childrearing capacity from that of capacity to give informed consent. Social welfare workers and mentally disabled persons themselves have convincingly argued that many, perhaps most, persons classified as "mildly retarded" are capable of understanding the issues involved in decisions about sterilization and birth control, and at the same time may feel undesirous or incapable of raising a child. In fact, the federal regulations do allow for such a possibility by leaving it open to the courts and clinicians to determine whether a particular mentally incompetent individual may be competent to exercise informed consent in reproductive matters and thus to become voluntarily sterilized under federally funded programs. How this will work out in practice, and whether the courts can be relied upon to assure that the "voluntary consent" of retarded persons is genuine and not manipulated, remains to be seen. Presumably, the "readjudication of capacity to consent" would *not* mean third-party consent, and would require that the retarded person herself or himself be adequately represented by an independent counsel or advocate.

The issue that remains, and to which the moratorium allows no exceptions, is that of profoundly or severely retarded persons who are not capable of voluntary consent, who may be unable to use temporary forms of birth control, who are at risk of pregnancy, and for whom such a pregnancy would by all objective standards present a real hardship. It seems altogether likely that, given both the sexual underdevelopment of such persons and their vulnerability, the vast majority of such pregnancies are the result of rape or incest. This raises, once again, the point made earlier—the danger that introducing sterilization as a "solution" in such cases may encourage neglect of adequate staffing, services, and other protections to guard against incidents of sexual assault. I know of no study that systematically documents pregnancy rates among populations of retarded women, institutionalized as well as deinstitutionalized, much less the circumstances in which those pregnancies arise (which are often not known, since the victims usually do not know how to report). One might agree that, for certain severely retarded persons, sterilization would be a better alternative for the individual involved than anything else available, and therefore not be morally objectionable. However, under existing conditions the position of the federal regulations seems reasonable: that lifting the moratorium even in these cases would create a greater danger, since it would allow sterilization as an alternative to the development of decent care and social programs that maximize the potentialities of *all* persons, even the most disabled. . . .

• • •

POSTSCRIPT

IS IT ETHICAL TO STERILIZE THE RETARDED WITHOUT CONSENT?

In a recent case involving a twenty-two-year-old woman with the mental age of a two or three year-old, the Wisconsin Supreme Court ruled that it did not have the jurisdiction to permit her parents to choose sterilization for her, thereby passing the responsibility for establishing a policy to the state legislature. But legislatures are unlikely to revise existing laws or to pass new ones in the current climate of concern for minority rights and activism against abortion and other technologies that limit reproduction. Many observers believe that a case-by-case approach, which takes into account the particular situation of the individual, is best anyway.

A careful review of the ethical and legal arguments for and against involuntary sterilization can be found in *Mental Retardation and Sterilization: A Problem of Competency and Paternalism*, edited by Ruth Macklin and Willard Gaylin (Plenum, 1981). This book also contains excerpts from the most important legal decisions. Also see M. Kindred, J. Cohen, D. Penrod, and T. Shaffer, editors, *The Mentally Retarded Citizen and the Law* (Free Press, 1976).

Two books that emphasize the range of disabilities among the retarded are Isabel P. Tobinault, *Sex, Society, and the Disabled* (Harper & Row, 1978), and Sol Gordon, *Love, Sex and Birth Control for the Mentally Retarded: A Guide for Parents* (Planned Parenthood, 1971).

ISSUE 5

SHOULD DOCTORS WITHHOLD THE TRUTH FROM DYING PATIENTS?

YES: Joseph Collins, from "Should Doctors Tell the Truth?" *Harper's Magazine* (August 1927)

NO: Sissela Bok, from *Lying: Moral Choice in Public and Private Life* (New York: Pantheon Books, 1978)

ISSUE SUMMARY

YES: The late Joseph Collins, who was a neurologist, argues that a physician's duty to be just, gracious, and benign to his patients often involves withholding the truth from them. He believes that many patients do not want to know the truth and would be injured by it.
NO: Philosopher Sissela Bok challenges the traditional physicians' view by arguing that the harm resulting from disclosure is less than they think and is outweighed by the benefits, including the important one of giving the patient the right to choose among treatments.

In his powerful short story, "The Death of Ivan Ilych," Leo Tolstoy graphically portrayed the physical agony and the social isolation of a dying man. But, he wrote, "What tormented Ivan Ilych most was the deception, the lie, which for some reason they all accepted, that he was not dying but was simply ill, and that he only need keep quiet and undergo a treatment and then something very good would result." Instrumental in setting up the deception is Ilych's doctor, who reassures him to the very end that all will be well. Hearing the banal news once again, "Ivan Ilych looks at him as much as to say: 'Are you really never ashamed of lying?' But the doctor does not wish to understand this question. . . ."

Unlike many of the ethical issues discussed in this volume, which have arisen as a result of modern scientific knowledge and technology, the question of whether to tell dying patients the truth is an old and persistent one. However, it has been given a new urgency because medical practice today is so complex that it is often difficult to know just what the "truth" really is. A dying patient's life can often be prolonged, although at great financial and personal cost, and many people differ over the definition of a "terminal" illness.

What must be balanced in this decision are two significant principles of ethical conduct: the obligation to tell the truth and the obligation not to harm others. Moral philosophers, beginning with Aristotle, have regarded truth as either an absolute value or one that, at the very least, is preferable to deception. The great German philosopher Immanuel Kant argued in the nineteenth century that there is no justification for lying (although some later commentators feel that his absolutist position has been overstated). Other philosophers have argued that deception is sometimes justified: For example, Henry Sidgwick, an early twentieth-century British philosopher, believed that it was entirely acceptable to lie to invalids and children to protect them from the shock of the truth. Although the question has been debated for centuries, no clear-cut answer has been reached. In fact, the case of a benevolent lie to a dying patient is often given as the prime example of an excusable deception.

If moral philosophers cannot agree, what guidance is there for the physician torn between his desire for truth and his desire to protect his patient from harm (and his admittedly paternalistic conviction that he knows best what will harm the patient)? None of the early medical codes and oaths offered any advice to physicians on what to tell patients, although they were quite explicit about the physicians' obligations to keep confidential what patients told them. The American Medical Association's 1847 "Code of Ethics" did endorse some forms of deception by noting that the physician has a sacred duty "to avoid all things which have a tendency to discourage the patient and to depress his spirits." The most recent (1980) AMA "Principles of Medical Ethics" says only that "A physician shall deal honestly with patients and colleagues. . . ." However, the American Hospital Association's "Patient's Bill of Rights," adopted in 1972, is more specific: "The patient has the right to obtain from his physician complete current information concerning his diagnosis, treatment, and prognosis in terms the patient can reasonably be expected to understand. When it is not medically advisable to give such information to the patient, the information should be made available to an appropriate person in his behalf."

In the following selection, Joseph Collins presents a classic defense of the physician's decision that sometimes the truth ought to be withheld from the patient, who may not wish to know or would be harmed by knowing. Sissela Bok counters with evidence that physicians often misread patients' wishes and that withholding the truth can often harm them more than disclosure.

YES

Joseph Collins

SHOULD DOCTORS TELL THE TRUTH?

This is not a homily on lying. It is a presentation of one of the most difficult questions that confront the physician. Should doctors tell patients the truth? Were I on the witness stand and obliged to answer the question with "yes" or "no," I should answer in the negative and appeal to the judge for permission to qualify my answer. The substance of this article is what that qualification would be.

Though few are willing to make the test, it is widely held that if the truth were more generally told, it would make for world-welfare and human betterment. We shall probably never know. To tell the truth is often to perpetrate a cruelty of which many are incapable. This is particularly true of physicians. Those of them who are not compassionate by nature are made so by experience. They come to realize that they owe their fellow-men justice, and graciousness, and benignity, and it becomes one of the real satisfactions in life to discharge that obligation. To do so successfully they must frequently withhold the truth from their patients, which is tantamount to telling them a lie. Moreover, the physician soon learns that the art of medicine consists largely in skillfully mixing falsehood and truth in order to provide the patient with an amalgam which will make the metal of life wear and keep men from being poor shrunken things, full of melancholy and indisposition, unpleasing to themselves and to those who love them. I propose therefore to deal with the question from a pragmatic, not a moral standpoint.

"Now you may tell me the truth," is one of the things patients have frequently said to me. Four types of individuals have said it: those who honestly and courageously want to know so that they may make as ready as possible to face the wages of sin while there is still time; those who do not want to know, and who if they were told would be injured by it; those who are wholly incapable of receiving the truth. Finally, those whose health is neither seriously disordered nor threatened. It may seem an exaggeration to say that in forty years of contact with the sick, the patients I have met who are in the first category could be counted on the fingers of one hand. The vast majority who demand the truth really belong in the fourth category, but there are sufficient in the second—with whom my concern chiefly is—to justify considering their case.

One of the astonishing things about patients is that the more serious the disease, the more silent they are about its portents and manifestations. The man who is constantly seeking reassurance that the vague abdominal pains indicative of hyperacidity are not symptoms of cancer often buries family and friends, some of whom have welcomed death as an escape from his burdensome iterations. On the other hand, there is the man whose first warning of serious disease is lumbago who cannot be persuaded to consult a physician until the disease, of which the lumbago is only a symptom, has so far progressed that it is beyond surgery. The seriousness of disease may be said to stand in direct relation to the reticence of its possessor. The more silent the patient, the more serious the disorder.

The patient with a note-book, or the one who is eager to tell his story in great detail, is rarely very ill. They are forever asking, 'Am I going to get well?" and though they crave assistance they are often unable to accept it. On the other hand, patients with organic disease are very chary about asking point blank either the nature or the outcome of their ailment. They sense its gravity, and the last thing in the world they wish to know is the truth about it; and to learn it would be the worst thing that could happen to them.

This was borne in upon me early in my professional life. I was summoned one night to assuage the pain of a man who informed me that he had been for some time under treatment for rheumatism—that cloak for so many diagnostic errors. His "rheumatism" was due to a disease of the spinal cord called locomotor ataxia. When he was told that he should submit himself to treatment wholly different from that which he had been receiving, the import of which any intelligent layman would have divined, he asked neither the nature nor the probable outcome of the disease. He did as he was counselled. He is now approaching seventy and, though not active in business, it still engrosses him.

Had he been told that he had a disease which was then universally believed to be progressive, apprehension would have depressed him so heavily that he would not have been able to offer the resistance to its encroachment which has stood him in such good stead. He was told the truth only in part. That is, he was told his "rheumatism" was "different"; that it was dependent upon an organism quite unlike the one that causes ordinary rheumatism; that we have preparations of mercury and arsenic which kill the parasite responsible for this disease, and that if he would submit himself to their use, his life would not be materially shortened, or his efficiency seriously impaired.

Many experiences show that patients do not want the truth about their maladies, and that it is prejudicial to their well-being to know it, but none that I know is more apposite than that of a lawyer, noted for his urbanity and resourcefulness in Court. When he entered my counseling room, he greeted me with a bonhomie that bespoke intimacy, but I had met him only twice—once on the golf links many years before, and once in Court where I was appearing as expert witness, prejudicial to his case.

He apologized for engaging my attention with such a triviality, but he had had pain in one shoulder and arm for the past few months, and though he was perfectly well—and had been assured of it by physicians in Paris, London, and Brooklyn—this pain was annoying and he had made up his mind to get rid of it. That I should not get a wrong slant on his condition, he submitted a number of laboratory reports furnished him by an osteopath to show that secretions and excretions susceptible of chemical examinations were quite normal. His determination seemed to be to prevent me from taking a view of his health which might lead me to counsel his retirement. He was quite sure that anything like a thorough examination was unnecessary but he submitted to it. It revealed intense and extensive disease of the kidneys. The pain in the network of nerves of the left upper-arm was a manifestation of the resulting autonintoxication.

I felt it incumbent upon me to tell him that his condition was such that he should make a radical change in his mode of life. I told him if he would stop work, spend the winter in Honolulu, go on a diet suitable to a child of three years, and give up exercise, he could look forward confidently to a recovery that would permit of a life of usefulness and activity in his profession. He assured me he could not believe that one who felt no worse than he did should have to make such a radical change in his mode of life. He impressed upon me that I should realize he was the kind of person who had to know the truth. His affairs were so diversified and his commitments so important that he *must* know. Completely taken in, I explained to him the relationship between the pain from which he sought relief and the disease, the degeneration that was going on in the excretory mechanisms of his body, how these were struggling to repair themselves, the procedure of recovery and how it could be facilitated. The light of life began to flicker from the fear that my words engendered, and within two months it sputtered and died out. He was the last person in the world to whom the truth should have been told. Had I lied to him, and then intrigued with his family and friends, he might be alive to-day.

The longer I practice medicine the more I am convinced that every physician should cultivate lying as a fine art. But there are many varieties of lying. Some are most prejudicial to the physician's usefulness. Such are: pretending to recognize the disease and understand its nature when one is really ignorant; asserting that one has effected the cure which nature has accomplished, or claiming that one can effect cure of a disease which is universally held to be beyond the power of nature or medical skill; pronouncing disease incurable which one cannot rightfully declare to be beyond cessation or relief.

There are other lies, however, which contribute enormously to the success of the physician's mission of mercy and salvation. There are a great number of instances in support of this but none more convincing than that of a man of fifty who, after twenty-five years of devotion to painting, decided that penury and old age were incompatible for him. Some of his friends had forsaken art for advertising. He followed their lead and in five years he was ready to gather the first ripe fruit of his labor. When he attempted to do so he was so immobilized by pain and rigidity that he had to forego work. One of those many persons who assume responsibility lightly assured him that if he would put himself in the hands of a certain osteopath he would soon be quite fit. The assurance was without foundation. He then consulted a physician who without examining him proceeded to treat him for what is considered a minor ailment.

Within two months his appearance gave such concern to his family that he was persuaded to go to a hospital, where the disease was quickly detected, and he was at once submitted to surgery. When he had recovered from the operation, learning that I was in the country of his adoption, he asked to see me. He had not been able, he said, to get satisfactory information from the surgeon or the physician; all that he could gather from them was that he would have to have supplementary X-ray or radium treatment. What he desired was to get back to his business which was on the verge of success, and he wanted assurance that he could soon do so.

He got it. And more than that, he got elaborate explanation of what surgical intervention had accomplished, but not a word of what it had failed to accomplish. A year of activity was vouchsafed him, and during that time he put his business in such shape that its eventual sale provided a modest competency for his family. It was not until the last few weeks that he knew the nature of his malady. Months of apprehension had been spared him by the deception, and he had been the better able to do his work, for he was buoyed by the hope that his health was not beyond recovery. Had he been told the truth, black despair would have been thrown over the world in which he moved, and he would have carried on with corresponding ineffectiveness.

The more extensive our field of observation and the more intimate our contact with human activity, the more we realize the finiteness of the human mind. Every follower of Hippocrates will agree that "judgment is difficult and experience fallacious." A disease may have only a fatal ending, but one does not know; one may know that certain diseases, such as general paresis, invariably causes death, but one does not know that tomorrow it may no longer be true. The victim may be reprieved by accidental or studied discovery or by the intervention of something that still must be called divine grace. . . .

• • •

NO

Sissela Bok

LIES TO THE SICK AND DYING

DECEPTION AS THERAPY

. . . A forty-six-year-old man, coming to a clinic for a routine physical check-up needed for insurance purposes, is diagnosed as having a form of cancer likely to cause him to die within six months. No known cure exists for it. Chemotherapy may prolong life by a few extra months, but will have side effects the physician does not think warranted in this case. In addition, he believes that such therapy should be reserved for patients with a chance for recovery or remission. The patient has no symptoms giving him any reason to believe that he is not perfectly healthy. He expects to take a short vacation in a week.

For the physician, there are now several choices involving truthfulness. Ought he to tell the patient what he has learned, or conceal it? If asked, should he deny it? If he decides to reveal the diagnosis, should he delay doing so until after the patient returns from his vacation? Finally, even if he does reveal the serious nature of the diagnosis, should he mention the possibility of chemotherapy and his reasons for not recommending it in this case? Or should he encourage every last effort to postpone death?

In this particular case, the physician chose to inform the patient of his diagnosis right away. He did not, however, mention the possibility of chemotherapy. A medical student working under him disagreed; several nurses also thought that the patient should have been informed of his possibility. They tried, unsuccessfully, to persuade the physician that this was the patient's right. When persuasion had failed, the student elected to disobey the doctor by informing the patient of the alternative of chemotherapy. After consultation with family members, the patient chose to ask for the treatment.

Doctors confront such choices often and urgently. What they reveal, hold back, or distort will matter profoundly to their patients. Doctors stress with corresponding vehemence their reasons for the distortion or concealment: not to confuse a sick person needlessly, or cause what may well be unnecessary pain or discomfort, as in the case of the cancer patient; not to leave a patient without hope, as in those many cases where the dying are not told the truth about their condition; or to improve the chances of cure, as where unwarranted optimism is expressed about some form of therapy. Doctors use information as part of the therapeutic regimen; it is given out in amounts, in admixtures, and according to timing believed best for patients. Accuracy, by comparison, matters far less.

Lying to patients has, therefore, seemed an especially excusable act. Some would argue that doctors, and *only* doctors, should be granted the right to manipulate the truth in ways so undesirable for politicians, lawyers, and others. Doctors are trained to help patients; their relationship to patients carries special obligations, and they know much more than laymen about what helps and hinders recovery and survival.

Even the most conscientious doctors, then, who hold themselves at a distance from the quacks and the purveyors of false remedies, hesitate to forswear all lying. Lying is usually wrong, they argue, but less so than allowing the truth to harm patients. B.C. Meyer echoes this very common view:

> [O]urs is a profession which traditionally has been guided by a precept that transcends the virtue of uttering truth for truth's sake, and that is, "so far as possible, do no harm."

Truth, for Meyer, may be important, but not when it endangers the health and well-being of patients. This has seemed self-evident to many physicians in the past—so much so that we find very few mentions of veracity in the codes and oaths and writings by physicians through the centuries. This absence is all the more striking as other principles of ethics have been consistently and movingly expressed in the same documents. . . .

Given such freedom, a physician can decide to tell as much or as little as he wants the patient to know, so long as he breaks no law. In the case of the man mentioned at the beginning of this chapter, some physicians might feel justified in lying for the good of the patient, others might be truthful. Some may conceal alternatives to the treatment they recommend; others not. In each case, they could appeal to the A.M.A. Principles of Ethics. A great many would choose to be able to lie. They would claim that not only can a lie avoid harm for the patient, but that it is also hard to know whether they have been right in the first place in making their pessimistic diagnosis; a "truthful" statement could therefore turn out to hurt patients unnecessarily. The concern for curing and for supporting those who cannot be cured then runs counter to the desire to be completely open. This concern is especially strong where the prognosis is bleak; even more so when patients are so affected by their illness or their medication that they are more dependent than usual, perhaps more easily depressed or irrational.

Physicians know only too well how uncertain a diagnosis or prognosis can be. They know how hard it is to give meaningful and correct answers regarding health and illness. They also know that disclosing their own uncertainty or fears can reduce those benefits that depend upon faith in recovery. They fear, too, that revealing grave risks, no matter how unlikely it is that these will come about, may exercise the pull of the "self-fulfilling prophecy." They dislike being the bearers of uncertain or bad news as much as anyone else. And last, but not least, sitting down to discuss an illness truthfully and sensitively may take much-needed time away from other patients.

These reasons help explain why nurses

and physicians and relatives of the sick and dying prefer not to be bound by rules that might limit their ability to suppress, delay, or distort information. This is not to say that they necessarily plan to lie much of the time. They merely want to have the freedom to do so when they believe it wise. And the reluctance to see lying prohibited explains, in turn, the failure of the codes and oaths to come to grips with the problems of truth-telling and lying.

But sharp conflicts are now arising. Doctors no longer work alone with patients. They have to consult with others much more than before; it they choose to lie, the choice may not be met with approval by all who take part in the care of the patient. A nurse expresses the difficulty which results as follows:

> From personal experience I would say that the patients who aren't told about their terminal illness have so many verbal and mental questions unanswered that many will begin to realize that their illness is more serious than they're being told. . . .

The doctor's choice to lie increasingly involves coworkers in acting a part they find neither humane nor wise. The fact that these problems have not been carefully thought through within the medical profession, nor seriously addressed in medical education, merely serves to intensify the conflicts. Different doctors then respond very differently to patients in exactly similar predicaments. The friction is increased by the fact that relatives often disagree even where those giving medical care to a patient are in accord on how to approach the patient. Here again, because physicians have not worked out to common satisfaction the question of whether relatives have the right to make such requests, the problems are allowed to be haphazardly resolved by each physician as he sees fit.

THE PATIENT'S PERSPECTIVE

The turmoil in the medical profession regarding truth-telling is further augmented by the pressures that patients themselves now bring to bear and by empirical data coming to light. Challenges are growing to the three major arguments for lying to patients: that truthfulness is impossible; that patients do not want bad news; and that truthful information harms them.

The first of these arguments . . . confuses "truth" and "truthfulness" so as to clear the way for occasional lying on grounds supported by the second and third arguments. At this point, we can see more clearly that it is a strategic move intended to discourage the question of truthfulness from carrying much weight in the first place, and thus to leave the choice of what to say and how to say it up to the physician. To claim that "since telling the truth is impossible, there can be no sharp distinction between what is true and what is false" is to try to defeat objections to lying before even discussing them. One need only imagine how such an argument would be received, were it made by a car salesman or a real estate dealer, to see how fallacious it is.

In medicine, however, the argument is supported by a subsidiary point: even if people might ordinarily understand what is spoken to them, patients are often not in a position to do so. This is where paternalism enters in. When we buy cars or houses, the paternalist will argue, we need to have all our wits about us; but when we are ill, we cannot always do so. We need help in making choices, even if help can be given only by keeping us in the dark. And the physician is trained and willing to provide such help.

It is certainly true that some patients cannot make the best choices for themselves when weakened by illness or drugs. But most still can. And even those who are incompetent have a right to have someone—their guardian or spouse perhaps—receive the correct information.

The paternalistic assumption of superiority to patients also carries great dangers for physicians themselves—it risks turning to contempt. The following view was recently expressed in a letter to a medical journal:

> As a radiologist who has been sued, I have reflected earnestly on advice to obtain Informed Consent but have decided to "take the risks without informing the patient" and trust to "God, judge, and jury" rather than evade responsibility through a legal gimmick. . . .
>
> [I]n a general radiologic practice many of our patients are uninformable and we would never get through the day if we had to obtain their consent to every potentially harmful study. . . .

The argument which rejects informing patients because adequate truthful information is impossible in itself or because patients are lacking in understanding, must itself be rejected when looked at from the point of view of patients. They know that liberties granted to the most conscientious and altruistic doctors will be exercised also in the "Medicaid Mills"; that the choices thus kept from patients will be exercised by not only competent but incompetent physicians; and that even the best doctors can make choices patients would want to make differently for themselves.

The second argument for deceiving patients refers specifically to giving them news of a frightening or depressing kind. It holds that patients do not, in fact, generally want such information, that they prefer not to have to face up to serious illness and death. On the basis of such a belief, most doctors in a number of surveys stated that they do not, as a rule, inform patients that they have an illness such as cancer.

When studies are made of what patients desire to know, on the other hand, a large majority say that they *would* like to be told of such a diagnosis. All these studies need updating and should be done with larger numbers of patients and non-patients. But they do show that there is generally a dramatic divergence between physicians and patients on the factual question of whether patients want to know what ails them in cases of serious illness such as cancer. In most of the studies, over 80 percent of the persons asked indicated that they would want to be told.

Sometimes this discrepancy is set aside by doctors who want to retain the view that patients do not want unhappy news. In reality, they claim, the fact that patients say they want it has to be discounted. The more someone asks to know, the more he suffers from fear which will lead to the denial of the information even if it is given. Informing patients is, therefore, useless; they resist and deny having been told what they cannot assimilate. According to this view, empirical studies of what patients say they want are worthless since they do not probe deeply enough to uncover this universal resistance to the contemplation of one's own death.

This view is only partially correct. For some patients, denial is indeed well established in medical experience. A number of patients (estimated at between 15 percent and 25 percent) will give evidence of denial of having been told about their illness, even when they repeatedly ask and are repeatedly informed. And nearly everyone experiences a period of denial at some point in the course of approaching death. Elisabeth Kubler-Ross sees denial as resulting often from premature and abrupt information by a stranger who goes through the process quickly to "get it over with." She holds that denial functions as a buffer after unexpected shocking news, permitting individuals to collect themselves and to mobilize other defenses. She describes prolonged denial in one patient as follows:

> She was convinced that the X-rays were "mixed up"; she asked for reassurance that her pathology report could not possibly be back so soon and that another patient's report must have been marked with her name. When none of this could be confirmed, she quickly asked to leave the hospital, looking for another physician in the vain hope "to get a better explanation for my troubles." This patient went "shopping around" for many doctors, some of whom gave her reassuring answers, others of whom confirmed the previous suspicion. Whether confirmed or not, she reacted in the same manner; she asked for examination and reexamination. . . .

But to say that denial is universal flies in the face of all evidence. And to take any claim to the contrary as "symptomatic" of deeper denial leaves no room for reasoned discourse. There is no way that such universal denial can be proved true or false. To believe in it is a metaphysical belief about man's condition, not a statement about what patients do and do not want. It is true that we can never completely understand the possibility of our own death, any more than being alive in the first place. But people certainly differ in the degree to which they can approach such knowledge, take it into account in their plans, and make their peace with it.

Montaigne claimed that in order to learn both to live and to die, men have to think about death and be prepared to accept it. To stick one's head in the sand, or to be prevented by lies from trying to discern what is to come, hampers freedom—freedom to consider one's life as a whole, with a beginning, a duration, an end. Some may request to be deceived rather than to see their lives as thus finite; others reject the information which would require them to do so; but most say that they want to know. Their concern for knowing about their condition goes far beyond mere curiosity or the wish to make isolated personal choices in the short time left to them; their stance toward the entire life they have lived, and their ability to give it meaning and completion, are at stake. In lying or withholding the facts which permit such discernment, doctors may reflect their own fears (which, according to one study, are much stronger than those of laymen) of facing questions about the meaning of one's life and the inevitability of death.

Beyond the fundamental deprivation that can result from deception, we are also becoming increasingly aware of all that can befall patients in the course of their illness when information is denied or distorted. Lies place them in a position where they no longer participate in choices concerning their own health, including the choice of whether to be a "patient" in the first place. A terminally ill person who is not informed that his illness is incurable and that he is near death cannot make decisions about the end of his life: about whether or not to enter a hospital, or to have surgery; where and with whom to spend his last days; how to put his affairs in order—these most personal choices cannot be made if he is kept in the dark, or given contradictory hints and clues.

It has always been especially easy to keep knowledge from terminally ill patients. They are most vulnerable, least able to take action to learn what they need to know, or to protect their autonomy. The very fact of being so ill greatly increases the likelihood of control by others. And the fear of being helpless in the face of such control is growing. At the same time, the period of dependency and slow deterioration of health and strength that people undergo has lengthened. There has been a dramatic shift toward institutionalization of the aged and those near death. (Over 80 percent of Americans now die in a hospital or other institution.)

Patients who are severely ill often suffer a further distancing and loss of control over their most basic functions. Electrical wiring, machines, intravenous administration of liquids, all create new dependency and at the same time new distance between the patient and all who come near. Curable patients are often willing to undergo such procedures; but when no cure is possible, these procedures merely intensify the sense of distance and uncertainty and can even become a substitute for comforting human acts. Yet those who suffer in this way often fear to seem troublesome by complaining. Lying to them, perhaps for the most charitable of purposes, can then cause them to slip unwittingly into subjection to new procedures, perhaps new surgery, where death is held at bay through transfusions, respirators, even resuscitation far beyond what most would wish.

Seeing relatives in such predicaments has caused a great upsurge of worrying about death and dying. At the root of this fear is not a growing terror of the *moment* of death, or even the instants before it. Nor is there greater fear of *being* dead. In contrast to the centuries of lives lived in dread of the punishments to be inflicted after death, many would now accept the view expressed by Epicurus, who died in 270 B.C.:

> Death, therefore, the most awful of evils, is nothing to us, seeing that, when we are, death is not come, and, when death is come, we are not.

The growing fear, if it is not of the moment of dying nor of being dead, is of all that which now precedes dying for so many: the possibility of prolonged pain, the increasing weakness, the uncertainty, the loss of powers and chance of senility, the sense of being a burden. This fear is further nourished by the loss of trust in health professionals. In part, the loss of trust results from the abuses which have been exposed—the Medicaid scandals, the old-age home profiteering, the commercial exploitation of those who seek remedies for their ailments; in part also because of the deceptive practices patients suspect, having seen how friends and relatives were kept in the dark; in part, finally, because of the sheer numbers of persons, often strangers, participating in the care of any one patient. Trust which might have gone to a doctor long known to the patient goes less easily to a team of strangers, no matter how expert or well-meaning.

It is with the working out of all that *informed consent** implies and the information it presupposes that truth-telling is coming to be discussed in a serious way for the first time in the health professions. Informed consent is a farce if the information provided is distorted or withheld. And even complete information regarding sur-

*The law requires that inroads made upon a person's body take place only with the informed voluntary consent of that person. The term "informed consent" came into common use only after 1960, when it was used by the Kansas Supreme Court in Nathanson vs. Kline, 186 Kan. 393, 350, p. 2d, 1093 (1960). The patient is now entitled to full disclosure of risks, benefits, and alternative treatments to any proposed procedure, both in therapy and in medical experimentation, except in emergencies or when the patient is incompetent, in which case proxy consent is required.

gical procedures or medication is obviously useless unless the patient also knows what the condition is that these are supposed to correct.

Bills of rights for patients, similarly stressing the right to be informed, are now gaining acceptance. This right is not new, but the effort to implement it is. Nevertheless, even where patients are handed the most elegantly phrased Bill of Rights, their right to a truthful diagnosis and prognosis is by no means always respected.

The reason why even doctors who recognize a patient's right to have information might still not provide it brings us to the third argument against telling all patients the truth. It holds that the information given might hurt the patient and that the concern for the right to such information is therefore a threat to proper health care. A patient, these doctors argue, may wish to commit suicide after being given discouraging news, or suffer a cardiac arrest, or simply cease to struggle, and thus not grasp the small remaining chance for recovery. And even where the outlook for a patient is very good, the disclosure of a minute risk can shock some patients or cause them to reject needed protection such as a vaccination or antibiotics.

The factual basis for this argument has been challenged from two points of view. The damages associated with the disclosure of sad news or risks are rarer than physicians believe; and the *benefits* which result from being informed are more substantial, even measurably so. Pain is tolerated more easily, recovery from surgery is quicker, and cooperation with therapy is greatly improved. The attitude that "what you don't know won't hurt you" is proving unrealistic; it is what patients do not know but vaguely suspect that causes them corrosive worry.

It is certain that no answers to this question of harm from information are the same for all patients. If we look, first, at the fear expressed by physicians that informing patients of even remote or unlikely risks connected with a drug prescription or operation might shock some and make others refuse the treatment that would have been best for them, it appears to be unfounded for the great majority of patients. Studies show that very few patients respond to being told of such risks by withdrawing their consent to the procedure and that those who do withdraw are the very ones who might well have been upset enough to sue the physician had they not been asked to consent before hand. It is possible that on even rarer occasions especially susceptible persons might manifest physical deterioration from shock; some physicians have even asked whether patients who die after giving informed consent to an operation, but before it actually takes place, somehow expire because of the information given to them. While such questions are unanswerable in any one case, they certainly argue in favor of caution, a real concern for the person to whom one is recounting the risks he or she will face, and sensitivity to all signs of distress.

The situation is quite different when persons who are already ill, perhaps already quite weak and discouraged, are told of a very serious prognosis. Physicians fear that such knowledge may cause the patients to commit suicide, or to be frightened or depressed to the point that their illness takes a downward turn. The fear that great numbers of patients will commit suicide appears to be unfounded. And if some do, is that a response so unreasonable, so much against the patient's best interest that physicians ought to make it a reason for concealment or lies? Many societies have allowed suicide in the past; our own has decriminalized it; and some are coming to make distinctions among the many suicides which ought to be prevented if at all possible, and those which ought to be respected.

Another possible response to very bleak news is the triggering of physiological mechanisms which allow death to come more quickly—a form of giving up or of preparing for the inevitable, depending on one's outlook. Lewis Thomas, studying responses in humans and animals, holds it not unlikely that:

> ... there is a pivotal movement at some stage in the body's reaction to injury or disease, maybe in aging as well, when the organism concedes that it is finished and the time for dying is at hand, and at this moment the events that lead to death are launched, as a coordinated mechanism. Functions are then shut off, in sequence, irreversibly, and, while this is going on, a neural mechanism, held ready for this occasion, is switched on....

Such a response may be appropriate, in which case it makes the moments of dying as peaceful as those who have died and been resuscitated so often testify. But it may also be brought on inappropriately, when the organism could have lived on, perhaps even induced malevolently, by external acts intended to kill. Thomas speculates that some of the deaths resulting from "hexing" are due to such responses. Levi-Strauss describes deaths from exorcism and the casting of spells in ways which suggest that the same process may then be brought on by the community.

It is not inconceivable that unhappy news abruptly conveyed, or a great shock given to someone unable to tolerate it, could also bring on such a "dying response," quite unintended by the speaker. There is every reason to be cautious and to try to know ahead of time how susceptible a patient might be to the accidental triggering—however rare—of such a response. One has to assume, however, that most of those who have survived long enough to be in a situation where their informed consent is asked have a very robust resistance to such accidental triggering of processes leading to death.

When, on the other hand, one considers those who are already near death, the "dying response" may be much less inappropriate, much less accidental, much less unreasonable. In most societies, long before the advent of modern medicine, human beings have made themselves ready for death once they felt its approach. Philippe Aries describes how many in the Middle Ages prepared themselves for death when they "felt the end approach." They awaited death lying down, surrounded by friends and relatives. They recollected all they had lived through and done, pardoning all who stood near their deathbed, calling on God to bless them, and finally praying. "After the final prayer all that remained was to wait for death, and there was no reason for death to tarry."

Modern medicine, in its valiant efforts to defeat disease and to save lives, may be dislocating the conscious as well as the purely organic responses allowing death to come when it is inevitable, thus denying those who are dying the benefits of the traditional approach to death. In lying to them, and in pressing medical efforts to cure them long past the point of possible recovery, physicians may thus rob individuals of an autonomy few would choose to give up.

Sometimes, then, the "dying response" is a natural organic reaction at the time when the body has no further defense. Sometimes it is inappropriately brought on by news too shocking or given in too abrupt a manner. We need to learn a great deal more about this last category, no matter how small. But there is no evidence that patients in general will be debilitated by truthful information about their condition.

Apart from the possible harm from information, we are coming to learn much more about the benefits it can bring patients. People follow instructions more carefully if they know what their disease is and why they are asked to take medication; any benefits from those procedures are therefore much more likely to come about.* Similarly, people recover faster from surgery and tolerate pain with less medication if they understand what ails them and what can be done for them.**

RESPECT AND TRUTHFULNESS

Taken all together, the three arguments defending lies to patients stand on much shakier ground as a counterweight to the right to be informed than is often thought. The common view that many patients cannot understand, do not want, and may be harmed by, knowledge of their condition, and that lying to them is either morally neutral or even to be recommended, must be set aside. Instead, we have to make a more complex comparison. Over against the right of patients to knowledge concerning themselves, the medical and psychological benefits to them from this knowledge, the unnecessary and sometimes harmful treatment to which they can be subjected if ignorant, and the harm to physicians, their profession, and other patients from deceptive practices, we have to set a severely restricted and narrowed paternalistic view—that *some* patients cannot understand, *some* do not want, and *some* may be harmed by, knowledge of their condition, and that they ought not to have to be treated like everyone else if this is not in their best interest.

Such a view is persuasive. A few patients openly request not to be given bad news. Others give clear signals to that effect, or are demonstrably vulnerable to the shock or anguish such news might call forth. Can one not in such cases infer implied consent to being deceived?

Concealment, evasion, withholding of information may at times be necessary. But if someone contemplates lying to a patient or concealing the truth, the burden of proof must shift. It must rest, here, as with all deception, on those who advocate it in any one instance. They must show why they fear a patient may be harmed or how they know that another cannot cope with the truthful knowledge. A decision to deceive must be seen as a very unusual step, to be talked over with colleagues and others who participate in the care of the patient. Reasons must be set forth and debated, alternatives weighed carefully. At all times, the correct information must go to *someone* closely related to the patient. . . .

● ● ●

*Barbara S. Hulka, J.C. Cassel, et al. "Communication, Compliance, and Concordance between Physicians and Patients with Prescribed Medications," *American Journal of Public Health,* Sept. 1976, pp. 847-53. The study shows that of the nearly half of all patients who do not follow the prescriptions of the doctors (thus foregoing the intended effect of these prescriptions), many will follow them if adequately informed about the nature of their illness and what the proposed medication will do.

**See Lawrence D. Egbert, George E. Batitt, et al., "Reduction of Postoperative Pain by Encouragement and Instruction of Patients," *New England Journal of Medicine,* 270, pp. 825-827, 1964.

See also: Howard Waitzskin and John D. Stoeckle, "The Communication of Information about Illness," *Advances in Psychosomatic Medicine,* Vol. 8, 1972, pp. 185-215.

POSTSCRIPT

SHOULD DOCTORS WITHHOLD THE TRUTH FROM DYING PATIENTS?

In its 1983 report, *Making Health Care Decisions,* the President's Commission for the Study of Ethical Problems in Medicine and Biomedical and Behavioral Research cited evidence from a survey it conducted indicating that ninety-four percent of the public would "want to know everything" about a diagnosis and prognosis, and ninety-six percent would want to know specifically about a diagnosis of cancer. To the question, "If you had a type of cancer that usually leads to death in less than a year, would you want your doctor to give you a realistic estimate of how long you had to live, or would you prefer that he not tell you?" Eighty-five percent said that they would want the realistic estimate. However, when physicians were asked a similar question about what they would disclose to a patient, only thirteen percent would give a "straight, statistical prognosis," and a third said that they would not give a definite time period but would stress that it wouldn't be a long one. Physicians, it appears, are more reluctant to tell the truth than the public (at least when faced with a hypothetical choice) is to hear it.

For a strong defense of the patient's right to know the truth, see Robert M. Veatch, *Death, Dying, and the Biological Revolution* (Yale, 1976), Chapter 6. A philosophical argument with a different view is Donald Vandeveer's article, "The Contractual Argument for Withholding Information," *Philosophy and Public Affairs* (Winter 1980). See also Mark Sheldon, "Truth Telling in Medicine," *Journal of the American Medical Association* (February 5, 1982).

ISSUE 6

IS KILLING THE SAME AS LETTING DIE?

YES: James Rachels, from "Active and Passive Euthanasia," *New England Journal of Medicine,* 292:2, January 9, 1975

NO: Tom L. Beauchamp and James F. Childress, from *Principles of Biomedical Ethics,* Second edition (New York: Oxford University Press, 1983)

ISSUE SUMMARY

YES: Philosopher James Rachels argues that the conventional distinction between active euthanasia (killing) and passive euthanasia (letting die) has no moral importance, and that active euthanasia can be more humane and justifiable than passive euthanasia.
NO: Philosophers Tom L. Beauchamp and James F. Childress, in rebutting Rachels's arguments, hold that the distinction is not only valid morally (it upholds certain principles such as "do no harm") but also practically (it avoids certain harmful consequences such as loss of trust by patients in physicians).

Like truth-telling, euthanasia is an old problem given new dimensions by the ability of modern medical technology to prolong life. The word itself is Greek (literally, "happy death") and the Greeks wrestled with the question of whether, in some cases, people would be better off dead. But the Hippocratic Oath in this instance was clear: "I will neither give a deadly drug to anybody if asked for it, nor will I make a suggestion to that effect." On the other hand, if the goal of medicine is not simply to prolong life but to reduce suffering, at some point the question of what measures should be taken or withdrawn will inevitably arise. The problem is: When death is inevitable, how far should one go in hastening it?

Cases of "mercy killing" often make headlines. These are usually cases in which distraught relatives, unable to bear the suffering of their loved ones (or their own suffering), kill the patient outright. Sometimes these people are charged with murder, and if the case comes to trial the defendant is most often acquitted or put on probation, for juries are reluctant to convict a person acting out of what appear to be benevolent motives. As dramatic as these cases may be, they are relatively unproblematic in a moral sense. No moral philosopher has constructed a justification for these acts of violence, as understandable as they may be on psychological grounds.

But the majority of cases in which euthanasia is raised as a possibility are among the most difficult ethical issues to resolve, for they involve the conflict between a physician's duty to preserve life and the burden on the patient and the family that is created by fulfilling that duty. One common distinction is between "active" euthanasia (that is, some positive act such as administering a lethal injection) and "passive" euthanasia (that is, an inaction such as deciding not to administer antibiotics when the patient has a severe infection). Another common distinction is between "voluntary" euthanasia (that is, the patient wishes to die and consents to the action that will make it happen) and "involuntary"—or better, "nonvoluntary"—euthanasia (that is, the patient is unable to consent, perhaps because he or she is in a coma).

There are varying views on whether euthanasia, in any form, can ever be permissible. Some philosophers and theologians, such as Arthur Dyck, believe that although it can be moral to withdraw life-prolonging treatments when they are futile, it can never be moral to take another's life, which is sacred. Others, such as law professor Yale Kamisar, agree on nonreligious grounds, believing that there is a danger that "legal machinery initially designed to kill those who are a nuisance to themselves may someday engulf those who are a nuisance to others." On the other hand, some philosophers, such as Peter Singer, defend voluntary euthanasia, claiming that a policy of permitting people to choose to die does not violate anyone's rights or autonomy and will not lead inevitably to genocide. (The Nazi example is often invoked in this argument, since involuntary euthanasia of the sick and mentally defective preceded the wholesale destruction of Jews and other non-Aryan groups.)

The two selections that follow take up one aspect of this large issue: the question of whether there is a moral distinction between killing and letting die. Such a distinction is at the basis of the American Medical Society's policy: "The intentional termination of the life of one human being by another—mercy killing—is contrary to that for which the medical profession stands. . . ." James Rachels attacks that distinction, asserting that our moral evaluation of such acts depends more on other factors, such as motivation and consequences. Tom L. Beauchamp and James F. Childress defend both the distinction and the AMA's policy, pointing out that since "the current practice of prohibiting killing while accepting some 'allowed deaths' has served as well, if not perfectly, it should be altered only with the utmost caution."

YES

James Rachels

ACTIVE AND PASSIVE EUTHANASIA

The distinction between active and passive euthanasia is thought to be crucial for medical ethics. The idea is that it is permissible, at least in some cases, to withhold treatment and allow a patient to die, but it is never permissible to take any direct action designed to kill the patient. This doctrine seems to be accepted by most doctors, and it is endorsed in a statement adopted by the House of Delegates of the American Medical Association on December 4, 1973:

> The intentional termination of the life of one human being by another—mercy killing—is contrary to that for which the medical profession stands and is contrary to the policy of the American Medical Association.
>
> The cessation of the employment of extraordinary means to prolong the life of the body when there is irrefutable evidence that biological death is imminent is the decision of the patient and/or his immediate family. The advice and judgment of the physician should be freely available to the patient and/or his immediate family.

However, a strong case can be made against this doctrine. In what follows I will set out some of the relevant arguments, and urge doctors to reconsider their views on this matter.

To begin with a familiar type of situation, a patient who is dying of incurable cancer of the throat is in terrible pain, which can no longer be satisfactorily alleviated. He is certain to die within a few days, even if present treatment is continued, but he does not want to go on living for those days since the pain is unbearable. So he asks the doctor for an end to it, and his family joins in the request.

Suppose the doctor agrees to withhold treatment, as the conventional doctrine says he may. The justification for his doing so is that the patient is in terrible agony, and since he is going to die anyway, it would be wrong to prolong his suffering needlessly. But now notice this. If one simply withholds treatment, it may take the patient longer to die, and so he may suffer more than he would if more direct action were taken and a lethal injection given. This fact provides strong reason for thinking that, once the initial decision not to prolong his agony has been made, active euthanasia is actually preferable to passive euthanasia, rather than the reverse. To say otherwise is to endorse the option that leads to more suffering rather than less, and is contrary to the humanitarian impulse that prompts the decision not to prolong his life in the first place.

Part of my point is that the process of being "allowed to die" can be relatively slow and painful, whereas being given a lethal injection is relatively quick and painless. Let me give a different sort of example. In the United States about one in 600 babies is born with Down's syndrome. Most of these babies are otherwise healthy—that is, with only the usual pediatric care, they will proceed to an otherwise normal infancy. Some, however, are born with congenital defects such as intestinal obstructions that require operations if they are to live. Sometimes, the parents and the doctor will decide not to operate, and let the infant die. Anthony Shaw describes what happens then:

> ... When surgery is denied [the doctor] must try to keep the infant from suffering while natural forces sap the baby's life away. As a surgeon whose natural inclination is to use the scalpel to fight off death, standing by and watching a salvageable baby die is the most emotionally exhausting experience I know. It is easy at a conference, in a theoretical discussion, to decide that such infants should be allowed to die. It is altogether different to stand by in the nursery and watch as dehydration and infection wither a tiny being over hours and days. This is a terrible ordeal for me and the hospital staff—much more so than for the parents who never set foot in the nursery.[1]

I can understand why some people are opposed to all euthanasia, and insist that such infants must be allowed to live. I think I can also understand why other people favor destroying these babies quickly and painlessly. But why should anyone favor letting "dehydration and infection wither a tiny being over hours and days"? The doctrine that says that a baby may be allowed to dehydrate and wither, but may not be given an injection that would end its life without suffering, seems so patently cruel as to require no further refutation. The strong language is not intended to offend, but only to put the point in the clearest possible way.

My second argument is that the conventional doctrine leads to decisions concerning life and death made on irrelevant grounds.

Consider again the case of the infants with Down's syndrome who need operations for congenital defects unrelated to the syndrome to live. Sometimes, there is no operation, and the baby dies, but when there is no such defect, the baby lives on. Now, an operation such as that to remove an intestinal obstruction is not prohibitively difficult. The reason why such operations are not performed in these cases is, clearly, that the child has Down's syndrome and the parents and the doctor judge that because of that fact it is better for the child to die.

But notice that this situation is absurd, no matter what view one takes of the lives and potentials of such babies. If the life of such an infant is worth preserving, what does it matter if it needs a simple operation? Or, if one thinks it better that such a baby should not live on, what difference does it make that it happens to have an obstructed intestinal tract? In either case, the matter of life and death is being decided on irrelevant grounds. It is the Down's syndrome, and not the intestines, that is the issue. The matter should be decided, if at all, on that basis, and not be allowed to depend on the essentially irrelevant question of whether the intestinal tract is blocked.

What makes this situation possible, of course, is the idea that when there is an intestinal blockage, one can "let the baby die," but when there is no such defect there is nothing that can be done, for one must not "kill" it. The fact that this idea leads to such results as deciding life or death on irrelevant grounds is another good reason why the doctrine should be rejected.

One reason why so many people think that there is an important moral difference between active and passive euthanasia is that they think killing someone is morally worse than letting someone die. But is it? Is killing, in itself, worse than letting die? To investigate this issue, two cases may be considered that are exactly alike except that one involves killing whereas the other involves letting someone die. Then, it can be asked whether this difference makes any difference to the moral assessments. It is important that the cases be exactly alike, except for this one difference, since otherwise one cannot be confident that it is this difference and not some other that accounts for any variation in the assessment of the two cases. So, let us consider this pair of cases:

In the first, Smith stands to gain a large inheritance if anything should happen to his six-year-old cousin. One evening while the child is taking his bath, Smith sneaks into the bathroom and drowns the child, and then arranges things so that it will look like an accident.

In the second, Jones also stands to gain if anything should happen to his six-year-old cousin. Like Smith, Jones sneaks in planning to drown the child in his bath. However, just as he enters the bathroom Jones sees the child slip and hit his head, and fall face down in the water. Jones is delighted; he stands by, ready to push the child's head back under if it is necessary, but it is not necessary. With only a little thrashing about, the child drowns all by himself, "accidentally," as Jones watches and does nothing.

Now Smith killed the child, whereas Jones "merely" let the child die. That is the only difference between them. Did either man behave better, from a moral point of view? If the difference between killing and letting die were in itself a morally important matter, one should say that Jones's behavior was less reprehensible than Smith's. But does one really want to say that? I think not. In the first place, both men acted from the same motive, personal gain, and both had exactly the same end in view when they acted. It may be inferred from Smith's conduct that he is a bad man, although that judgment may be withdrawn or modified if certain further facts are learned about him—for example, that he is mentally deranged. But would not the very same thing be inferred about Jones from his conduct? And would not the same further considerations also be relevant to any modification of this judgment? Moreover, suppose Jones pleaded, in his own defense, "After all, I didn't do anything except just stand there and watch the child drown. I didn't kill him; I only let him die." Again, if letting die were in itself less bad than killing, this defense should have at least some weight. But it does not. Such a "defense" can only be regarded as a grotesque perversion of moral reasoning. Morally speaking, it is no defense at all.

Now, it may be pointed out, quite properly, that the cases of euthanasia with which doctors are concerned are not like this at all. They do not involve personal gain or the destruction of normal healthy children. Doctors are concerned only with cases in which the patient's life is of no further use of him, or in which the patient's life has become or will soon become a terrible burden. However, the point is the same in these cases: the bare difference between killing and letting die does not, in itself, make a moral difference. If a doctor lets a patient die, for humane reasons, he is in the same moral position as if he had given the patient a lethal injection for humane reasons. If his decision was wrong—if, for example, the patient's illness was in fact curable—the decision would be equally regrettable no matter which method was used to carry it out. And if the doctor's decision was the right one, the method used is not in itself important.

The AMA policy statement isolates the crucial issue very well: the crucial issue is "the intentional termination of the life of one human being by another." But after identifying this issue, and forbidding "mercy killing," the statement goes on to deny that the cessation of treatment is the intentional termination of life. This is where the mistake comes in, for what is the cessation of treatment, in these circumstances, if it is not "the intentional termination of the life of one human being by another"? Of course it is exactly that, and if it were not, there would be no point to it.

Many people will find this judgment hard to accept. One reason, I think, is that it is very easy to conflate the question of whether killing is, in itself, worse than letting die, with the very different question of whether most actual cases of killing are more reprehensible than most actual cases of letting die. Most actual cases of killing are clearly terrible (think, for example, of all the murders reported in the newspapers), and one hears of such cases every day. On the other hand, one hardly ever hears of a case of letting die, except for the action of doctors who are motivated by humanitarian reasons. So one learns to think of killing in a much worse light than of letting die. But this does not mean that there is something about killing that makes it in itself worse than letting die, for it is not the bare difference between killing and letting die that makes the difference in these cases. Rather, the other factors—the murderer's motive of personal gain, for example, contrasted with the doctor's humanitarian motivation—account for different reactions to the different cases.

I have argued that killing is not in itself any worse than letting die; if my contention is right, it follows that active euthanasia is not any worse than passive euthanasia. What arguments can be given on the other side? The most common, I believe, is the following:

"The important difference between active and passive euthanasia is that, in passive euthanasia, the doctor does not do anything to bring about the patient's death. The doctor does nothing, and the patient dies of whatever ills already afflict him. In active euthanasia, however, the doctor does something to bring about the patient's death: he kills him. The doctor who gives the patient with cancer a lethal injection has himself caused his patient's death; whereas if he merely ceases treatment, the cancer is the cause of the death."

A number of points need to be made here. The first is that it is not exactly correct to say that in passive euthanasia the doctor does nothing, for he does do one thing that is very important: he lets the patient die. "Letting someone die" is certainly different, in some respects, from other types of action—mainly in that it is a kind of action that one may perform by way of not performing certain other actions. For example, one may let a patient die by way of not giving medication, just as one may insult someone by way of not shaking his hand. But for any purpose of moral assessment, it is a type of action nonetheless. The decision to let a patient die is subject to moral appraisal in the same way that a decision to kill him would be subject to moral appraisal: it may be assessed as wise or unwise, compassionate or sadistic, right or wrong. If a doctor deliberately let a patient die who was suffering from a routinely curable illness, the doctor would certainly be to blame for what he had done, just as he would be to blame if he had needlessly killed the patient. Charges against him would then be appropriate. If so, it would be no defense at all for him to insist that he didn't "do anything." He would have done something very serious indeed, for he let his patient die.

Fixing the cause of death may be very important from a legal point of view, for it may determine whether criminal charges are brought against the doctor. But I do not think that this notion can be used to show a moral difference between active and passive euthanasia. The reason why it is considered bad to be the cause of someone's death is that death is regarded as a great evil—and so it is. However, if it has been decided that euthanasia—even passive euthanasia—is desirable in a given case, it has also been decided that in this instance death is no greater an evil than the patient's continued existence. And if this is true, the usual reason for not wanting to be the cause of someone's death simply does not apply.

Finally, doctors may think that all of this is only of academic interest—the sort of thing that philosophers may worry about but that has no practical bearing on their own work. After all, doctors must be concerned about the legal consequences of what they do, and active euthanasia is clearly forbidden by the law. But even so, doctors should also be concerned with the fact that the law is forcing upon them a moral doctrine that may well be indefensible, and has a considerable effect on their practices. Of course, most doctors are not now in the position of being coerced in this matter, for they do not regard themselves as merely going along with what the law requires. Rather, in statements such as the AMA policy statement that I have quoted, they are endorsing this doctrine as a central point of medical ethics. In that statement, active euthanasia is condemned not merely as illegal but as "contrary to that for which the medical profession stands," whereas passive euthanasia is approved. However, the preceding considerations suggest that there is really no moral difference between the two, considered in themselves (there may be important moral differences in some cases in their *consequences,* but as I pointed out, these differences may make active euthanasia, and not passive euthanasia, the morally preferable option). So, whereas doctors may have to discriminate between active and passive euthanasia to satisfy the law, they should not do any more than that. In particular, they should not give the distinction any added authority and weight by writing it into official statements of medical ethics.

NOTE

1 A. Shaw, "Doctor, Do We Have a Choice?" *The New York Times Magazine,* January 30, 1972, p. 59.

• • •

NO

Tom L. Beauchamp and James F. Childress

PRINCIPLES OF BIOMEDICAL ETHICS

KILLING AND LETTING DIE

. . . [A] sixty-eight-year-old doctor, who suffered severely from terminal carcinoma of the stomach, collapsed with a massive pulmonary embolism. He survived because one of his young colleagues performed a pulmonary embolectomy. Upon recovery the doctor-patient requested that no steps should be taken to prolong his life if he suffered another cardiovascular collapse. He even wrote an authorization to this effect for the hospital records. He reasoned that his pain was too much to bear given his dismal prospects. He thus asked to be *allowed to die* under certain conditions, but he did not ask to be *killed.* In [another] case . . . a defective infant needed an operation to correct a tracheoesophogeal fistula. The parents and physicians determined that survival was not in this infant's best interests and decided to allow the infant to die rather than to perform an operation. In both cases, we need to ask whether certain actions, such as intentionally not trying to overcome a cardiovascular collapse and not performing an operation, can legitimately be described as "allowing to die" rather than "killing," and whether such actions are justifiable.

For many people, it is important to distinguish killing and letting die, and to prohibit the former while authorizing the latter in some range of cases. For example, after prohibiting "mercy killing" or the "intentional termination of the life of one human being by another,"[1] the AMA House of Delegates held that cessation of treatment is morally justified when the patient and/or the patient's immediate family, with the advice and judgment of the physician, decide to withhold or stop the use of "extraordinary means to prolong life when there is irrefutable evidence that biological death is imminent." Although several terms in this statement—such as "extraordinary," "irrefutable," and "imminent"—need careful examination, it is clear that the statement authorizes some instances of allowing to die by withholding or stopping treatment, while it excludes killing. Whether letting particular patients die—such as the sixty-eight-year-old man suffering from terminal carcinoma of the stomach and the defective infant needing an operation—is morally acceptable would depend on several conditions. But if their deaths involve killing rather than being merely "allowed deaths," they are not justifiable according to the AMA House of Delegates' statement.

In recent years, the distinction between killing and letting die has come under frequent attack. Some critics focus on developments in biomedical technology that appear to make it difficult to classify acts as instances either of killing or of letting die. Unplugging the respirator is now a standard example of this problem. Other critics dismiss the distinction itself, holding that it is a "moral quibble" without any "moral bite." As we explore the arguments for and against this distinction, it is important to emphasize that acceptance or rejection of the *distinction* does not necessarily determine *moral conclusions* about particular cases. For instance, it is possible to reject the distinction and to hold that some cases of what have been called "killing" and "letting die" are morally permissible, or that all cases are morally prohibited; and it is also possible to affirm the distinction and yet to hold that most cases of letting die and all cases of killing are morally wrong. Even if the distinction is morally significant, the label "killing" or the label "letting die" should not dictate a conclusion about a particular case. For example, it would be absurd to affirm the moral significance of the distinction and then to accept *all* cases of letting die as morally fitting. Even instances of letting die must meet other criteria such as the detriment-benefit calculation, and some cases of allowed death involve egregious negligence.

In a widely discussed argument for rejecting both the distinction between active and passive euthanasia and the AMA's policy statement, James Rachels contends that killing is not, in itself, worse than letting die.[2] That is, the "bare difference" between acts of killing and acts of letting die is not in itself a morally relevant difference. Part of his strategy is to sketch two cases that differ only in that one involves killing, while the other involves allowing to die. He contends that if there is no morally relevant difference between these cases, the "bare difference" between killing and allowing to die is demonstrated to be morally irrelevant. In his two cases, two young men want their six-year-old cousins dead so that they can gain large inheritances. Smith drowns his cousin while the boy is taking a bath. Jones plans to drown his cousin, but as he enters the bathroom he sees the boy slip and hit his head; Jones stands by, doing nothing, while the boy drowns. Smith killed his cousin; Jones merely allowed his cousin to die.

While we agree with Rachels that both acts are equally reprehensible because of the motives, ends, and actions, we do not accept his conclusion that these examples show that the distinction between killing and letting die is morally irrelevant. Several rejoinders to Rachels are in order. First, Rachels's cases and the cessations of treatment envisioned by the AMA are so markedly disanalogous that it is not clear what Rachels's argument shows. In some cases of unjustified acts, including both of Rachels's examples, we are not interested in moral distinctions per se. As Richard Trammell points out, some examples have a "masking" or "sledgehammer" effect; the fact that "one cannot distinguish the taste of two wines when both are mixed with green persimmon juice, does not imply that there is no distinction between the wines."[3] Since Rachel's examples involve two morally justified acts by agents whose motives and intentions are despicable, it is not surprising that some *other* features of their situations, such as killing and letting die, do not strike us as morally compelling considerations.

Second, while Rachels's cases involve two *unjustified* actions, one of killing and the other of letting die, the AMA statement distinguished cases of *unjustified killing* from cases of *justified letting die*. The AMA statement does not, however, claim that the moral difference is identical to the distinction between killing and letting die. It does not even imply that the "bare difference" between (passive) letting die and (active) killing is the only difference or even a morally sufficient difference between the justified and unjustified cases. Its point is rather that the justified actions in medicine are confined to (passive) letting die. While the AMA statement holds that "mercy killing" in medicine is unjustified in all circumstances, it does not hold that letting die is right in all circumstances or that killing outside medicine is always wrong. For an act that results in an earlier death for the patient to be justified, it is necessary that it be describable as an act of "letting die," but this description is not sufficient to justify the act; nor is the bare description of killing sufficient to make *all* acts of killing wrong. This AMA pronouncement is meant to hold only in the context of the physician-patient relationship.

Third, in Rachels's cases Smith and Jones are *morally* responsible and *morally* blameworthy for the deaths of their respective cousins, even if Jones, who allowed his cousin to drown, is not *causally* responsible. The law might find only Smith who killed his cousin, guilty of homicide (because of the law's theory of proximate cause), but morality condemns both actions because of the agents' motives and their commissions and omissions. While we would not condemn a nonswimmer for failing to jump into deep water to try to rescue a drowning child, we find Jones's actions reprehensible because he (morally) should have rescued the child. Even if he had no other special duties to the child, the duty of beneficence . . . requires affirmative action. The point of the cases envisioned by the AMA is that the physician is always morally prohibited from killing patients but is not morally bound to preserve life in *all* cases. According to the AMA, the physician has a right—and perhaps a duty—to stop treatment if and only if three conditions are met: (1) the life of the body is being preserved by extraordinary means, (2) there is irrefutable evidence that biological death is imminent, and (3) the patient and/or the family consents.

Fourth, even if the distinction between killing and letting die is morally irrelevant in some contexts, it does not follow that it is always morally irrelevant. The fact that the distinction does not show up in every sort of case does not mean that it is morally unimportant under all circumstances. Rachels does effectively undermine any attempt to rest judgments about ending life on the "bare difference" between killing and letting die, but his target may be a straw man. Many philosophers and theologians have argued that there are *independent* moral, religious, and other reasons for defending the distinction and for prohibiting killing while authorizing allowing to die in some circumstances.

One theologian has argued, for example, that we can discern the moral significance of the distinction between killing and letting die only by "placing it in the religious context out of which it grew."[4] That context is the Biblical story of God's actions toward his creatures. In that context it makes *sense* to talk about "placing patients in God's hands," just as it is important not to usurp God's prerogatives by desperately struggling to prolong life when the patient is irreversibly dying. But even if the distinction between killing and letting die originated within a religious context, and even if it makes more sense in that context than in some others, it can be defended on nontheological grounds without being reduced to a claim about a "bare difference." However important the religious context was for the origin of the distinction, religious doctrines are not presupposed by the distinction and independent moral grounds are sufficient to support it.

Some nontheological arguments in favor of the distinction between killing and allowing to die invoke both moral and practical considerations. They hold that the distinction enables us to express and maintain certain principles such as nonmaleficence and to avoid certain harmful consequences. Probably no single reason by itself is sufficient to support the moral relevance of the distinction and thus to prohibit killing while permitting some intentionally allowed deaths. But several reasons together indicate that the distinction is worth retaining or, in effect, that our current practices should be maintained with some clarifications and modifications. We now turn to this set of reasons.

The most important arguments for the distinction between killing and letting die depend on a distinction between *acts* and *practices*.[5] It is one thing to justify an act, i.e., to hold that it is right; it is another to justify a general practice. [M]any beliefs about principles and consequences are applied to practices or rules rather than directly to acts. For example, we might justify a rule of confidentiality because it encourages people to seek therapy and because it promotes respect for persons and their privacy. Such a rule might, however, lead to undesirable results in *particular* cases. Likewise, a rule that prohibits "active killing," while permitting some "allowed deaths," may be justifiable, even though it excludes some acts of killing that in and of themselves might appear to be justifiable. Such a rule would not permit us to kill a patient who suffers from terrible pain, who rationally asks for "mercy," i.e., to be killed, and who will probably die within three weeks. According to the rule of double effect, we should, of course, use measures to alleviate the patient's pain even though these would hasten death; we should allow the patient to die, but not kill the patient. It may be necessary to prohibit by rule and policy some acts that do not appear to be wrong in some circumstances in order to maintain a viable practice that, for the most part, expresses our principles and avoids seriously undesirable consequences. Thus, although particular acts of killing may not violate the duty of nonmaleficence and may even be humane and compassionate, a policy of authorizing killing would probably violate the duty of nonmaleficence by creating a grave risk of harm in many cases.

According to one line of argument, the prohibition of killing even for "mercy" expresses principles and values that provide a basis of trust between patients and health care professionals. Trust involves the expectation that others will respect moral limits. When we trust medical practitioners, we expect them to promote our welfare and, at least, to do us no harm without a corresponding prospect of benefit. The prohibition of killing in medical contexts is a basic expression of the ethos of care for the patient's life and health as well as the duty of maleficence. Some claim that it is instrumentally as well as symbolically important, for its removal would weaken a "climate, both moral and legal, which we are not able to do without."[6] David Louisell, for example, contends that "Euthanasia would threaten the patient-physician relationship: confidence might give way to suspicion.... Can the physician, historic battler for life, become an affirmative agent of death without jeopardizing the trust of his dependents?"[7] . . .

If rules permitting active killing were introduced into a society, it is not implausible to suppose that the society over time would move increasingly in the direction of involuntary euthanasia—e.g., in the form of killing defective newborns for such reasons as the avoidance of social burdens. There could be a general reduction of respect for human life as a result of the official removal of some barriers to killing. Rules against killing in a moral code are not isolated; they are threads in a fabric of rules, based in part on nonmaleficence, that support respect for human life. The more threads we remove, the weaker the fabric becomes. If we focus on attitudes and not merely rules, the general attitude of respect for life may be eroded by shifts in particular areas. Determination of the probability of such an erosion depends not only on the connectedness of rules and attitudes, but also on various forces in the society....

In addition to fears of abuse, including abuse of the mentally disturbed and others who cannot consent, there are other legitimate fears. First, easy resort to killing to relieve pain and suffering may divert attention and resources from other strategies that may be effective, such as the hospice movement. Second, consider the following two types of wrongly diagnosed patients.[8]

1. Patients wrongly diagnosed as hopeless, and who will survive even if a treatment *is* ceased (in order to allow a natural death).
2. Patients wrongly diagnosed as hopeless, and who will survive only if the treatment is *not ceased* (in order to allow a natural death).

If a social rule of allowing some patients to die were in effect, doctors and families who followed it would only lose patients in the second category. But if killing were permitted, at least some of the patients in the first category would be needlessly lost. Thus, a rule prohibiting killing would save some lives that would be lost if *both* killing and allowing to die were permitted. Of course, such a consequence is not a decisive reason for a policy of (only) allowing to die, for the numbers in categories (1) and (2) are likely to be small and other reasons for killing, such as extreme pain and autonomous choice, might be weighty. But it is certainly *a* morally relevant reason.

Proponents of the practice of killing some patients appeal to a range of exceptional cases to show the utility of the practice. Among the strongest reasons for killing some patients is to relieve unbearable and uncontrollable pain and suffering. No one would deny that pain and suffering can so ravage and dehumanize patients that death appears to be in their best interests. Prolonging life and refusing to kill in such circumstances may appear to be cruel and even to violate the duty of nonmaleficence. Often proponents of "mercy killing" appeal to nonmedical situations to show that killing may be more humane and compassionate than letting die—as, for example, in the case of a truck driver inextricably trapped in a burning wreck who cries out for "mercy" and asks to be killed. In such tragic situations we are reluctant to say that those who kill at the behest of the victim act wrongly. Furthermore, juries often find persons who have killed a suffering relative not guilty by reason of temporary insanity.

There are, nevertheless, serious objections to building into *medical practice* an explicit exception licensing physicians to kill their patients in order to relieve uncontrollable pain and suffering. One objection is that it is not clear that many, if any, cases in medical practice are really parallel to the person trapped in a burning wreck. The physician may be able to relieve pain and suffering short of killing—even if death is hastened—by means that are not available to a bystander at the scene of an accident. A second objection holds that we should not construct a social or professional ethic on borderline situations and emergency cases, even if medical practitioners confront some cases of unmanageable pain and suffering. It is dangerous to generalize from emergencies, for hard cases may make bad social and professional ethics as well as bad law. As Charles Fried writes,

> The concept of emergency is only a tolerable moral concept if somehow we can truly think of it as exceptional, if we can truly think of it as a circumstance that, far from defying our usual moral universe, suspends it for a limited time and thus suspends usual moral principles. It is when emergencies become usual that we are threatened with moral disintegration, dehumanization.[9]

Third, there are ways to "accept" acts of killing in exceptional circumstances without altering the rules of practice in order to accomodate them. As mentioned earlier, juries often find those who kill their suffering relatives not guilty by reason of temporary insanity, as occurred in the Zygmaniak case in New Jersey.[10] In June 1973, George Zygmaniak was in a motorcycle accident that left him paralyzed from the neck down. This paralysis was considered to be irreversible, and Zygmaniak begged his brother, Lester, to kill him. Three days later, Lester brought a sawed-off shotgun into the hospital and shot his brother in the head, after having told him, "Close your eyes now, I'm going to shoot you." Verdicts like "not guilty by reason of temporary insanity" do not *justify* the act of killing a suffering relative. They differ from a verdict of not guilty on grounds of self-defense, for self-defense does justify killing, at least in some circumstances. Verdicts like not guilty by reason of temporary insanity thus function to *excuse* the agent by finding that he or she lacked the conditions of responsibility necessary to be legally guilty.

Others have proposed that we maintain the legal rule against killing even if physicians and others sometime have to engage in justified conscientious or civil disobedience. Concurring with Robert Veatch, Paul Ramsey holds that "civil disobedience—the courage to go against the rules when morally warranted—may be better than to allow for exceptions in a rule of general practice."[11] But what conditions might justify conscientious refusals in medical practice to follow the rule against killing patients? According to Ramsey, when dying patients are totally inaccessible to our care, when our care is a matter of indifference to them because of intractable pain or a deep coma, "there is no longer any morally significant distinction between omission and commission, between standing aside ess

'ching them."[12] "Total is a limit of care itself; for an become totally useless. It is not clear, however, that Ramsey's distinction between dying and nondying patients can carry his argument. Nor is it clear whether he considers someone in a deep and prolonged state of unconsciousness as dying, and if so, whether such a view is justifiable. In addition, it is necessary to ask whether Ramsey's exception can be limited to the cases that he endorses; it too may be the thin edge of the wedge. Nevertheless, even if pain and suffering of a certain magnitude can in principle justify active killing, as long as other conditions are met, they may only justify acts of conscientious refusal to follow the rule of practice, not basic changes in the rule itself.

Finally, which side in the debate has the burden of proof—the proponents or the opponents of a practice of selective killing? Anthony Flew has argued that supporters of the current practice of prohibiting killing must bear the burden of proof because the prohibition of *voluntary* euthanasia violates the principle of liberty by refusing to respect individual autonomy.[13] However, a policy of voluntary euthanasia, based on either a negative right to die (a right to noninterference) or a positive right to die (a right to be killed), would involve such a change in society's vision of the medical profession and medical attitudes that a shift in the burden of proof to the proponents of change is inevitable. The prohibition of killing is not arbitrary even when cases of voluntary request are factored in. It expresses some important moral principles, values, and attitudes whose loss, or serious alteration, could have major negative consequences. Because the current practice of prohibiting killing while accepting some "allowed deaths" has served us well, if not perfectly, it should be altered only with the utmost caution. Lines are not easy to draw and maintain, but in general we have been able to follow the line between killing and letting die in medical practice. Before we undertake any major changes, we need strong evidence that these changes are really needed in order to avoid important harms or secure important benefits, and that the good effects will outweigh the bad effects. . . .

NOTES

1 It is a mistake to view these expressions as synonymous, though the present statement appears to.
2 James Rachels, "Active and Passive Euthanasia," *New England Journal of Medicine* 292 (January a9, 1975): 78-80. For valuable discussions of the distinction between killing and letting die, see Bonnie Steinbock, ed., *Killing and Letting Die*; and John Ladd, ed., *Ethical Issues Relating to Life and Death* (New York: Oxford University Press, 1979).
3 Richard L. Trammell, "Saving and Taking Life," *Journal of Philosophy* 72 (1975): 131-37
4 Gilbert Meilaender, "The Distinction Between Killinq and Allowing to Die," *Theological Studies* 37 (1976): 467-70.
5 See John Rawls, "Two Concepts of Rules," *Philosphical Review* 64 (1955): 3-32.
6 G.J. Hughes, S.J., "Killing and Letting Die," *The Month* 236 (1975):42-45.
7 David Louisell, "Euthanasia and Biothanasia: On Dying and Killing," *Linacre Quarterly* 40 (1973): 234-58.
8 We owe most of this argument to James Rachels.
9 Charles Fried, "Rights and Health Care—Beyond Equity and Efficiency," *New England Journal of Medicine* 293 (July 31, 1975): 245.
10 For a discussion of this case, see Paige Mitchell, *Act of Love: The Killing of George Zygmaniak* (New York: Knopf, 1976).
11 See Paul Ramsey, *Ethics at the Edges of Life*, p. 217; Robert Veatch, *Death, Dying, and the Biological Revolution* (New Haven, Conn.: Yale University Press, 1976) p. 97.
12 Ramsey, *Ethics at the Edges of Life*, pp. 195, 214, 216; cf. Ramsey, *The Patient as Person*, pp. 161-64.
13 Antony Flew, "The Principle of Euthanasia," *Euthanasia and the Right to Death: The Case of Voluntary Euthanasia*, ed. A.B. Downing (London: Peter Owen, 1969), pp. 30-48.

• • •

POSTSCRIPT

IS KILLING THE SAME AS LETTING DIE?

In 1982 the American Medical Association reaffirmed its stand on euthanasia. An opinion from its Judicial Council declared: "For humane reasons, with informed consent a physician may do what is medically necessary to alleviate severe pain, or cease or omit treatment to let a terminally ill patient die, but he should not intentionally cause death." The Catholic view on euthanasia was forcefully stated in a Vatican declaration of May 5, 1980: ". . . (N)othing and no one can in any way permit the killing of an innocent human being, whether a foetus or an embryo, an infant or an adult, an old person, or one suffering from an incurable disease, or a person who is dying. Furthermore, no one is permitted to ask for this act of killing, either for himself or herself or for another person entrusted to his or her care, nor can he or she consent to it. . . ."

However, the competent patient's right to refuse treatment is well established in law and ethics. Several states have "right to die" laws, although they do not all work equally well in achieving their aims. For a recent proposal see "The Right to Refuse Treatment: A Model Act," by the Legal Advisors Committee of Concern for Dying (*American Journal of Public Health,* August 1983).

The most comprehensive review of all issues concerned with treatment of dying patients is *Deciding to Forego Life-Sustaining Treatment,* a report of the President's Commission for the Study of Ethical Problems in Medicine and Biomedical and Behavioral Research (Government Printing Office, 1983). *Death, Dying, and Euthanasia,* edited by Dennis J. Horan and David Mall, is a collection of articles from various points of view (University Publications of America, 1980). Also see Bonnie Steinbock, editor, *Killing and Letting Die* (Prentice-Hall, 1980); Marvin Kohl, editor, *Beneficent Euthanasia* (Prometheus Books, 1975); and John Behnke and Sissela Bok, editors, *The Dilemmas of Euthanasia* (Doubleday, 1975).

ISSUE 7

SHOULD TREATMENT BE WITHHELD FROM NEWBORNS WITH BIRTH DEFECTS?

YES: Raymond S. Duff and A.G.M. Campbell, from "Moral and Ethical Dilemmas in the Special Care Nursery," *New England Journal of Medicine* 289 (October 25, 1973)

NO: C. Everett Koop, from "Ethical and Surgical Considerations in the Care of the Newborn with Congenital Abnormalities," in *Infanticide and the Handicapped Newborn,* edited by Dennis J. Horan and Melinda Delahoyde (Provo, Utah: Brigham Young University Press, 1982)

ISSUE SUMMARY

YES: Pediatricians Raymond Duff and A.G.M. Campbell conclude that the prognosis for meaningful life is so poor in some newborns with birth defects that parents and physicians are justified in rejecting further treatment for them.
NO: C. Everett Koop, a pediatric surgeon who is now Surgeon General of the United States, calls withholding treatment from newborns "infanticide" and faults the medical profession for acceding to the wishes of the families instead of protecting their patients.

The birth of a baby can be one of life's most joyous moments; but, if the baby is born with some severe defect, it can be one of its most tragic. Throughout history, the fate of abnormal babies has varied: Some societies have sanctioned killing them outright—the practice of infanticide; others have prohibited it officially, but without complete success; and some have given such infants special recognition, though often as "freaks of nature." For the most part, these birth-defective babies died, because there was little that anyone could do to correct the defects. Today, however, because of remarkable advances in medical technology and the development of a new medical specialty—neonatology, or the care of newborns—many infants who would almost certainly have died even a few decades ago can now be saved. But with this advance has come a terrible dilemma: Is it right to save a baby's life when its future is bleak or perhaps hopeless?

There are three types of cases in which the dilemma typically arises: First, some babies are born with a genetic defect—commonly known as Down's syndrome—which causes mental retardation. Some of these babies also have defects of the heart and esophagus, which must be corrected by surgery or they will die. The surgery does not affect their retardation, which may be mild or severe although this cannot be predicted at birth. Second, some babies are born with neural tube defects—that is, the spinal cord has not closed during fetal development. One form is *spina bifida,* in which there is an open lesion on the spinal cord. Some cases are very severe and include mental retardation; others are quite mild. The lesion can be closed surgically; if it is not, the child is vulnerable to infections and likely to die at an early age. But the surgery does not remove the defect entirely. A third category of babies are those born prematurely; some congenital or inborn birth defect may be present, but often the babies' main problem is that their organs, particularly their lungs, are too immature to sustain life. Through aggressive measures, including mechanical respirators, even babies with a birth weight of one thousand grams (two pounds, three ounces) have a good chance of surviving, and those of 750 grams (under two pounds) can often be saved. But sometimes their condition, and the treatment itself, creates permanent problems such as neurological or learning disabilities. Some babies treated in this way can not be weaned from the respirator and live on for months in neonatal intensive care units.

In many, perhaps most, of these cases there is no question about what to do: Parents and physicians want the babies treated to the maximum extent possible. In other cases there is also no moral problem, because there is nothing that can be done to save the baby's life. But in the difficult, in-between area—where treatment is possible but the outcome is uncertain or where the child will have a defect no matter what is done—there are sharp disagreements about what decision should be made and who should make it. All the questions about euthanasia that were raised about adults in the previous selections are present here as well, but with an added ethical dimension, since the babies are totally dependent on others to make decisions for them.

In the following selections two clashing views emerge. Raymond Duff and A.G.M. Campbell draw on their experiences in the Yale University Special Care Nursery to bolster their belief that in some cases withholding treatment is the right thing to do and that the parents should be involved in this decision. C. Everett Koop finds this conclusion totally unacceptable, especially from doctors, and describes cases in which parents have come to accept their children's handicaps. As an "ethical physician," he says, "I must come down on the side of life."

YES

Raymond S. Duff and A.G.M. Campbell

MORAL AND ETHICAL DILEMMAS IN THE SPECIAL-CARE NURSERY

Between 1940 and 1970 there was a 58 per cent decrease in the infant death rate in the United States.[1] This reduction was related in part to the application of new knowledge to the care of infants. Neonatal mortality rates in hospitals having infant intensive-care units have been about ½ those reported in hospitals without such units.[2] There is now evidence that in many conditions of early infancy the long-term morbidity may also be reduced.[3] Survivors of these units may be healthy, and their parents grateful, but some infants continue to suffer from such conditions as chronic cardiopulmonary disease, short-bowel-syndrome or various manifestations of brain damage; others are severely handicapped by a myriad of congenital malformations that in previous times would have resulted in early death. Recently, both lay and professional persons have expressed increasing concern about the quality of life for these severely impaired survivors and their families.[4, 5] Many pediatricians and others are distressed with the long-term results of pressing on and on to save life at all costs and in all circumstances. Eliot Slater[6] stated, "If this is one of the consequences of the sanctity-of-life ethic, perhaps our formulation of the principle should be revised."

The experiences described in this communication document some of the grave moral and ethical dilemmas now faced by physicians and families. They indicate some of the problems in a large special-care nursery where medical technology has prolonged life and where "informed" parents influence the management decisions concerning their infants.

RESULTS

In total, there were 299 deaths: each was classified in one of two categories; deaths in Category 1 resulted from pathologic conditions in spite of the treatment given; 256 (86 per cent) were in this category. Of these, 66 per cent

From "Moral and Ethical Dilemmas in the Special Care Nursery," by Raymond S. Duff and A.G.M. Campbell, *New England Journal of Medicine,* vol. 289, October 25, 1973. Reprinted by permission of the author.

were the result of respiratory problems or complications associated with extreme prematurity (birth weight under 1000 g). Congenital heart disease and other anomalies accounted for an additional 22 per cent.

Deaths in Category 2 were associated with severe impairment, usually from congenital disorders; 43 (14 per cent) were in this group. These deaths or their timing was associated with discontinuance or withdrawal of treatment. The mean duration of life in Category 2 was greater than that in Category 1. This was the result of a mean life of 55 days for eight infants who became chronic cardiopulmonary cripples but for whom prolonged and intensive efforts were made in the hope of eventual recovery. They were infants who were dependent on oxygen, digoxin and diuretics, and most of them had been treated for the idiopathic respiratory-distress syndrome with high oxygen concentrations and positive-pressure ventilation.

Some examples of management choices in Category 2 illustrate the problems. An infant with Down's syndrome and intestinal atresia, like the much-publicized one at Johns Hopkins Hospital,[7] was not treated because his parents thought that surgery was wrong for their baby and themselves. He died seven days after birth. Another child had chronic pulmonary disease after positive-pressure ventilation with high oxygen concentrations for treatment of severe idiopathic respiratory-distress syndrome. By five months of age, he still required 40 per cent oxygen to survive, and even then, he was chronically dyspneic and cyanotic. He also suffered from cor pulmonale, which was difficult to control with digoxin and diuretics. The nurses, parents and physicians considered it cruel to continue, and yet difficult to stop. All were attached to this child, whose life they had tried so hard to make worthwhile. The family had endured high expenses (the hospital bill exceeding $15,000), and the strains of the illness were believed to be threatening the marriage bonds and to be causing sibling behavioral disturbances. Oxygen supplementation was stopped, and the child died in about three hours. The family settled down and 18 months later had another baby, who was healthy.

A third child had meningomyelocele, hydrocephalus and major anomalies of every organ in the pelvis. When the parents understood the limits of medical care and rehabilitation, they believed no treatment should be given. She died at five days of age.

We have maintained contact with most families of children in Category 2. Thus far, these families appear to have experienced a normal mourning for their losses. Although some have exhibited doubts that the choices were correct, all appear to be as effective in their lives as they were before this experience. Some claim that their profoundly moving experience has provided a deeper meaning in life, and from this they believe they have become more effective people.

Members of all religious faiths and atheists were participants as parents and as staff in these experiences. There appeared to be no relation between participation and a person's religion. Repeated participation in these troubling events did not appear to reduce the worry of the staff about the awesome nature of the decisions.

DISCUSSION

That decisions are made not to treat severely defective infants may be no surprise to those familiar with special-care facilities. All laymen and professionals familiar with our nursery appeared to set some limits upon their application of treatment to extend life or to investigate a pathologic process. For example, an experienced nurse said about one child, "We lost him several weeks ago. Isn't it time to quit?" In another case, a house officer said to a physician investigating an aspect of a child's disease, "For this child, don't you think it's time to turn off your curiosity so you can turn on your kindness?" Like many others, these children eventually acquired the "right to die."

Arguments among staff members and families for and against such decisions were based on varied notions of the rights and interests of defective infants, their families, professionals and society. They were also related to varying ideas about prognosis. Regarding the infants, some contended that individuals should have a right to die in some circumstances such as anencephaly, hydranencephaly, and some severely deforming and incapacitating conditions. Such very defective individuals were considered to have little or no hope of achieving meaningful "humanhood."[8] For example, they have little or no capacity to love or be loved. They are often cared for in facilities that have been characterized as "hardly more than dying bins,"[9] an assessment with which, in our experience, knowledgeable parents (those who visited chronic-care facilities for placement of their children) agreed. With institutionalized well children, social participation may be essentially nonexistent, and maternal deprivation severe; this is known to have an adverse, usually disastrous, effect upon the child.[10] The situation for the defective child is probably worse, for he is restricted socially both by his need for care and by his defects. To escape "wrongful life,"[11] a fate rated as worse than death, seemed right. In this regard, Lasagna[12] notes, "We may, as a society, scorn the civilizations that slaughtered their infants, but our present treatment of the retarded is in some ways more cruel."

Others considered allowing a child to die wrong for several reasons. The person most involved, the infant, had no voice in the decision. Prognosis was not always exact, and a few children with extensive care might live for months, and occasionally years. Some might survive and function satisfactorily. To a few persons, withholding treatment and accepting death was condemned as criminal.

Families had strong but mixed feelings about management decisions. Living with the handicapped is clearly a family affair, and families of deformed infants thought there were limits to what they could bear or should be expected to bear. Most of them wanted maximal efforts to sustain life and to rehabilitate the handicapped; in such cases, they were supported fully. However, some families, especially those having children with severe defects, feared that they and their other children would become socially enslaved, economically deprived, and permanently stigmatized, all perhaps for a lost cause. Such a state of "chronic sorrow" until death has been described by Olshansky.[13] In some cases, families considered the death of the child right both for the child and for the family. They asked if that choice could be theirs or their doctors.

As Feifel has reported,[14] physicians on the whole are reluctant to deal with the issues. Some, particularly specialists based in the medical center, gave specific reasons for this disinclination. There was a feeling that to "give up" was disloyal to the cause of the profession. Since major research, teaching and patient-care efforts were being made, professionals expected to discover, transmit and apply knowledge and skills; patients and families were supposed to co-operate fully even if they were not always grateful. Some physicians recognized that the wishes of families went against their own, but they were resolute. They commonly agreed that if they were the parents of very defective children, with-holding treatment would be most desirable for them. However, they argued that aggressive management was indicated for others. Some believed that allowing death as a management option was euthanasia and must be stopped for fear of setting a "poor ethical example" or for fear of personal prosecution or damage to their clinical departments or to the medical center as a whole. Alexander's report on Nazi Germany[15] was cited in some cases as providing justification for pressing the effort to combat disease. Some persons were concerned about the loss through death of "teaching material." They feared the training of professionals for the care of defective children in the future and the advancing of the state of the art would be compromised. Some parents who became aware of this concern thought their children should not become experimental subjects.

Practicing pediatricians, general practitioners and obstetricians were often familiar with these families and were usually sympathetic with their views. However, since they were more distant from the special-care nursery than the specialists of the medical center, their influence was often minimal. As a result, families received little support from them, and tension in community-medical relations was a recurring problem.

Infants with severe types of meningomyelocele precipitated the most controversial decisions. Several decades ago, those who survived this condition beyond a few weeks usually became hydrocephalic and retarded, in addition to being crippled and deformed. Without modern treatment, they died earlier.[16] Some may have been killed or at least not resuscitated at birth.[17] From the early 1960's, the tendency has been to treat vigorously all infants with meningomyelocele. As advocated by Zachary[18] and Shurtleff,[19] aggressive management of these children became the rule in our unit as in many others. Infants were usually referred quickly. Parents routinely signed permits for operation though rarely had they seen their children's defects or had the nature of various management plans and their respective prognoses clearly explained to them. Some physicians believed that parents were too upset to understand the nature of the problems and the options for care. Since they believed informed consent had no meaning in these circumstances, they either ignored the parents or simply told them that the child needed an operation on the back as the first step in correcting several defects. As a result, parents often felt completely left out while the activities of care proceeded at a brisk pace.

Some physicians experienced in the care of these children and familiar with the impact of such conditions upon families had early reservations about this plan of care.[20] More recently, they were influenced by the pessimistic appraisal of vigorous management schemes in some cases.[3] Meningomyelocele, when treated vigorously, is associated with higher survival rates,[19] but the achievement of satisfactory rehabilitation is at best difficult and usually impossible for almost all who are severely affected. Knowing this, some physicians and some families[24] decide against treatment of the most severely affected. If treatment is not carried out, the child's condition will usually deteriorate from further brain damage, urinary-tract infections and orthopedic difficulties, and death can be expected much earlier. Two thirds may be dead by three months, and over 90 per cent by one year of age. However, the quality of life during that time is poor, and the strains on families are great, but not necessarily greater than with treatment.[22] Thus, both treatment and nontreatment constitute unsatisfactory dilemmas to everyone, especially for the child and his family. When maximum treatment was viewed as unacceptable by families and physicians in our unit, there was a growing tendency to seek early death as a management option, to avoid that cruel choice of gradual, often slow, but progressive deterioration of the child who was required under these circumstances in effect to kill himself. Parents and the staff then asked if his dying needed to be prolonged. If not, what were the most appropriate medical responses?

Is it possible that some physicians and some families may join in a conspiracy to deny the right of a defective child to live or to die? Either could occur. Prolongation of the dying process by resident physicians having a vested interest in their careers has been described by Sudnow.[23] On the other hand, from the fatigue of working long and hard some physicians may give up too soon, assuming that their cause is lost. Families, similarly, may have mixed motives. They may demand death to obtain relief from the high costs and the tensions inherent in suffering, but their sense of guilt in this thought may produce the opposite demand, perhaps in violation of the sick person's rights. Thus, the challenge of deciding what course to take can be most tormenting for the family and the physician. Unquestionably, not facing the issue would appear to be the easier course, at least temporarily; no doubt many patients, families, and physicians decline to join in an effort to solve the problems. They can readily assume that what is being done is right and sufficient and ask no questions. But pretending there is no decision to be made is an arbitrary and potentially devastating decision of default. Since families and patients must live with the problems one way or another in any case, the physician's failure to face the issues may constitute a victimizing abandonment of patients and their families in times of greatest need. As Lasagna[12] pointed out, "There is no place for the physician to hide."

Can families in the shock resulting from the birth of a defective child understand what faces them? Can they give truly "informed consent" for treatment or withholding treatment? Some of our colleagues answer no to both questions. In our opinion, if families regardless of background are heard sympathetically and at length and are given information and answers to their questions in words they understand, the problems of their children as well as the expected benefits and limits of any proposed care can be understood clearly in practically all instances. Parents *are* able to understand the implications of such things as chronic dyspnea, oxygen dependency, incontinence, paralysis, contractures, sexual handicaps and mental retardation.

Another problem concerns who decides for a child. It may be acceptable for a person to reject treatment and bring about his own death. But it is quite a different situation when others are doing this for him. We do not know how often families and their physicians will make just decisions for severely handicapped children. Clearly, this issue is central in evaluation of the process of decision making that we have described. But we also ask, if these parties cannot make such decisions justly, who can?

We recognize great variability and often much uncertainty in prognoses and in family capacities to deal with defective newborn infants. We also acknowledge that there are limits of support that society can or will give to assist handicapped persons and their families. Severely deforming conditions that are associated with little or no hope of a functional existence pose painful dilemmas for the laymen and professionals who must decide how to cope with severe handicaps. We believe the burdens of decision making must be borne by families and their professional advisers because they are most familiar with the respective situations. Since families primarily must live with and are most affected by the decisions, it therefore appears that society and the health professions should provide only general guidelines for decision making. Moreover, since variations between situations are so great, and the situations themselves so complex, it follows that much latitude in decision making should be expected and tolerated. Otherwise, the rules of society or the policies most convenient for medical technologists may become cruel masters of human beings instead of their servants. Regarding any "allocation of death"[24] policy we readily acknowledge that the extreme excesses of Hegelian "rational utility" under dictatorships must be avoided.[15] Perhaps it is less recognized that the uncontrolled application of medical technology may be detrimental to individuals and families. In this regard, our views are similar to those of Waitzkin and Stoekle.[25] Physicians may hold excessive power over decision making by limiting or controlling the information made available to patients or families. It seems appropriate that the profession be held accountable for presenting fully all management options and their expected consequences. Also, the public should be aware that professionals often face conflicts of interest that may result in decisions against individual preferences.

What are the legal implications of actions like those described in this paper? Some persons may argue that the law has been broken, and others would contend otherwise. Perhaps more than anything else, the public and professional silence on a major social taboo and some common practices has been broken further. That seems appropriate, for out of the ensuing dialogue perhaps better choices for patients and families can be made. If working out these dilemmas in ways such as those we suggest is in violation of the law, we believe the law should be changed.

NOTES

1 Wegman ME: Annual summary of vital statistics—1970. Pediatrics 48:979-983, 1971

2 Swyer PR: The regional organization of special care for the neonate. Pediatr Clin North Am 17:761-776, 1970

3 Rawlings G, Reynold EOR, Stewart A, et al: Changing prognosis for infants of very low birth weight. Lancet 1:516-519, 1971

4 Freeman E: The god committee. New York Times Magazine, May 21, 1972, pp 84-90

5 Lorber J: Results of treatment of myelomeningocele. Dev Med Child Neurol 13:279-303, 1971

6 Slater E: Health service or sickness service. Br Med J 4:734-736, 1971

7 Report of the Joseph P. Kennedy Foundation International Symposium on Human Rights, Retardation and Research. Washington, DC. The John F. Kennedy Center for the Performing Arts, October 16, 1971

8 Fletcher J: Indicators of humanhood: a tentative profile of man. The Hastings Center Report Vol 2, No 5. Hastings-on-Hudson, New York, Institute of Society, Ethics and the Life Sciences. November, 1972. pp 1-4

9 Freeman HE, Brim OG Jr, Williams G: New dimensions of dying. The Dying Patient. Edited by OG Brim Jr. New York. Russell Sage Foundation. 1970. pp xiii-xxvi

10 Spitz RA: Hospitalism: an inquiry into the genesis of psychiatric conditions in early childhood. Psychoanal Study Child 1:53-74, 1945

11 Engelhardt HT Jr: Euthanasia and children: the injury of continued existence. J Pediatr 83:170-171, 1973

12 Lasagna L: Life, Death and the Doctor. New York, Alfred A Knopf, 1968

13 Olshansky S: Chronic sorrow: a response to having a mentally defective child. Soc Casework 43:190-193, 1962

14 Feifel H: Perception of death. Ann NY Acad Sci 164:669-677, 1969

15 Alexander L: Medical science under dictatorship. N Engl J Med 241:39-47, 1949
16 Laurence KM and Tew BJ: Natural history of spina bifida cystica and cranium bifidum cysticum: major central nervous system malformations in South Wales. Part IV. Arch Dis Child 46:127-138, 1971
17 Forrest DM: Modern trends in the treatment of spina bifida: early closure in spina bifida: results and problems. Proc R Soc Med 60:763-767, 1967
18 Zachary RB: Ethical and social aspects of treatment of spina bifida. Lancet 2:274-276, 1968
19 Shurtleff DB: Care of the myelodysplastic patient. Ambulatory Pediatrics. Edited by M Green, R Haggerty. Philadelphia, WB Saunders Company, 1968, pp 726-741
20 Matson DD: Surgical treatment of myelomeningocele. Pediatrics 42:225-227, 1968
21 Mac Keith RC: A new look at spina bifida aperta. Dev Med Child Neurol 13:277-278, 1971
22 Hide DW, Williams HP, Ellis HL: The outlook for the child with a myelomeningocele for whom early surgery was considered inadvisable. Dev Med Child Neurol 14:304-307, 1972
23 Sudnow D: Passing On. Englewood Cliffs, New Jersey, Prentice Hall, 1967
24 Manning B: Legal and policy issues in the allocation of death. The Dying Patient. Edited by OG Brim Jr. New York. Russell Sage Foundation, 1970, pp 253-274
25 Waitzkin H, Stoeckle JD: The communication of information about illness. Adv Psychosom Med 8:180-215, 1972

• • •

NO

C. Everett Koop

ETHICAL AND SURGICAL CONSIDERATIONS IN THE CARE OF THE NEWBORN WITH CONGENITAL ABNORMALITIES

. . . Infanticide is the killing of a born infant by direct means or by withholding something necessary for its survival. This practice in the United States is extraordinarily important to those who are interested in the sanctity of human life because infanticide might never have come about had it not been for abortion on demand. When I read, in the months following the January 22, 1973 decision of the Supreme Court in *Roe v. Wade,* various references to Justice Blackmun's majority opinion in that case, my blood ran cold. You will remember that he considered the Hippocratic Oath which forbids abortion to be irrelevant. He spurned whatever morality he might have gleaned from the Judeo-Christian heritage of this country and turned instead to the pagan religions of Rome, of Greece, and of Persia. Although those countries practiced abortion, it was infanticide and euthanasia which were more important inhumanities in their cultures.

The second important thing to remember about infanticide is that it is euthanasia in an age group. There are many semantic differences in the English language on both sides of the Atlantic and infanticide is one of them. Infanticide in Great Britain usually means the killing of a born infant by the infant's mother. Infanticide in this country is the killing of a born infant by medical personnel in a hospital either by a direct act or much more commonly by the withholding of something necessary for the survival of that infant. Its hidden importance in reference to our concerns in the future is that I am certain the day will come when the euthanasia forces will say, "Why are you concerned about euthanasia? We have had euthanasia of infants for a long time and there has been no outcry."

The third important thing concerning infanticide is that it is being practiced by a segment of the medical profession from whom we have traditionally expected more—pediatricians and pediatric surgeons—and it is being ignored by a segment of our society from whom the victim has a right to expect more—namely, the law.

7. SHOULD TREATMENT BE WITHHELD FROM NEWBORNS?

The medical profession has slipped its anchor and drifted away from the commitment which put the patient first in the recognition of the fact that he needed the help a physician could provide. This principle was rather universally understood in medicine not too long ago when morality was based on certain absolutes that the individual perceived as right or wrong. I am distressed that in an era of moral relativism, the life of a handicapped child can be forfeited to alleviate suffering in the family. If the practice of infanticide is a perversion of the former morality in medicine, that is bad enough. But if the situation is compounded by the fact that the law has turned its back as though infanticide did not exist, then we are indeed in trouble, for who knows the direction the extension of this philosophy will take next?

For almost thirty-five years now I have devoted the major part of my professional life to the management of children born with a congenital defect. I was, however, a surgeon of the skin and its contents in my early years. Therefore, my experience with congenital defects is broader than just the field that ordinarily is now called general pediatric surgery. Although in my more recent years my interests have been confined to those congenital anomalies incompatible with life but nevertheless amenable to surgical correction, there was a day when I was concerned with the management of cleft lips and palates, orthopedic defects, spina bifida and its complications, congenital heart disease, and major urologic defects.

I know what can be accomplished in the habilitation of a child born less than perfect. I know what can be done with that child's family. I know that these children become loved and loving, that they are creative, and that their entrance into a family is frequently looked back upon in subsequent years as an extraordinarily positive experience. Those who never have had the privilege of working with handicapped children who are being habilitated into our society after the correction of a congenital defect frequently tell me that such a child should be allowed to die or even encouraged to die because its life could obviously be nothing but unhappy and miserable. Yet it has been my constant experience that disability and unhappiness do not go hand in hand. The most unhappy children I have known have been completely normal. On the other hand, there is remarkable joy and happiness in the lives of most handicapped children; yet some have borne burdens that I would have indeed found very difficult to endure.

The first medical effort I know of in this country to educate the profession in the management of a defective newborn where death was one of the options in treatment is the film *Who Shall Survive?* produced by the Joseph P. Kennedy Foundation.[1] It depicts the manner in which a child with both Down's syndrome and duodenal atresia was given nothing by mouth until it expired from dehydration and starvation fifteen days later. Whatever was the intent of those who produced and financed this film, when it is seen during orientation week by new medical students across the country it is interpreted as an acceptable example of the management of a difficult problem in neonatology.

The first medical article along these lines to attract wide attention is entitled "Dilemmas of the Newborn Intensive Care Nursery," by Drs. Raymond S. Duff and A.G.M. Campbell of Yale University School of Medicine.[2] They acknowledge that over a two-year period about 14 percent of the deaths in their special care unit were those they permitted to happen because it was their considered judgment after discussion with the family that these children's lives were not worth living. It is impossible for the physician not to influence the family by innuendo alone; how much more if he counsels: "If this were my own child. . . ." The written word can never truly compete with the spoken word in matters such as this. I have to acknowledge that when I read the Duff and Campbell report, my emotions were a combination of fury and frustration. Yet, when I talk with Dr. Duff, I recognize that we have different concerns, and probably different understandings, of the ethics of the situation. My focus is on the life of the child; his is on the well-being of the family. My ethics might be said to be based on moral rules concerning absolutes of right and wrong, whereas I would suspect that his ethical principles are based more on a balance between the advantages to the patient and the disadvantages to the family.

My concerns about death as an option in the management of a handicapped newborn are centered not only on withholding treatment from the patient, but also on the implications of this form of management when extended to other children and to adults. This is because I believe in the "thin edge of the wedge" theory and in the dangers of the "slippery slope," whereas Dr. Duff does not see the slippery slope in the same light.

Drs. Duff and Campbell state in their article: "Survivors of these neonatal intensive care units may be healthy and their parents grateful, but in some instances continue to suffer from such conditions as chronic pulmonary disease, short bowel syndrome or various manifestations of brain damage. Others are severely handicapped by a myriad of congenital malformations that in previous times have resulted in death."[3] Because a newborn child has the possibility of having dyspnea, oxygen dependence, incontinence, paralysis, a contracture, or a sexual handicap does not necessarily entitle the physician to decide that the child's life is not worth living. If we decide that this is a reason for terminating a child's life, how long will it be before the same thinking is extended to adults who already have these same signs and symptoms and might be considered candidates for some type of euthanasia program?

Drs. Duff and Campbell also state: "Often too, the parents' or siblings' rights to relief from the seemingly pointless, crushing burdens were important considerations."[4] It seems to me that this is solving a social problem by inattention to a newborn handicapped child resulting in his death. I do not think this is the proper use of medical expertise. As stated previously, society is the loser when the patient becomes the impersonal consumer and the profession is delivering a service.

When a double standard exists for the management of the newborn with a handicap, one can expect a double standard to follow for the care of the nonhandicapped newborns and for older patients as well. . . .

I have recently written the script for, acted in, and narrated several documentary films, collectively entitled *Whatever Happened to the Human Race?,* that I have undertaken with Francis A. Schaeffer, an American-born theologian-philosopher who lives in Switzerland.[5] The second of these films is on the subject of infanticide. I think one of the most compelling scenes in any of the films is one held in my living room where four of my patients born with defects incompatible with life and who were operated upon by me on the first day or two of life were assembled with four other patients who had developed lethal problems in early childhood. They were not coached in any way concerning what answer they were to give to my questions. They were told we were making some documentary movies and were writing a book on the general topic of *Whatever Happened to the Human Race?* We allowed time for them to talk with each other for about an hour in order to feel comfortable before being asked to participate in the film.

The patients at the time ranged in age from eleven to thirty-three years. One patient had been born with a number of major congenital anomalies down the midline of his body requiring, up to then, thirty-seven operative procedures for correction. Another was born without an esophagus, requiring transplantation of the colon to replace that absent organ. Still another was born with a tumor of the tongue necessitating almost total amputation of that structure in a series of operations. The fourth youngster with congenital defects was born with no rectum, no innervation of the bladder, and with major defects of the esophagus.

The other four children all had tumors. One was a benign tumor of the bones of the face, which had required a number of operations for correction and we still had not achieved perfection. The other three had cancers of the adrenal gland, of the parotid gland, and of the uterus, respectively. There can be no doubt about how such young people feel concerning the joy of living, despite the time-consuming and usually painful medical and surgical procedures they have endured to correct birth defects or situations discovered in early childhood. Here are samples of their comments:

> Because the start was a little abnormal, it doesn't mean you're going to finish that way. I'm a normal, functioning human being, capable of doing anything anybody else can.
>
> At times it got very hard, but life is certainly worth living. I married a wonderful guy and I'm just so happy.
>
> At the beginning it was a little difficult going back to school after surgery, but then things started looking up, with a little perseverance and support. I am an anesthetist and I'm happily married. Things are going great for me.
>
> I really think that all my operations and all the things I had wrong with me were worth it, because I really enjoy life and I don't really let the things that are wrong with me bother me.
>
> If anything, I think I've had an added quality to my life—an appreciation of life. I look forward to every single morning.
>
> Most of the problems are what my parents went through with the surgery. I've now been teaching high school for eight years and it's a great joy.
>
> They spend millions of dollars to send men to the moon. I think they can spend any amount necessary to save someone's life. A human life is so important because it's a gift—not something you can give, so you really don't have the right to take it either.
>
> I really don't consider myself handicapped. Life is just worth living. What else can I say?[6]

In another part of the film we talk to a young man who is now a graduate student. He was a thalidomide baby, born without a left leg and without arms below the elbows. When we asked this young man what he thought about those who say that people born with such serious birth defects should be eliminated, this, in part, was his reply.

> They don't really see that what they are talking about is murder. I know, when I was born, the first thing my dad said to my mom was that "this one needs our

love more." An individual with a handicap needs our love and needs us to help him grow into the being that God has made him to be. They are advocating that we destroy these children before they're even given a chance to live and to conquer their handicaps.

I'm very glad to be alive. I live a full, meaningful life. I have many friends and many things that I want to do in life. I think the secret of living with a handicap is realizing who you are—that you are a human being, somebody who is very special—looking at the things that you *can* do in spite of your handicap, and maybe even through your handicap.[7]

Anxious to know in my own patients what perceptions parents had years after their encounter with a surgical procedure to save a handicapped newborn's life, a study was done on thirty-one families in which I personally had operated on a child more than fifteen years before for the correction of esophageal atresia.[8] When fifty-three parents were asked what type of overall effect the situation had on the family, only two said the effect was strong and negative. Seven said the effect was mild and negative, ten said it was strong and positive, and fourteen claimed the effect was mild and positive. Eighteen parents thought there was *no* impact on the family....

If any group of physicians knows what can be accomplished by surgery on the handicapped newborn—and the proper support of the patient and his family in subsequent years—it is pediatric surgeons. Drs. Anthony Shaw, Judson G. Randolph, and Barbara Manard surveyed members of the surgical section of the American Academy of Pediatrics in reference to the management of newborns with handicaps.[9] Of the 400 pediatric surgeons queried, 267 (67 percent) completed questionnaires. A separate group of 308 pediatricians completed 190 questionnaires (62 percent). The first question was, "Do you believe that the life of each and every newborn infant should be saved if it is within our ability to do so?" Eighty percent of those surgeons with my kind of background answered no.[10]

Here are some other readily remembered statistics. Seventy-six percent of the pediatric surgeons would acquiesce in the parents' decision to refuse consent for surgery in a newborn with intestinal obstruction if the infant also had Down's syndrome, or mongolism.[11] An almost unbelievable fact is that 8 percent of the surgeons (respondents) said they would acquiesce to the parents' wishes if the child had nothing other than simple intestinal atresia, the operation which is almost 100 percent successful and life after which is completely normal.[12]

To return to the infant with duodenal obstruction, which is fatal but easily correctable, and Down's syndrome, the following percentages are significant. Twenty-three percent of the pediatric surgeons group would move the parents in the direction of not signing a consent for surgery and an operative permit making it the physician's decision whether or not to let the baby die; nevertheless, if the family desired surgery the surgeon would perform it.[13] Over half of the same group said they would provide the parents with all known facts and make the decision completely the parents'. (Surely the bias of the doctor would show through.) Only 16 percent would try to persuade the parents to allow surgery but would not take them to court on refusal. Three percent would get a court order if the parents refused consent for operation.[14]

The schizophrenic nature of these replies is indicated by the fact that if they acquiesce to the parents' decision to withhold lifesaving surgery 63 percent would have stopped all supportive treatment, 30 percent would have given oral feedings which of course would be vomited immediately, but less than .05 percent would have terminated the infant's life by an injection of a drug such as morphine. . . .[15]

I practice medicine in the realm of trust between my patient's family and me. I do withhold treatment from patients under certain circumstances, but if I do, I have to know three things: an extraordinary amount about the disease process in question, an extraordinary amount about my patient, and an extraordinary amount about the relationship of my patient to the disease process in question. If I do not know all of these three, then I must, as an ethical physician, in any decision process come down on the side of life. . . .

NOTES

1 *Report of the Joseph P. Kennedy Foundation Int'l Symposium on Human Rights, Retardation and Research,* Oct. 16, 1971. For an extended version of the Johns Hopkins case study, *see* Gustafson, "Mongolism, Parental Desires and the Right to Life," 16 *Perspectives in Biology & Med.* 529 (1973).

2 Duff & Campbell, "Moral and Ethical Dilemmas In The Special-Care Nursery," 289 *New Eng. J. Med.* 890 (1973).

3 *Id.* at 890.

4 *Id.* at 891.

5 F. Schaeffer & C.E. Koop, *Whatever Happened to the Human Race?* (1979).

6 *Id.* at 64-65.

7 *Id.* at 65.

8 Koop et al., "The Social, Psychological and Economic Problems of the Patient's Family After Secondary Repair of Esophegeal Atresia," 17 *Kinderchirurgie* (Supp. July, 1975).

9 Shaw, Randolph, & Manard, "Ethical Issues in Pediatrics Surgery: A National Survey of Pediatricians and Pediatric Surgeons," *60 Pediatrics 588* (1977).

10 *Id.* at 589. Of 259 responses from pediatric surgeons, 17 percent said yes and 83 percent said no. "Because the respondents [were] not a random sample of either [pediatric surgeons or pediatricians] but represented self-selected subgroups of entire populations, the use of inferential statistics is inappropriate." *Id.*

11. *Id.* at 590. Fifty percent of the pediatricians' group responded that they would acquiesce in such a decision.

12 *Id.* at 590-91. The authors note, however, that these respondents' answers to other questions indicated that most had read the question too hastily. These physicians were not more likely than others to refuse to operate on a baby with Down's syndrome. *Id.* at 591.

13 *Id.* at 591-92.

14 *Id.* Several of those who responded checked more than one option. (The pediatric surgeons usually chose to move the parents in the direction of not signing, and also to provide the parents with information and make the decision completely theirs.)

15 *Id.* at 592-93. It is interesting to note the difference between the responses of the pediatric surgeons and the pediatricians. Generally, the pediatricians were more willing to attempt to save the infant's life.

● ● ●

POSTSCRIPT

SHOULD TREATMENT BE WITHHELD FROM NEWBORNS WITH BIRTH DEFECTS?

In April 1982 a baby, known only as "Baby Doe," was born in Bloomington, Indiana, with Down's syndrome and other defects. The parents, on the physician's advice, decided not to authorize surgery for the child and to withhold nutrition as well. The case was reported to the local authorities by a concerned nurse and was brought to court, where a judge upheld the parents' decision. "Baby Doe" died after six days. That case, as well as others, has resulted in federal action to prevent the deaths of such babies. In March 1983 the Department of Health and Human Services issued a regulation establishing a "hotline," which people could call if they wanted to report a case of "child abuse or neglect" in a hospital nursery. The caller could remain anonymous, and an investigative squad would immediately be dispatched to the hospital to investigate. A federal judge ruled the regulation invalid on procedural grounds, but it was reproposed in July 1983. Medical professionals are opposed to the regulation, considering it an unwarranted governmental intrusion into the very complex process of decision making; the rule, they say, will make people fearful of hospitals and doctors, and will hurt the very children it is designed to protect.

See "Disconnecting the Baby Doe Hotline," and "Baby Doe Redux: Doctors as Child Abusers" by George J. Annas (*Hastings Center Report,* June 1983 and October 1983). The special problems of decision making for premature infants is discussed in Carson Strong's "The Tiniest Newborns" (*Hastings Center Report,* February 1983). John A. Robertson and Norman Fost point out the need for professional consensus on treatment decisions in "Passive Euthanasia of Defective Newborn Infants: Legal Considerations," *Journal of Pediatrics* (May 1976). For a view supporting treatment, see Paul Ramsey, *Ethics at the Edges of Life* (Yale, 1978), Chapters 5-8. Also see Chester A. Swinyard, editor, *Decision Making and the Defective Newborn* (Thomas, 1977).

ISSUE 8

CAN SUICIDE BE RATIONAL?

YES: Mary Rose Barrington, from "Apologia for Suicide," in M. Pabst Battin and David J. Mayo, editors, *Suicide: The Philosophical Issues* (New York: St. Martins Press, 1980)

NO: Herbert Hendin, M.D., from "The Right to Suicide," in *Suicide in America* (New York: W.W. Norton & Company, 1982)

ISSUE SUMMARY

YES: Mary Rose Barrington, a British solicitor (attorney), argues that humane and advanced societies must embrace the notion of "rational suicide" in a world that is increasingly crowded and populated by the aged, who would prefer a "planned death" to a long wait to be "arbitrarily extinguished."

NO: Psychiatrist Herbert Hendin emphasizes that suicide is a pathological response to life's problems and that instead of intellectual attempts to rationalize or glorify suicide, we need efforts to improve our lives together.

Suicide in literature and history has a romantic and even mythic quality: Consider Romeo, who could not live without his Juliet; the altruistic suicide in 1912 of Captain Oates, who walked out to his death in the Antarctic snow in an attempt to help Robert Scott and his other doomed companions; and the suicides of members of the French Resistance who chose death rather than reveal the names of their comrades under Nazi torture. Even the suicide in 1963 of Sylvia Plath, the young American poet who put her head in a gas oven (fully expecting, it now appears, to be rescued at the last minute), has been idealized. Many famous suicides—Marilyn Monroe, for example—have become legendary.

The realities of suicide, however, are more mundane. Although much of the discussion focuses on the terminally ill, very few dying people actually kill themselves. Suicide rates vary from country to country, but around the world suicide is among the first five causes of death for white males from ten to fifty-five years of age, and the second cause of death for white males from the ages of fifteen to nineteen (accidental death is first). In this country, the suicide rate among women and among young people is increasing, and it is highest of all among young black men. Those who are most likely to succeed in suicide attempts are older men who are divorced, widowed, or single; who abuse alcohol or drugs; or who are physically or mentally ill.

Suicide has been known since primitive times; however, the word did not appear until the seventeenth century. Until then it was known as "self-homicide" or "self-murder." The idea that taking one's own life can be a moral choice has a mixed history. It has been both approved and condemned, glorified and vilified. Early peoples generally had a horror of suicide, believing that the ghost of the suicide would return. The Athenians buried suicides outside the city and away from other graves, with the hand that did the self-murdering buried apart. Neither the Old Testament nor the New Testament directly prohibit suicide, and early Christianity was marked by a penchant for suicide and martyrdom. But by the sixth century, Christian theologians legislated against it, spurred on by St. Augustine's conviction that because each soul is immortal, each life is equally valuable. To reject life is to reject the gift of God, he said. St. Thomas Aquinas declared that not only was suicide a violation of a duty to God but it also violated the natural law and harmed the community. Kant argued on philosophical grounds that suicide degrades the worth of human life and is always immoral. By the eighteenth century, suicide had been made illegal in most European countries. Suicide continues to be considered a sin by the Catholic Church and a crime in many places.

But the opposing view also has deep roots. In Plato's *Phaedo* (the account of the trial and death of Socrates), Socrates declares that there are times when a person would be better off dead. Socrates chose to drink the hemlock fixed as the method of execution by the Athenian court; he, in some sense, committed suicide. In the first century A.D., the Roman philosopher Seneca wrote: "The wise man will live as long as he ought, not as long as he can." The nineteenth-century Scottish philosopher David Hume provided a more modern justification for suicide. He found that it involved no "transgression of our duty either to God, our neighbor, or ourselves." Perhaps the most persuasive contemporary philosopher who argues that suicide can be moral is Richard B. Brandt. He says: "The most that the moral critic of suicide could hold, then, is that there is *some* moral obligation not to do what one knows will cause one's death; but he surely cannot deny that circumstances exist in which there are obligations to do things which, in fact, will result in one's death."

The contemporary debate focuses not so much on whether people have a right to suicide but on whether it is rational—that is, the most sensible choice to make in a given situation. If it is not rational, then it should be prevented. Mary Rose Barrington believes that our current crisis of overpopulation and an aging society makes suicide a rational choice for the elderly. "To insist on the obligation of old people to live through a period of decline and helplessness," she says, "seems to me to be lacking in a feeling for the demands of human *self*-respect." Arguing against this position and also against the other claims that suicide is rational, Herbert Hendin presents clinical evidence that potential suicides are disturbed people who need help rather than approval.

YES

Mary Rose Barrington

APOLOGIA FOR SUICIDE

Of the many disagreeable features inherent in the human condition, none is more unpalatable than mortality. Many people declare that they find the concept of survival and immortal life both inconceivable and preposterous; but they will usually admit to a minimal pang at the thought of being snuffed out in due course and playing no further part in the aeons to come. That aeons have already passed before they were born is a matter that few people take to heart, and they tend on the whole to be rather glad not to have experienced the hardships of life before the era of the Public Health Acts and pain-killing drugs. To cease from being after having once existed seems altogether different and altogether terrible. This is an odd conclusion, bearing in mind that whereas before birth one must be reckoned to have had no effect on the course of events at all, the very act of birth and the shortest of lives may produce incalculable and possibly cataclysmic effects by indirect causation. Viewed in this light we might all be filled with satisfaction to think that our every move will send ripples of effects cascading down time. In fact, speculations of this kind do little if anything to satisfy the immortal longings, and even though being remembered kindly by others is generally felt to be something of a comfort, absolute death remains absolutely appalling. Many people who have no religious convictions save themselves from despair by filing away in their minds some small outside chance that they might, after all, survive, perhaps as some semi-anonymous cog in a universal system; many others resolutely refuse to give any thought to death at all.

If human convictions and behavior were a direct function of logical thinking, one would expect that the more firmly a person believed in the survival of his soul in an existence unhampered by the frequently ailing body, the more ready he would be to leave this world and pass on to the next. Nothing of the sort appears to be the case, at least for those whose religion is based on the Old Testament. Self-preservation is presented in such religions as a duty, though

From "Apologia for Suicide," by Mary Rose Barrington in *Suicide: The Philosophical Issues,* edited by M. Pabst Battin and David J. Mayo.

one that is limited by some inconsistent provisos. Thus a person may sacrifice his life to save others in war, or he may die a martyr's death in a just cause; but if he were to reason that there was not enough food in the family to go round, and therefore killed himself to save the others from starvation (a fate, like many others, considerably worse than death), this would be regarded as the sin, and erstwhile crime, of suicide. Whether performed for his own benefit or to benefit others, the act of suicide would be condemned as equivalent to breaking out from prison before the expiry of the term fixed, a term for which there can be no remission.

The old notions about suicide, with an influence still lingering on, are well summarized by Sir William Blackstone in his famous *Commentaries on the Laws of England* (1765-9): "The suicide is guilty of a double offence: one spiritual, in invading the prerogative of the Almighty and rushing into his immediate presence uncalled for; the other temporal, against the King, who hath an interest in the preservation of all his subjects."[1]

Religious opposition to suicide is of decreasing importance as people become ever more detached from dogmas and revelationary teachings about right and wrong. The important matter to be considered is that while the humanist, the agnostic or the adherent of liberal religion seldom condemns suicide as a moral obliquity, he appears on the whole to find it as depressing and horrifying as the religious believer for whom it is sinful. There are many reasons for this, some good, and some regrettable.

Indoctrination against suicide is regrettably to be found at all levels. In itself the tendentious expression "to commit suicide" is calculated to poison the unsuspecting mind with its false semantic overtones, for, apart from the dangerous practice of committing oneself to an opinion, most other things committed are, as suicide once was, criminal offences.[2] People are further influenced by the unhappy shadow cast over the image of suicide by the wide press coverage given to reports of suicide by students who are worried about their examinations, or girls who are upset over a love affair, or middle-aged people living alone in bed-sitting-rooms who kill themselves out of depression—troubles that might all have been surmounted, given time. In pathetic cases such as these, it is not, as it seems to me, the act of suicide that is horrifying, but the extreme unhappiness that must be presumed to have induced it. Death from despair is the thing that ought to make us shudder, but the shudder is often extended to revulsion against the act of suicide that terminates the despair, an act that may be undertaken in very different circumstances.

The root cause of the widespread aversion to suicide is almost certainly death itself rather than dislike of the means by which death is brought about. The leaf turns a mindless face to the sun for one summer before falling for ever into the mud; death, however it comes to pass, rubs our clever faces in the same mud, where we too join the leaves. The inconceivability of this transformation in status is partly shot through with an indirect illumination, due to the death of others. Yet bereavement is not death. Here to mourn, we are still here, and the imagination boggles at the notion that things could ever be otherwise. Not only does the imagination boggle, as to some extent it must, but the mind unfortunately averts. The averted mind acknowledges, in a theoretical way, that death does indeed happen to people here and there and now and then, but to some extent the attitude to death resembles the attitude of the heavy smoker to lung cancer; he reckons that if he is lucky it will not happen to *him*, at least not yet, and perhaps not ever. This confused sort of faith in the immortality of the body must underlie many a triumphal call from the hospital ward or theatre, that the patient's life has been saved—and he will therefore die next week instead of this week, and in rather greater discomfort. People who insist that life must always be better than death often sound as if they are choosing eternal life in contrast to eternal death, when the fact is that they have no choice in the matter; it is death now, or death later. Once this fact is fully grasped it is possible for the question to arise as to whether death now would not be preferable.

Opponents of suicide will sometimes throw dust in the eyes of the uncommitted by asking at some point why one should ever choose to go on living if one once questions the value of life; for as we all know, adversity is usually round the corner, if not at our heels. Here, it seems to me, a special case must be made out for people suffering from the sort of adversity with which the proponents of euthanasia are concerned: namely, an apparently irremediable state of physical debility that makes life unbearable to the sufferer. Some adversities come and go; in the words of the Anglo-Saxon poet reviewing all the disasters known to Norse mythology, "That passed away, so may this." Some things that do not pass away include inoperable cancers in the region of the throat that choke their victims slowly to death. Not only do they not pass away, but like many extremely unpleasant conditions they cannot be alleviated by pain-killing drugs. Pain itself can be controlled, provided the doctor in charge is prepared to put the relief of pain before the prolongation of life; but analgesics will not help a patient to live with total incontinence, reduced to the status of a helpless baby after a life of independent adulthood. And for the person who manages to avoid these grave afflictions there remains the spectre of senile decay, a physical and mental crumbling into a travesty of the normal person. Could anything be more reasonable than for a person faced with these living deaths to weigh up the pros and cons of living out his life until his heart finally fails, and going instead to meet death half-way?

It is true, of course, that, all things being equal, people do want to go on living. If we are enjoying life, there seems no obvious reason to stop doing so and be mourned by our families and forgotten by our friends. If we are not enjoying it, then it seems a miserable end to die in a trough of depression, and better to wait for things to become more favourable. Most people, moreover, have a moral obligation to continue living, owed to their parents while they are still alive, their children while they are dependent, and their spouses all the time. Trained professional workers may even feel that they have a duty to society to continue giving their services. Whatever the grounds, it is both natural and reasonable that without some special cause nobody ever wants to die *yet*. But must these truisms be taken to embody the whole truth about the attitude of thinking people to life and death? A psychiatrist has been quoted as saying: "I don't think you can consider anyone normal who tries to take his own life."[3] The abnormality of the suicide is taken for granted, and the possibility that he might have been doing something sensible (for him) is not presented to the mind for even momentary consideration. It might as well be argued that no one can be considered normal who does not want to procreate as many children as possible, and this was no doubt urged by the wise men of yesterday; today the tune is very different, and in this essay we are concerned with what they may be singing tomorrow.

There is an obvious connection between attitudes to birth and to death, since both are the fundamentals of life. The experience of this century has shown that what may have appeared to be ineradicably basic instincts can in fact be modified in an advanced society, and modified not merely by external pressures, but by corresponding feedback movement from within. Primitive people in general take pride in generating large families, apparently feeling in some deep-seated way that motherhood proves the femaleness of the female, and that fatherhood proves the maleness of the male, and that the position in either case is worth proving very amply. This simple pride is not unknown in advanced countries, although public applause for feats of childbearing is at last beginning to freeze on the fingertips, and a faint rumble of social disapproval may be heard by an ear kept close to the ground. The interesting thing is that it is not purely financial considerations that have forced people into limiting their progeny, and least of all is it the public weal; people have actually come to prefer it. Women want to lead lives otherwise than as mothers; men no longer feel themselves obliged to assert their virility by pointing to numerous living tokens around them; and most parents prefer to concentrate attention and affection upon a couple rather than a pack. The modification in this apparently basic drive to large-scale procreation is now embraced not with reluctance, but with enthusiasm. My thesis is that humane and advanced societies are ripe for a similar and in many ways equivalent swing away from the ideal of longevity to the concept of a planned death.

It may be worth pausing here to consider whether the words "natural end," in the sense usually ascribed to the term, have much bearing on reality. Very little is "natural" about our present-day existence, and least natural of all is the prolonged period of dying that is suffered by so many incurable patients solicitously kept alive to be killed by their disease. The sufferings of animals (other than man) are heart-rending enough, but a dying process spread over weeks, months or years seems to be one form of suffering that animals are normally spared. When severe illness strikes them they tend to stop eating, sleep and die. The whole weight of Western society forces attention on the natural right to live, but throws a blanket of silence over the natural right to die. If I seem to be suggesting that in a civilized society suicide ought to be considered a quite proper way for a well-brought-up person to end his life (unless he has the good luck to die suddenly and without warning), that is indeed the tenor of my argument; if it is received with astonishment and incredulity, the reader is referred to the reception of recommendations made earlier in the century that birth control should be practised and encouraged. The idea is no more extraordinary, and would be equally calculated to diminish the sum total of suffering among humankind.

This will probably be taken as, or distorted into, a demand for the infliction of the death penalty on retirement. And yet the bell tolls for me no less than for others. Apart from the possibility that he may actually have some sympathy for the aged, no one casting a fearful eye forward into the future is likely to advocate treatment of the old that he would not care to see applied to himself, lest he be hoist with his own petard. It cannot be said too many times that so long as people are blessed with reasonable health, reasonable independence and reasonable enjoyment of life, they have no more reason to contemplate suicide than people who are half their age, and frequently half as sprightly as many in their seventies and eighties today. Attention is here being drawn to people who unfortunately have good reason to question whether or not they want to exercise their right to live; the minor infirmities of age, and relative weakness, and a slight degree of dependence on younger people who regard the giving of a helping hand as a natural part of the life-cycle, do not give rise to any such question. The question arises when life becomes a burden rather than a pleasure.

Many middle-aged people are heard to express the fervent wish that they will not live to be pain-ridden cripples, deaf, dim-sighted or feeble-minded solitaries, such that they may become little else than a burden to themselves and to others. They say they *hope* they will die before any of these fates descend upon them, but they seldom affirm that they *intend* to die before that time; and when the time comes, it may barely cross their minds that they could, had they then the determination, take the matter into their own hands. The facile retort will often be that this merely goes to show that people do not really mean what they say and that like all normal, sensible folk, they really want to live on for as long as is physically possible. But this, I would suggest, is a false conclusion. They mean exactly what they say, but the conditions and conditioning of society make it impossible for them to act in accordance with their wishes. To face the dark reality that the future holds nothing further in the way of joy or meaningful experience, and to face the fact without making some desperate and false reservation, to take the ultimate decision and act upon it knowing that it is a gesture that can never be repeated, such clearsightedness and resolution demand a high degree of moral strength that cannot but be undermined by the knowledge that this final act of self-discipline would be the subject of headshakings, moralizings and general tut-tutting.

How different it would be if a person could talk over the future with his family, friends and doctors, make arrangements, say farewells, take stock of his life, and know that his decision about when and how to end his life was a matter that could be the subject of constructive and sympathetic conference, and even that he could have his chosen ones around him at the last. As things are at present, he would always be met with well-meant cries of "No, no, you mustn't talk like that," and indeed anyone taking a different line might feel willy-nilly that his complicity must appear unnatural and lacking in affection. We feel that we *ought* to become irrational at the idea that someone we care for is contemplating ending his own life, and only the immediate spectacle of intense suffering can shock us out of a conditioned response to this situation. The melancholy result is that a decision that cries out for moral support has to be taken in cheerless isolation, and if taken at all is usually deferred until the victim is in an advanced state of misery.

But supposing the person contemplating suicide is not in fact undergoing or expecting to undergo severe suffering, but is merely an elderly relation, probably a mother, in fragile health, or partially disabled, and though not acutely ill is in need of constant care and attention. It would be unrealistic to deny the oppressive burden that is very often cast on the shoulders of a young to middle-aged person, probably a daughter, by the existence of an ailing parent, who may take her from her career when she is a young woman in her thirties or forties, and leave her, perhaps a quarter of a century later, an elderly, exhausted woman, demoralized over the years by frequently having had to choke back the wish that her mother would release her by dying. Even in a case such as this, human feeling does demand, I would think, that the younger person must still respond to intimations of suicide with a genuinely felt, "No, no."

But what of the older person's own attitude? Here we arrive at the kernel of the violent and almost panic-stricken reaction of many people to the idea of questioning whether it is better, in any given situation, to be or not to be. For if there is no alternative to continued living, then no choice arises, and hence there can be no possibility of an older person, who is a burden to a younger person, feeling a sense of obligation to release the captive attendant from willing or unwilling bondage, no questioning of the inevitability of the older person's living out her full term. But what if there were a real choice? What if a time came when, no longer able to look after oneself, the decision to live on for the maximum number of years were considered a mark of heedless egoism? What if it were to be thought that *dulce et decorum est pro familia mori?* This is a possibility that makes many people shrink from the subject, because they find the prospect too frightful to contemplate. Is it (to be charitable) because they always think themselves into the position of the younger person, so that "No, no" rises naturally to their lips, or is it (to be uncharitable) because they cannot imagine themselves making a free sacrifice of this sort?

This very controversial issue is, it may be remarked, outside the scope of voluntary euthanasia, which is concerned exclusively with cases where a patient is a burden to *himself,* and whether or not he is a burden to others plays no part whatever. The essence of voluntary euthanasia is the cooperation of the doctor in making crucial decisions; the "burden to others," on the contrary, must make all decisions and take all responsibility himself for any actions he might take. The issue cannot, however, be ignored, because the preoccupation of many opponents of voluntary euthanasia with its supposed implications, suggests that few people have any serious objection to the voluntary termination of a gravely afflicted life. This principal theme is usually brushed aside with surprising haste, and opponents pass swiftly on to the supposed evils that would flow from making twilight existence optional rather than obligatory. It is frequently said that hard-hearted people would be encouraged to make their elderly relatives feel that they had outlived their welcome and ought to remove themselves, even if they happened to be enjoying life. No one can say categorically that nothing of the sort would happen, but the sensibility of even hard-hearted people to the possible consequences of their own unkindness seems just as likely. A relation who had stood down from life in a spirit of magnanimity and family affection would, after an inevitable period of heart-searching and self-recrimination, leave behind a pleasant memory; a victim of callous treatment hanging like an accusing albatross around the neck of the living would suggest another and rather ugly story. Needless to say, whoever was responsible would not in any event be the sort of person to show consideration to an aged person in decline.

Whether or not some undesirable fringe results would stem from a free acceptance of suicide in our society, the problem of three or four contemporaneous generations peopling a world that hitherto has had to support only two or three is with us here and now, and will be neither generated nor exacerbated by a fresh attitude to life and death. The disabled, aged parent, loved or unloved, abnegating or demanding, is placed in one of the tragic dilemmas inherent in human existence, and one that becomes more acute as standards of living rise. One more in the mud-hut is not a problem in the same way as one more in a small, overcrowded urban dwelling; and the British temperament demands a privacy incompatible with the more sociable Mediterranean custom of packing a grandmother and an aunt or two in the attic. Mere existence presents a mild problem; disabled existence presents a chronic problem. The old person may have no talent for being a patient, and the young one may find it intolerable to be a nurse. A physical decline threatens to be accompanied by an inevitable decline in the quality of important human relationships—human relationships, it is worth repeating, not superhuman ones. Given superhuman love, patience, fortitude and all other sweet-natured qualities in a plenitude not normally present in ordinary people, there would be no problem. But the problem is there, and voluntary termination of life offers a possible solution that may be better than none at all. The young have been urged from time immemorial to have valiant hearts, to lay down their lives for their loved ones when their lives have hardly started; it may be that in time to come the disabled aged will be glad to live in a society that approves an honourable death met willingly, perhaps in the company of another "old soldier" of the same generation, and with justifiable pride. Death taken in one's own time, and with a sense of purpose, may in fact be far more bearable than the process of waiting to be arbitrarily extinguished.[4] A patient near the end of his life who arranged his death so as, for example, to permit an immediate transfer of a vital organ to a younger person, might well feel that he was converting his death into a creative act instead of waiting passively to be suppressed.

A lot of kindly people may feel that this is lacking in respect for the honourable estate of old age; but to insist on the obligation of old people to live through a period of decline and helplessness seems to me to be lacking in a feeling for the demands of human *self*-respect. They may reply that this shows a false notion of what constitutes self-respect, and that great spiritual qualities may be brought out by dependence and infirmity, and the response to such a state. It is tempting in a world dominated by suffering to find all misery purposeful, and indeed in some situations the "cross-to-bear" and the willing bearer may feel that they are contributing a poignant note to some cosmic symphony that is richer for their patience and self-sacrifice. Since we are talking of options and not of compulsions, people who felt like this would no doubt continue to play their chosen parts; but what a truly ruthless thing to impose those parts on people who feel that they are meaningless and discordant, and better written out. . . .

NOTES

1 Sir William Blackstone, *Commentaries on the Laws of England,* 18th edition, ed. Arthur Ryland (London: Sweet, Pheney, Maxwell, Stevens & Sons, 1829), Vol. IV, p. 189.
2 Professor Flew points out the greater virtues of the French "*se suicider.*" See Antony Flew, "The Principle of Euthanasia," in A.B. Downing, ed., *Euthanasia and the Right to Death* (London: Peter Owen, 1969), p. 46, n. 13. We should perhaps be grateful not to be burdened with an expression like the German "*Selbstmord,*" i.e., "self-murder."
3 Reported in *The Observer* (June 26, 1967).
4 It will be noted that reference is made here in all cases to the aged. In a longer exposition I would argue that very different considerations apply to the young disabled who have not yet enjoyed a full life span, and who should be given far greater public assistance to enable them to enjoy life as best they can.

● ● ●

NO

Herbert Hendin

THE RIGHT TO SUICIDE

Partly as a response to the failure of suicide prevention, partly in reaction to commitment abuses, and perhaps mainly in the spirit of accepting anything that does not physically harm anyone else, we see suicide increasingly advocated as a fundamental human right. Many such advocates deplore all attempts to prevent suicide as an interference with that right. It is a position succinctly expressed by Nietzsche when he wrote, "There is a certain right by which we may deprive a man of life, but none by which we may deprive him of death."[1] Taken from its social and psychological context, suicide is regarded by some purely as an issue of personal freedom.

The psychiatrist Thomas Szasz has been an articulate contemporary spokesman for this point of view.[2] Szasz believes we rationalize an oppressive policy toward deviations like suicide and drug abuse by calling them illnesses and use psychiatrists and psychologists as enforcers of that policy. While not advocating drug use, Szasz believes that "dangerous drugs, addicts and pushers are the scapegoats of our modern, secular, therapeutically imbued societies," and that "the ritual persecution of these pharmacological and human agents must be seen against the historical backdrop of the ritual persecution of other scapegoats, such as witches, Jews, and madmen."[3] Of suicide prevention, Szasz writes, "He who does not accept and respect those who want to reject life does not truly accept and respect life itself." Causing one's own death, Szasz goes on, "should be called 'suicide' only by those who disapprove of it; and should be called 'death control' by those who approve of it."[4]

The often transient and ambivalent quality of the impulse to commit suicide is not recognized by Szasz, who believes that successful suicides intend to die and that unsuccessful ones do not. Here the clinical evidence contradicts him. Ambivalence toward suicide is indicated by the fact that three-fourths of all suicides communicate their intentions, often with the hope that something will be done to make their suicide unnecessary. In a high proportion of cases, such communications are varied, repeated, and expressed to more than one individual. Studies of those who have survived serious suicide attempts have revealed that a fantasy of being rescued is frequently present.

What has misled Szasz and the clinicians who make a rigid separation between those who survive suicide attempts and those who do not is the evidence that many so-called attempted suicides are not even ambivalent about suicide—they clearly want to live. This in no way contradicts the clinical evidence that a large number of those who kill themselves are ambivalent in the sense that they do something irrevocable in a state of uncertainty.

Many people have speculated that if you could talk to someone who was in midair after jumping from a tall tower, you might find out that he no longer was so sure he wanted to die. Over the past thirty years I have seen four people who survived six-story suicide jumps. Two wished to survive as soon as they had jumped, two said they did not, but one of the latter two who professed to be furious at having survived made no subsequent suicide attempts.

Moreover, in a majority of cases, we do not know at once how serious the individual is about suicide. It is estimated that only one out of ten suicide attempts results in death, a figure that tends to confirm the view that suicidal individuals are not unambivalently intent on dying. Similarly, studies of the subsequent mortality rates of survivors show that only about 1 percent of all survivors kill themselves within one year. If for no other reason than the persuasive evidence of ambivalence surrounding suicide, some intervention—even if it is very short-term and narrowly circumscribed—seems clearly warranted and desirable.

Most suicidal patients who come to hospitals do so as a consequence of injuries sustained in their suicide attempts. Are we to refuse treatment for such injuries out of respect for the patient's suicidal intent? Most of these patients recovering from their injuries in hospitals have not asked for help; some will accept it and others will reject it when it is offered. Should we not even offer it unless the patient explicitly requests it? Few who argue for the "right to suicide" are likely to make the same argument with regard to a suicidal child or adolescent.

Szasz claims that man's inhumanity, demonstrable in such practices as slavery in the United States and totalitarianism in the Soviet Union and in Nazi Germany, refutes the contention that we value everyone's life or the suicide's life more than he does. Presumably we should recognize that we are intrinsically evil and cease to try or pretend to try to be otherwise.

Szasz, who is passionately eloquent in defending the right to suicide and the right to use or sell drugs, seems to show little sympathy for the desperately wretched lives of drug abusers and of those who would kill themselves. His position would be more understandable if his legitimate concerns about social and medical coercion were accompanied by a corresponding concern for the plight of those whose lives are self-destructively out of control, many of whom want help. As it is, Szasz invites a policy of indifference to them. His argument that social help undermines individual autonomy has been used in the past to justify opposition to every form of social reform.

Szasz makes no claim, however, that society should help, support, or encourage the suicide in his efforts to kill himself. He believes that it would be sufficient if society recognized that it had no right to interfere. But those arguing for "the right to suicide" go further. Many supporters of euthanasia see suicide in a social context, believe that context makes evident the social utility of suicidal death, and want social support, encouragement, and even help in carrying out suicide.

Much of the argument for suicide focuses on the elderly. The increasing number of old people, the inadequate care provided by nursing homes, and the economic cost to both families and society of caring for the infirm elderly are used to support the view that suicide must be accepted, encouraged, and protected. Mary Rose Barrington, a solicitor of the Supreme Court of the Judicature of England and a past chairperson of the Voluntary Euthanasia Society, tells us that "the problem of three or four contemporary generations peopling a world that heretofore has had to support only two or three is with us here and now."[5] What a sad commentary on us and our culture it would be if our response to the social changes required by the increasing number of the elderly were to be euthanasia.

Many of those who once advocated euthanasia for elderly, infirm suffering patients have broadened their position to include the right to suicide for everyone. Reflecting this change, the British Voluntary Euthanasia Society is now called EXIT.

Barrington and Eliot Slater, an English psychiatrist and advocate of euthanasia, include chronic illness—regardless of what age—as a justification for suicide. Slater tells us, "If a chronically sick man dies, he ceases to be a burden on himself, on his family, on the health services and on the community. If we can do nothing to get a patient better, but do our best to retard the process of dying—extend it perhaps over months and years—we are adding to the totality of ill health and incapacity. To take an obvious example, transplant surgery, in providing a spare set for people who have run through the pair of kidneys, liver and heart, increases the number of people in the community who at one time are suffering from diseases of the kidneys, liver and heart. There is, of course, absolutely no limit to the burdens we can go on piling up, by trying to keep badly damaged individuals alive."[6] Such social Darwinism, if carried to a logical conclusion, would force us to cease our efforts to help and perhaps to encourage the suicide of all who are disabled, chronically ill, or handicapped.

Barrington tells us that, unlike people, animals when struck by severe illness have the good sense to stop eating and die. Actually, some human beings do so too; they are usually people whose spirit has been so crushed by life that they offer little resistance to illness. Some primitive cultures, such as that of Alor, demonstrated a cultural tendency toward such a response, but Alor was a society that crushed the adaptive capacity of most of its inhabitants. We need not believe that suffering is good for the character in order to understand that the capacity to deal with adversity, including illness, is one of the features of psychosocial stability. . . .

We need not argue the issue of whether it is rational for an individual with a painful terminal illness to refuse extraordinary life-saving measures or to arrange more actively to end his life. Most would agree it is, and that is precisely why supporters of the "right to suicide" or "death control" position are constantly presenting the case of a patient suffering from incurable, painful cancer as the case on which they based their argument. In reality, however, such understandable cases form only a small percentage of all suicides, or potential suicides. The majority of suicides confront us with the problem of understanding people whose situation does not seem, from an outsider's viewpoint, hopeless or often even critical. The knowledge that there are more suicides by people who wrongly believe themselves to be suffering from cancer than there are suicides by those who actually have cancer puts the problem in some perspective.

Such advocates of the "right to suicide" as Barrington and Slater think our opposition to suicide is based on our fear of accepting and dealing with death. They wish to raise our consciousness on the matter. Barrington, for example, writes, "People who insist that life must always be better than death often sound as if they are choosing eternal life in contrast to eternal death, when the fact is that they have no choice in the matter; it is death now, or death later. Once this fact is fully grasped it is possible for the question to arise as to whether death now would not be preferable." She also believes that consciousness is best raised early, and she suggests that children be encouraged to write compositions "envisaging why and in what circumstances they propose to end their lives."[7]

The "right to suicide" advocates propose for all of us a heightened consciousness about death, a consciousness that is in fact intrinsic to the adaptation of suicidal individuals. The person facing imminent death who is in intractable pain and arranges to end his life may be a suicide in the dictionary definition of the term, but not in the psychological sense. The suicide is more apt to be someone for whom death must be imminent when it is not, for whom death is a necessary part of his or her adaptation to life, and for whom the possibility of self-inflicted death may make life more bearable.

Potentially suicidal people make death the center of their existence. As the poet Anne Sexton, who went on to kill herself, put it, "talking death" is "life" for suicides.[8] They are often people who take continued comfort from the fact that if things get too bad they can or will end their lives. In dealing with the preoccupation with death, they are concerned with how and when death can be implemented; some find comfort in persuading others to join them in their preoccupation. A recent psychiatric report of a small "epidemic" of suicide and suicide attempts on a college campus was traced to one young man who had dealt with his own preoccupation with suicide by involving others in what amounted to a suicide club.[9] A constructive effort to deal with a similar preoccupation with death was made by a professional woman I saw who was absorbed with killing herself and had made one almost fatal attempt, while making a second career for herself as a volunteer worker in a suicide prevention center. In trying to persuade others to stay alive, she was trying to persuade herself.

Albert Camus states at the opening of *The Myth of Sisyphus*, "There is but one truly serious philosophical problem, and that is suicide. Judging whether life is or is not worth living amounts to answering the fundamental question of philosophy."[10] This statement, quoted approvingly in books and articles on suicide, echoes the "Is life worth living?" question posed in a famous essay on suicide by William James, who was evidently seriously suicidal for a significant period in his life.[11] The young [man] who spent his high school years making lists of reasons why he should keep living reflects in a less sophisticated manner the problem with which James and Camus were wrestling. Both James and Camus ultimately affirm the value of life, but whether or not to end one's life is not the central question for most people.

Individuals who spend years planning

their death are suicidal. Such persons may wait for the first sign of serious illness associated with age to kill themselves, but they have been suicidal for a long time. Yet in the current climate such people are sometimes regarded as an avant-garde who can guide us in matters of life and death.

A good example is provided in the well-publicized case of Jo Roman, a Manhattan artist and former social worker. After years of advocating choosing the time of one's own death, she called her friends in to say good-bye, arranged to have the group's conversation videotaped, then spent the evening with her husband and a close friend before taking a fatal overdose of pills. She was 62 and had been diagnosed as having a breast tumor that would have been treatable by mastectomy, but she did not wish to have that done. In a letter that she requested be sent to *The New York Times* following her suicide, she said that she was carrying out her suicide "more than a decade earlier than she had planned." She explained that before the cancer was diagnosed fourteen months earlier, she had planned to end her life around 1992, when she would have been 75. Her videotapes on her advocacy of "self-termination" were subsequently shown in an educational television documentary. The *Times* reporter accepted the story very much at face value, depicting her as a pioneer.[12]

A somewhat comparable story had been written for the magazine section of the same newspaper the year before by a man who had decided to kill himself if he was told that a colostomy would be necessary to save him from a rectal cancer. He, too, was determined not to accept a mutilating procedure and felt he would rather die than do so. Both individuals believed their decisions were not simply private matters but examples that they hoped would help to change social attitudes.

Although mastectomies and colostomies are traumatic procedures for anyone to undergo, the majority of people who need them fortunately do choose to live, and their commitments to life and to other people are such that most of them make satisfactory adjustments. It would be sadly preposterous if the attitude that people who need such surgical procedures should choose death instead were to become prevalent.

A related illustration is provided by a vigorous, handsome doctor of 52 who killed himself after a minor heart attack. A bachelor, he prided himself on his appearance, his ability as a tennis player, and his sexual conquests. He spent his social life in a series of casual affairs with women, becoming acutely uncomfortable if a relationship lasted more than a month. He took his heart attack as an even greater attack on his self-image and lifestyle and defended himself by suicide.

People whose investment in their appearance and intactness is so great that they will die rather than accept the changes of age or disease are likely to be ones whose capacity for caring for others is impaired. Mrs. Roman, the *Times* story noted only parenthetically, had given her two children away at the time of an earlier divorce, when they were six and four, to a friend who had raised them. Her story had some similarities to that of a recent patient I had seen who had decided to die rather than undergo removal of a malignant but operable tumor. The woman had been suicidal before the diagnosis of the tumor, although the tumor strengthened her determination to kill herself. She, too, had given her young children to her parents to raise following an earlier divorce.

Even without a knowledge of suicide,

common sense would indicate that there is something morbid about people who, while still vigorous and healthy, spend their time worrying about controlling the circumstances of their death. Before glorifying these pioneers of "self-termination," we would do well to remember that these individuals who accept life only on their own terms have much in common psychodynamically with much less romanticized suicides.

Media attempts to glorify suicide would be less significant if they were not accompanied by a marked increase in intellectual attempts to find a rational basis for suicide. More and more philosophers are being drawn into discussions of the ethics of suicide, so that Camus's remark that suicide is the essential question for philosophy is truer now than when he made it. Most such writing attempts to defuse the absolute nature of suicide by a process of intellectual assimilation. The issues of living and dying are rationalized into a language and style that at times seem more appropriate to descriptive economics. The German psychiatrist-philosopher Alfred Hoche addressed the problem at the beginning of this century, but his approach is typical of current evaluations of the right to die in terms of the cost-effectiveness of life to one's self.

Hoche proposed the term *Bilanz Selbstmord* or "balance sheet suicide" to refer to cases in which individuals assumed to be mentally unimpaired dispassionately took stock of their life situation and, having found it unacceptable or untenable and foreseeing no significant change for the better, decided to end their lives.[13] Richard Brandt, past president of the American Philosophical Association, in a modern version of balance sheet suicide, tries to outline how we can evaluate which decision to make.[14] He sees a close analogy between a rational decision for suicide and the decision of the directors of a firm to declare bankruptcy and go out of business. He is aware that depression may impair one's judgment about future probabilities, but he seems to feel that the aware individual can make allowance for this possible error in his calculations.

Neither Hoche's nor Brandt's arguments are convincing. The tendency to think that life can be measured on a balance scale is itself a characteristic of suicidal people. Their thought processes often seem tailored to narrow possibilities, for their rigidity often makes them unable to see alternative solutions, while depression alters their judgment about possibilities for the future. . . .

Theoretical formulations of the moral or philosophical merits of suicide, divorced from clinical knowledge of suicidal individuals, bear little relation to the issues at work in suicidal individuals and have little value for the development of social policy. Commonly overlooked by such formulations is the extraordinary coerciveness associated with suicidal behavior. From the attempt to coerce life by making grandiose conditions on reality that reality cannot fulfill to the "If you love me, you will be willing to die with me!" test put to a reluctant partner in a suicide pact, self-destruction and destructiveness to others go hand in hand. The suicide pact is in fact, not covenant affirming, but often a form of tyranny, affirming one partner's desire to control the life of the other. The coercive grandiosity of the Reverend Jim Jones, in a bizarre and exaggerated way, suggests the social relations of many who are suicidal and who bind others to them "even unto death.". . .

Although our efforts to prevent individual suicides should not be of the sort that devalue life even more than suicide does, when pathology is psychosocial—when the community has a stake in it—personal rights are not without limits. Some years ago I wrote that if suicidal people were to organize to recruit others to their point of view, as happens in Robert Louis Stevenson's story "The Suicide Club," society should be able to intervene.[15] The emergence of and growing acclaim for societies that exist to facilitate the suicide of their members in England and in the United States should be regarded with alarm. They are not merely distributing "how to do it" information. They are the avant-garde of a larger attempt to seek social approval and institutionalization for suicide. If they succeed, their success will be a reflection of how, as a culture, we are turning from efforts to improve our lives together toward the lesser goal of helping each other die.

NOTES

1 Nietzsche, *Human, All-Too-Human,* trans. H. Zimmern (Edinburgh: Foulis, 1909), p. 88.

2 Szasz, *The Myth of Mental Illness: Foundations of a Theory of Personal Conduct,* rev. ed. (New York: Harper & Row, 1974); idem, *Law, Liberty, and Psychiatry: An Inquiry into the Social Uses of Mental Health Practices* (New York: Collier Books, 1968); idem, *Ceremonial Chemistry: The Ritual Persecution of Drugs, Addicts, and Pushers* (Garden City, N.Y.: Anchor Books, 1974); idem, *The Second Sin* (Garden City, N.Y.: Anchor Books, 1974); idem, "The Ethics of Suicide," *Antioch Review* 31 (1971): 7-17.

3 Szasz, *Ceremonial Chemistry,* pp. xi, xii.

4 Szasz, *The Second Sin,* pp. 75, 76.

5 Barrington, "Apologia for Suicide," in *Suicide: The Philosophical Issues,* ed. M.P. Battin and D. Mayo (New York: St. Martin's, 1980), p. 98.

6 Slater, "Choosing the Time to Die," in ibid., pp. 202-3.

7 Barrington, "Apologia for Suicide," p. 101.

8 Quoted by J. Oates in "The Art of Suicide," in *Suicide: The Philosophical Issues,* ed. Battin and Mayo, p. 165.

9 W. Binns, D. Kerkinan, and S. Schroeder, "Destructive Group Dynamics: An Account of Some Peculiar Interrelated Incidents of Suicide and Suicidal Attempts in a University Dormitory," *Journal of the American College Health Association* 14 (1966): 350-56.

10 Camus, *The Myth of Sisyphus and Other Essays,* trans. J. O'Brien (New York: Vintage Books, 1959), p. 3.

11 James, *Is Life Worth Living?* (Philadelphia: Weston, 1896).

12 *New York Times,* 17 June 1979.

13 Hoche, "Vom Sterben," in *Aus der Werkstatt* (Munich: Jehmann, 1935), pp. 210-32.

14 Brandt, "The Morality and Rationality of Suicide," in *A Handbook for the Study of Suicide,* ed. S. Perlin (New York: Oxford University Press, 1975), pp. 61-76.

15 Stevenson, *The Suicide Club* (New York: Beres, 1941).

• • •

POSTSCRIPT

CAN SUICIDE BE RATIONAL?

In March 1983 the well-known writer Arthur Koestler and his wife Cynthia were found dead—double suicides—in their London apartment. In his seventies, Koestler had been ill for several years, but his wife was much younger and presumably in good health. Both had been active supporters of Exit—the British organization that endorses the idea of rational suicide and provides explicit information on how to achieve it. In this country an organization called Hemlock has the same aims. The Koestlers' suicides raised the further ethical question of the extent of marital devotion: Was her suicide rational or the result of depression?

Tom L. Beauchamp's article, "Suicide and the Value of Life" in *Matters of Life and Death,* edited by Tom Regan (Random House, 1980) is a comprehensive discussion of the philosophical aspects of suicide. The concept of suicide is clarified by R.F. Holland in "Suicide," reprinted in *Moral Problems,* second edition, edited by James Rachels (Harper & Row, 1975). Thomas S. Szasz in "The Ethics of Suicide" (*Antioch Review,* Spring 1971) argues against suicide intervention on the grounds that it interferes with individual liberty. A. Alvarez's *The Savage God: A Study of Suicide* is both a study of suicide in literature and history and an account of the author's own failed attempt. See also *A Handbook for the Study of Suicide,* edited by Seymour Perlin (Oxford, 1975), which contains Richard Brandt's views; and Philip E. Devine, *The Ethics of Homicide* (Cornell, 1978), a condemnation of suicide.

ISSUE 9

IS IT A THERAPIST'S DUTY TO WARN POTENTIAL VICTIMS OF VIOLENCE?

YES: Justice Mathew O. Tobriner, from Majority opinion in *Tarasoff* v. *Regents of the University of California* (California Supreme Court, July 1, 1976)

NO: Justice William P. Clark, from Dissenting opinion in *Tarasoff* v. *Regents of the University of California* (California Supreme Court, July 1, 1976)

ISSUE SUMMARY

YES: Mathew O. Tobriner, a justice in the Supreme Court of California, asserts that when a physician or a psychotherapist learns in the course of treatment that a mentally ill patient plans to commit a violent act against a third person, the public interest requires that the therapist warn that person, even if it violates the patient's right to privacy.

NO: William P. Clark, a justice in the same court, dissents from the majority view. He argues that unless patients can be assured of confidentiality, those who need treatment will not seek it and that in order to protect themselves against lawsuits and prosecution for a failure to warn, therapists will commit patients to mental hospitals, often unnecessarily.

"If I tell you a secret, will you promise not to tell anyone?" This simple question familiar from childhood, captures two important features of human relationships: the need to confide one's fears and hopes to another person and the need to trust that person not to reveal the secret. If the person who receives the confidence agrees not to reveal it, he or she has made a promise. All ethical systems place a high value on promise-keeping.

When this exchange occurs in a professional relationship—between patient and physician or therapist; client and attorney; or priest and confessor—there is even more at stake. The professional, as part of achieving that status, has accepted an ethical code that states that confidentiality will be maintained. One of the earliest formulations of this concept is found in the Hippocratic Oath, which is still sworn to by all physicians: "What I may see or hear in the course of the treatment or even outside of the treatment in regard to the life of men, which on no account one must spread abroad, I will keep to myself. . . ."

But no value is absolute, and some exceptions to the rule of confidentiality are well established. For example, considerations of public health underlie laws that require physicians to report certain contagious diseases such as syphilis, measles, meningitis, and (most recently) acquired immune deficiency syndrome (AIDS). Similarly, a physician must report cases of gunshot wounds to the authorities, since a crime may have been committed. Physicians, and social workers and others are required by law to report suspected cases of child abuse, so that a child who is being harmed physically or mentally can be protected.

These examples show that a threat to the health of the public or a crime against another person (as in the case of child abuse) can clearly override an individual's rights to confidentiality. But in recent years a new question has arisen: As Sissela Bok, a philosopher who has written extensively on secrets, puts it: "Does a professional owe confidentiality to clients who reveal plans or acts that endanger others directly?" The question, she says, arises equally for the lawyer whose client lets it be known that he plans a bank robbery, for the pediatrician who suspects that a mother drugs her children to keep them quiet, and for the psychiatrist whose patient reveals his violent jealousy of his wife. This last situation will be addressed in the following two selections. If, in the course of psychological therapy, a person makes threats against someone else, should the therapist be required to breach confidentiality and warn the potential victim? The problem is particularly common in the treatment of mental patients. It is imperative for therapeutic reasons that patients feel free to express their innermost thoughts and fantasies. However, if their threats are real, the victim can be seriously harmed or—as in the case of Tatiana Tarasoff, to be described below—even killed. A complicated factor is the difficulty (some say the impossibility) of predicting accurately whether a person will actually commit the violent act he or she announces.

The two selections that follow are from the same court ruling. In writing the majority opinion in the case of *Tarasoff* v. *Board of Regents of the University of California,* Justice Mathew O. Tobriner explains the court's opinion that the public interest in protecting against violent assault outweighs its interest in safeguarding the confidential character of psychotherapeutic communication. Justice William B. Clark dissented from his colleagues' view, arguing that imposing a duty on therapists to warn potential victims will impair the treatment of many who would never become violent and will actually result in more violence because those who need treatment will not seek it. The ones who will be protected, he says, are the therapists, who will commit patients to mental hospitals rather than risk a lawsuit or prosecution.

YES Justice Mathew O. Tobriner

MAJORITY OPINION IN *TARASOFF v. REGENTS OF THE UNIVERSITY OF CALIFORNIA*

On October 27, 1969, Prosenjit Poddar killed Tatiana Tarasoff. Plaintiffs, Tatiana's parents, allege that two months earlier Poddar confided his intention to kill Tantiana to Dr. Lawrence Moore, a psychologist employed by the Cowell Memorial Hospital at the University of California at Berkeley. They allege that on Moore's request, the campus police briefly detained Poddar, but released him when he appeared rational. They further claim that Dr. Harvey Powelson, Moore's superior, then directed that no further action be taken to detain Poddar. No one warned plaintiffs of Tatiana's peril. . . .

We shall explain that defendant therapists cannot escape liability merely because Tatiana herself was not their patient. When a therapist determines, or pursuant to the standards of his profession should determine, that his patient presents a serious danger of violence to another, he incurs an obligation to use reasonable care to protect the intended victim against such danger. The discharge of this duty may require the therapist to take one or more of various steps, depending upon the nature of the case. Thus it may call for him to warn the intended victim or others likely to apprise the victim of the danger, to notify the police, or to take whatever other steps are reasonably necessary under the circumstances. . . .

PLAINTIFFS' COMPLAINTS

. . . Plaintiff's first cause of action, entitled "Failure to Detain a Dangerous Patient," alleges that on August 20, 1969, Poddar was a voluntary outpatient receiving therapy at Cowell Memorial Hospital. Poddar informed Moore, his therapist, that he was going to kill an unnamed girl, readily identifiable as Tatiana, when she returned home from spending the summer in Brazil. Moore, with the concurrence of Dr. Gold, who had initially examined Poddar, and Dr. Yandell, assistant to the director of the department of psychiatry,

From Majority Opinion, *Tarasoff v. Regents of the University of California*, California Supreme Court, July 1. 1976.

decided that Poddar should be committed for observation in a mental hospital. Moore orally notified Officers Atkinson and Teel of the campus police that he would request commitment. He then sent a letter to Police Chief William Beall requesting the assistance of the police department in securing Poddar's confinement.

Officers Atkinson, Brownrigg, and Halleran took Poddar into custody, but, satisfied that Poddar was rational, released him on his promise to stay away from Tatiana. Powelson, director of the department of psychiatry at Cowell Memorial Hospital, then asked the police to return Moore's letter, directed that all copies of the letter and notes that Moore had taken as therapist be destroyed, and "ordered no action to place Prosenjit Poddar in 72-hour treatment and evaluation facility."

Plantiffs' second cause of action, entitled "Failure to Warn on a Dangerous Patient," incorporates the allegations of the first cause of action, but adds the assertion that defendants negligently permitted Poddar to be released from police custody without "notifying the parents of Tatiana Tarasoff that their daughter was in grave danger from Prosenjit Poddar." Poddar persuaded Tatiana's brother to share an apartment with him near Tatiana's residence; shortly after her return from Brazil, Poddar went to her residence and killed her.

Plantiffs' third cause of action, entitled "Abandonment of a Dangerous Patient," seeks $10,000 punitive damages against defendant Powelson. Incorporating the crucial allegations of the first cause of action, plaintiffs charge that Powelson "did the things herein alleged with intent to abandon a dangerous patient, and said acts were done maliciously and oppressively."

Plaintiffs' fourth cause of action, for "Breach of Primary Duty to Patient and the Public," states essentially the same allegations as the first cause of action, but seeks to characterize defendants' conduct as a breach of duty to safeguard their patient and the public. Since such conclusory labels add nothing to the factual allegations of the complaint, the first and fourth causes of action are legally indistinguishable. . . .

. . . We direct our attention . . . to the issue of whether plaintiffs' second cause of action can be amended to state a basis for recovery.

PLAINTIFFS CAN STATE A CAUSE OF ACTION AGAINST DEFENDANT THERAPISTS FOR NEGLIGENT FAILURE TO PROTECT TATIANA

The second cause of action can be amended to allege that Tatiana's death proximately resulted from defendant's negligent failure to warn Tatiana or others likely to apprise her of her danger. Plaintiffs contend that as amended, such allegations of negligence and proximate causation, with resulting damages, establish a cause of action. Defendants, however, contend that in the circumstances of the present case they owed no duty of care to Tatiana or her parents and that, in the absence of such duty, they were free to act in careless disregard of Tatiana's life and safety.

In analyzing this issue, we bear in mind that legal duties are not discoverable facts of nature, but merely conclusory expressions that, in cases of a particular type, liability should be imposed for damage done. "The assertion that liability must . . . be denied because defendant bears no 'duty' to plaintiff 'begs the essential question—whether the plaintiff's interests are entitled to legal protection against the defendant's conduct. . . . [Duty] is not sacrosanct in itself, but only an expression of the sum total of those considerations of policy which lead the law to say that the particular plaintiff is entitled to protection.' "

In the landmark case of *Rowland v. Christian* (1968), Justice Peters recognized that liability should be imposed "for an injury occasioned to another by his want of ordinary care or skill" as expressed in section 1714 of the Civil Code. Thus, Justice Peters, quoting from *Heaven v. Pender* (1883) stated: " 'Whenever one person is by circumstances placed in such a position with regard to another . . . that if he did not use ordinary care and skill in his own conduct . . . he would cause danger of injury to the person or property of the other, a duty arises to use ordinary care and skill to avoid such danger.' "

We depart from "this fundamental principle" only upon the "balancing of a number of considerations"; major ones "are the foreseeability of harm to the plaintiff, the degree of certainty that the plaintiff suffered injury, the closeness of the connection between the defendant's conduct and the injury suffered, the moral blame attached to the defendant's conduct, the policy of preventing future harm, the extent of the burden to the defendant and consequences to the community of imposing a duty to exercise care with resulting liability for breach, and the availability, cost and prevalence of insurance for the risk involved."

The most important of these considerations in establishing duty is foreseeability. As a general principle, a "defendant owes a duty of care to all persons who are foreseeably endangered by his conduct, with respect to all risks which make the conduct unreasonably dangerous." As we shall explain, however, when the avoidance of foreseeable harm requires a defendant to control the conduct of another person, or to warn of such conduct, the common law has traditionally imposed liability only if the defendant bears some special relationship to the dangerous person or to the potential victim. Since the relationship between a therapist and his patient satisfies this requirement, we need not here decide whether foreseeability alone is sufficient to create a duty to exercise reasonable care to protect a potential victim of another's conduct.

Although, as we have stated above, under the common law, as a general rule, one person owed no duty to control the conduct of another nor to warn those endangered by such conduct, the courts have carved out an exception to this rule in cases in which the defendant stands in some special relationship to either the person whose conduct needs to be controlled or in a relationship to the foreseeable victim of that conduct. Applying this exception to the present case, we note that a relationship of defendant therapists to either Tatiana or Poddar will suffice to establish a duty of care: as explained in section 315 of the Restatement Second of Torts, a duty of care may arise from either "(a) a special relation . . . between the actor and the third person which imposes a duty upon the actor to control the third person's conduct, or (b) a special relation . . . between the actor and the other which gives to the other a right of protection."

Although plaintiff's pleadings assert no special relation between Tatiana and defendant therapists, they establish as between Poddar and defendant therapists the special relation that arises between a patient and his doctor or psychotherapist. Such a relationship may support affirmative duties for the benefit of third persons. Thus, for example, a hospital must exercise reasonable care to control the behavior of a patient which may endanger other persons. A doctor must also warn a patient if the patient's condition or medication renders certain conduct, such as driving a car, dangerous to others.

Although the California decisions that recognize this duty have involved cases in which the defendant stood in a special relationship *both* to the victim and to the person whose conduct created the danger, we do not think that the duty should logically be constricted to such situations. Decisions of other jurisdictions hold that the single relationship of a doctor to his patient is sufficient to support the duty to exercise reasonable care to protect others against dangers emanating from the patient's illness. The courts hold that a doctor is liable to persons infected by his patient if he negligently fails to diagnose a contagious disease, or having diagnosed the illness, fails to warn members of the patient's family.

Since it involved a dangerous mental patient, the decision in *Merchants Nat. Bank & Trust Co. of Fargo v. United States* (1967) comes closer to the issue. The Veterans Administration arranged for the patient to work on a local farm, but did not inform the farmer of the man's background. The farmer consequently permitted the patient to come and go freely during nonworking hours; the patient borrowed a car, drove to his wife's residence and killed her. Notwithstanding the lack of any "special relationship" between the Veterans Administration and the wife, the court found the Veterans Administration liable for the wrongful death of the wife.

In their summary of the relevant rulings Fleming and Maximov conclude that the "case law should dispel any notion that to impose on the therapists a duty to take precautions for the safety of persons threatened by a patient, where due care so requires, is in any way opposed to contemporary ground rules on the duty relationship. On the contrary, there now seems to be sufficient authority to support the conclusion that by entering into a doctor-patient relationship the therapist becomes sufficiently involved to assume some responsibility for the safety, not only of the patient himself, but also of any third person whom the doctor knows to be threatened by the patient." [Fleming & Maximov, *The Patient or His Victim: The Therapist's Dilemma* (1974) 62 Cal. L. Rev. 1025. 1030.]

Defendants contend, however, that imposition of a duty to exercise reasonable care to protect third persons is unworkable because therapists cannot accurately predict whether or not a patient will resort to violence. In support of this argument amicus ["friend of the court"] representing the American Psychiatric Association and other professional societies cites numerous articles which indicate that therapists, in the present state of the art, are unable reliably to predict violent acts; their forecasts, amicus claims, tend consistently to overpredict violence, and indeed are more often wrong than right. Since predictions of violence are often erroneous, amicus concludes, the courts should not render rulings that predicate the liability of therapists upon the validity of such predictions.

The role of the psychiatrist, who is indeed a practitioner of medicine, and that of the psychologist who performs an allied function, are like that of the physician who must conform to the standards of the profession and who must often make diagnoses and predictions based upon such evaluations. Thus the judgment of the therapist in diagnosing emotional disorders and in predicting whether a patient presents a serious danger of violence is comparable to the judgment which doctors and professionals must regularly render under accepted rules of responsiblity.

We recognize the difficulty that a therapist encounters in attempting to forecast whether a patient presents a serious danger of violence. Obviously we do not require that the therapist, in making that determination, render a perfect performance; the therapist need only exercise "that reasonable degree of skill, knowledge, and care ordinarily possessed and exercised by members of [that professional specialty] under similar circumstances." Within the broad range of reasonable practice and treatment in which professional opinion and judgment may differ, the therapist is free to exercise his or her own best judgment without liability; proof, aided by hindsight, that he or she judged wrongly is insufficient to establish negligence.

In the instant case, however, the pleadings do not raise any question as to failure of defendant therapists to predict that Poddar presented a serious danger of violence. On the contrary, the present complaints allege that defendant therapists did in fact predict that Poddar would kill, but were negligent in failing to warn.

Amicus contends, however, that even when a therapist does in fact predict that a patient poses a serious danger of violence to others, the therapist should be absolved of any responsibility for failing to act to protect the potential victim. In our view, however, once a therapist does in fact determine, or under applicable professional standards reasonably should have determined, that a patient poses a serious danger of violence to others, he bears a duty to exercise reasonable care to protect the foreseeable victim of that danger. While the discharge of this duty of due care will necessarily vary with the facts of each case, in each instance the adequacy of the therapist's conduct must be measured against the traditional negligence standard of the rendition of reasonable care under the circumstances. As explained in Felming and Maximov, *The Patient or His Victim: The Therapist's Dilemma* (1974), "... the ultimate question of resolving the tension between the conflicting interests of patient and potential victim is one of social policy, not professional expertise.... In sum, the therapist owes a legal duty not only to his patient, but also to his patient's would-be victim and is subject in both respects to scrutiny by judge and jury."...

The risk that unnecessary warnings may be given is a reasonable price to pay for the lives of possible victims that may be saved. We would hesitate to hold that the therapist who is aware that his patient expects to attempt to assassinate the President of the United States would not be obligated to warn the authorities because the therapist cannot predict with accuracy that his patient will commit the crime.

Defendants further argue that free and open communication is essential to psychotherapy; that "unless a patient... is assured that... information [revealed by him] can and will be held in utmost confidence, he will be reluctant to make the full disclosure upon which diagnosis and treatment... depends." The giving of a warning, defendants contend, constitutes a breach of trust which entails the revelation of confidential communications.

We recognize the public interest in supporting effective treatment of mental illness and in protecting the rights of patients to privacy and the consequent public importance of safeguarding the confidential character of psychotherapeutic communication. Against this interest, however, we must weigh the public interest in safety from violent assault. The Legislature has undertaken the difficult task of balancing the countervailing concerns. In Evidence

Code section 1014, it established a broad rule of privilege to protect confidential communications between patient and psychotherapist. In Evidence Code section 1024, the Legislature created a specific and limited exception to the psychotherapist-patient privilege: "There is no privilege ... if the psychotherapist has reasonable cause to believe that the patient is in such mental or emotional condition as to be dangerous to himself or to the person or property of another and that disclosure of the communication is necessary to prevent the threatened danger."

We realize that the open and confidential character of psychotherapeutic dialogue encourages patients to express threats of violence, few of which are ever executed. Certainly a therapist should not be encouraged routinely to reveal such threats; such disclosures could seriously disrupt the patient's relationship with his therapist and with the persons threatened. To the contrary, the therapist's obligations to his patient require that he not disclose a confidence unless such disclosure is necessary to avert danger to others, and even then that he do so discreetly, and in a fashion that would preserve the privacy of his patient to the fullest extent compatible with the prevention of the threatened danger.

The revelation of a communication under the above circumstances is not a breach of trust or a violation of professional ethics; as stated in the Principles of Medical Ethics of the American Medical Association (1957), section 9; "A physician may not reveal the confidence entrusted to him in the course of medical attendance... *unless he is required to do so by law or unless it becomes necessary in order to protect the welfare of the individual or of the community.*" (Emphasis added.) We conclude that the public policy favoring protection of the confidential character of patient-psychotherapist communications must yield to the extent to which disclosure is essential to avert danger to others. The protective privilege ends where the public peril begins.

Our current crowded and computerized society compels the interdependence of its members. In this risk-infested society we can hardly tolerate the further exposure to danger that would result from a concealed knowledge of the therapist that his patient was lethal. If the exercise of reasonable care to protect the threatened victim requires the therapist to warn the endangered party or those who can reasonably be expected to notify him, we see no sufficient societal interest that would protect and justify concealment. The containment of such risks lies in the public interest. For the foregoing reasons, we find that plaintiffs' complaints can be amended to state a cause of action against defendants Moore, Powelson, Gold, and Yandell and against the Regents as their employer, for breach of a duty to exercise reasonable care to protect Tatiana....

● ● ●

NO — Justice William P. Clark

DISSENTING OPINION IN *TARASOFF v. REGENTS OF THE UNIVERSITY OF CALIFORNIA*

Until today's majority opinion, both legal and medical authorities have agreed that confidentiality is essential to effectively treat the mentally ill, and that imposing a duty on doctors to disclose patient threats to potential victims would greatly impair treatment. Further, recognizing that effective treatment and society's safety are necessarily intertwined, the Legislature has already decided effective and confidential treatment is preferred over imposition of a duty to warn.

The issue whether effective treatment for the mentally ill should be sacrificed to a system of warnings is, in my opinion, properly one for the Legislature, and we are bound by its judgment. Moreover, even in the absence of clear legislative direction, we must reach the same conclusion because imposing the majority's new duty is certain to result in a net increase in violence. . . .

COMMON LAW ANALYSIS

Entirely apart from the statutory provisions, the same result must be reached upon considering both general tort principles and the public policies favoring effective treatment, reduction of violence, and justified commitment.

Generally, a person owes no duty to control the conduct of another. Exceptions are recognized only in limited situations where (1) a special relationship exists between the defendant and injured party, or (2) a special relationship exists between defendant and the active wrongdoer, imposing a duty on defendant to control the wrongdoer's conduct. The majority does not contend the first exception is appropriate to this case.

Policy generally determines duty. Principal policy considerations include foreseeability of harm, certainty of the plaintiff's injury, proximity of the defendant's conduct to the plaintiff's injury, moral blame attributable to defendant's conduct, prevention of future harm, burden on the defendant, and consequences to the community.

Overwhelming policy considerations weigh against imposing a duty on psycho-

From Dissenting Opinion, *Tarasoff v. Regents of the University of California*, California Supreme Court, July 1, 1976.

therapists to warn a potential victim against harm. While offering virtually no benefit to society, such a duty will frustrate psychiatric treatment, invade fundamental patient rights and increase violence.

The importance of psychiatric treatment and its need for confidentiality have been recognized by this court. "It is clearly recognized that the very practice of psychiatry vitally depends upon the reputation in the community that the psychiatrist will not tell." [Slovenko, *Psychiatry and a Second Look at the Medical Privilege* (1960) 6 Wayne L.Rev.175, 188.]

Assurance of confidentiality is important for three reasons.

DETERRENCE FROM TREATMENT

First, without substantial assurance of confidentiality, those requiring treatment will be deterred from seeking assistance. It remains an unfortunate fact in our society that people seeking psychiatric guidance tend to become stigmatized. Apprehension of such stigma—apparently increased by the propensity of people considering treatment to see themselves in the worst possible light—creates a well-recognized reluctance to seek aid. This reluctance is alleviated by the psychiatrist's assurance of confidentiality.

FULL DISCLOSURE

Second, the guarantee of confidentiality is essential in eliciting the full disclosure necessary for effective treatment. The psychiatric patient approaches treatment with conscious and unconscious inhibitions against revealing his innermost thoughts. "Every person, however well-motivated, has to overcome resistances to therapeutic exploration. These resistances seek support from every possible source and the possibility of disclosure would easily be employed in the service of resistance." (Goldstein & Katz, *Psychiatrist-Patient Privilege: The GAP Proposal and the Connecticut Statute,* 36 Conn. Bar J., 175, 179; see also, 118 Am.J.Psych. 734, 735.) Until a patient can trust his psychiatrist not to violate their confidential relationship, "the unconscious psychological control mechanism of repression will prevent the recall of past experiences." [Butler, *Psychotherapy and Griswold: Is Confidentiality a Privilege or a Right?* (1971) 3 Conn.L.Rev. 599, 604.]

SUCCESSFUL TREATMENT

Third, even if the patient fully discloses his thoughts, assurance that the confidential relationship will not be breached is necessary to maintain his trust in his psychiatrist—the very means by which treatment is effected. "[T]he essence of much psychotherapy is the contribution of trust in the external world and ultimately in the self, modelled upon the trusting relationship established during therapy" (Dawidoff, *The Malpractice of Psychiatrists,* 1966 Duke L.J. 696, 704.) Patients will be helped only if they can form a trusting relationship with the psychiatrist. All authorities appear to agree that if the trust relationship cannot be developed because of collusive communication between the psychiatrist and others, treatment will be frustrated.

Given the importance of confidentiality to the practice of psychiatry, it becomes clear the duty to warn imposed by the majority will cripple the use and effectiveness of psychiatry. Many people, potentially violent—yet susceptible to treatment—will be deterred from seeking it; those seeking it will be inhibited from making revelations necessary to effective treatment; and, forcing the psychiatrist to violate the patient's trust will destroy the interpersonal relationship by which treatment is effected.

VIOLENCE AND CIVIL COMMITMENT

By imposing a duty to warn, the majority contributes to the danger to society of violence by the mentally ill and greatly increases the risk of civil commitment—the total deprivation of liberty—of those who should not be confined. The impairment of treatment and risk of improper commitment resulting from the new duty to warn will not be limited to a few patients but will extend to a large number of the mentally ill. Although under existing psychiatric procedures only a relatively few receiving treatment will ever present a risk of violence, the number making threats is huge, and it is the latter group—not just the former—whose treatment will be impaired and whose risk of commitment will be increased.

Both the legal and psychiatric communities recognize that the process of determining potential violence in a patient is far from exact, being fraught with complexity and uncertainty.

In fact precision has not even been attained in predicting who of those having already committed violent acts will again become violent, a task recognized to be of much simpler proportions.

This predictive uncertainty means that the number of disclosures will necessarily be large. As noted above, psychiatric patients are encouraged to discuss all thoughts of violence, and they often express such thoughts. However, unlike this court, the psychiatrist does not enjoy the benefit of overwhelming hindsight in seeing which few, if any, of his patients will ultimately become violent. Now, confronted by the majority's new duty, the psychiatrist must instantaneously calculate potential violence from each patient on each visit. The difficulties researchers have encountered in accurately predicting violence will be heightened for the practicing psychiatrist dealing for brief periods in his office with heretofore nonviolent patients. And, given the decision not to warn or commit must always be made at the psychiatrist's civil peril, one can expect most doubts will be resolved in favor of the psychiatrist protecting himself.

Neither alternative open to the psychiatrist seeking to protect himself is in the public interest. The warning itself is an impairment of the psychiatrist's ability to treat, depriving many patients of adequate treatment. It is to be expected that after disclosing their threats, a significant number of patients, who would not become violent if treated according to existing practices, will engage in violent conduct as a result of unsuccessful treatment. In short, the majority's duty to warn will not only impair treatment of many who would never become violent but worse, will result in a net increase in violence.

The second alternative open to the psychiatrist is to commit his patient rather than to warn. Even in the absence of threat of civil liability, the doubts of psychiatrists as to the seriousness of patient threats have led psychiatrists to overcommit to mental institutions. This overcommitment has been authoritatively documented in both legal and psychiatric studies. This practice is so prevalent that it has been estimated that "as many as twenty harmless persons are incarcerated for every one who will commit a violent act." [Steadman & Cocozza, *Stimulus/Response: We Can't Predict Who Is Dangerous* (Jan. 1975) 8 Psych. Today 32, 35.]

Given the incentive to commit created by the majority's duty, this already serious situation will be worsened. . . .

● ● ●

POSTSCRIPT

IS IT A THERAPIST'S DUTY TO WARN POTENTIAL VICTIMS OF VIOLENCE?

The decision in *Tarasoff* was widely criticized by lawyers and mental health professionals. Nevertheless, the doctrine that therapists have a duty to warn potential victims has been endorsed by several other courts. In one New Jersey case, a court held a psychiatrist liable for failing to warn a former girlfriend who was killed by an adolescent patient—even though the patient had never expressed any intent to harm her and had talked only about his jealous feelings. However, some courts have limited the duty to warn to known, identifiable victims rather than the public at large and have excluded cases of suicide or property damage.

Prosenjit Poddar, the man who killed Tatiana Tarasoff, was convicted of second-degree murder but the conviction was overturned on appeal because the jury had been incorrectly instructed. Since more than five years had elapsed since the crime, the state decided not to retry Poddar but to release him if he would promise to return to India, which he did.

In 1978, two years after the *Tarasoff* decision, a study of a thousand California therapists, reported in the *Stanford Law Review*, suggested that the decision had led them to give more credence to threats expressed by patients. A quarter of the respondents indicated that patients were less willing to talk about violent thoughts after they had been warned that such material might not be held confidential. Many therapists felt anxious about knowing the limits of the duty to warn, and some refused to take on patients where violence might be discussed.

For the aftermath of the decison, see Vanessa Merton, "Confidentiality and the 'Dangerous' Patient: Implications of *Tarasoff* for Psychiatrists and Lawyers," *Emory Law Journal* (Vol. 31, 1982). On confidentiality in general, see *Secrets* by Sissela Bok (Pantheon, 1982). LeRoy Walters discusses the philosophical justifications for the principle of medical confidentiality in "Ethical Aspects of Medical Confidentiality," in Tom L. Beauchamp and LeRoy Walters, *Contemporary Issues in Bioethics,* second edition (Wadsworth, 1982). See also Robert M. Veatch, *Case Studies in Medical Ethics* (Harvard, 1977), Chapter 5; and Louis Everstine, et al., "Threats to Confidentiality," *American Psychologist* (September 1980).

ISSUE 10

SHOULD THE INSANITY DEFENSE BE ABOLISHED?

YES: Stephen Cohen, "It's a Mad, Mad Verdict," *The New Republic* (July 12, 1982)

NO: Richard J. Bonnie, "The Moral Basis of the Insanity Defense," *American Bar Association Journal* 69 (January 1983)

ISSUE SUMMARY

YES: Professor of law Stephen Cohen argues that the insanity defense as it now exists should be abolished because the psychiatric detection of mental illness is so unreliable and because it is so difficult to tell whether mental illness has impaired the defendant's capacity for free will.

NO: Professor of law Richard J. Bonnie counters with the view that the insanity defense should not be abandoned because it is fundamentally wrong to condemn and punish a person whose rational control over his or her behavior was impaired by mental illness.

On June 21, 1982, a jury found John W. Hinckley, Jr., "Not guilty by reason of insanity" for the crimes of shooting and wounding President Ronald Reagan, Press Secretary James Brady, a Secret Service guard, and a District of Columbia policeman. The prosecution, according to the verdict, had certainly proved that Hinckley had fired the gun (that was never questioned) but had failed to prove beyond a reasonable doubt that he was sane when he did it. Hinckley was not set free but was ordered confined to St. Elizabeths Hospital, a mental institution.

The verdict stunned the American public. Almost immediately bills were introduced in Congress and in the states to abolish or amend the insanity plea or to introduce a new verdict of "Guilty but mentally ill." Something, it appeared, was terribly wrong when a person who clearly had committed a certain act and who did not appear to be "crazy"—indeed, who had carefully planned the event—escaped the full punishment of the law.

The Hinckley verdict, dramatic as it was, is only the most recent in a series of cases that have raised serious questions about the insanity defense. Even before the shooting of the president, legal scholars and psychiatrists had been considering whether the defense was being misused, whether it was of moral or practical value, and how it might be amended.

The idea that the insane should not be punished for acts that would be criminal if committed by normal people dates to the twelfth century. Medieval scholars developed the notion that only persons who are morally blameworthy—that is, who intentionally commit a crime and understand the significance of what they do—should be punished. The modern formulation of this idea is known as "McNaughtan's Rule," because it resulted from a case in 1843 in England when Daniel McNaughtan shot and killed the secretary to Robert Peel, then prime minister. McNaughtan's defense was that he was suffering from delusions that Peel's political party was persecuting him. In clarifying the grounds on which McNaughtan was acquitted, the House of Lords said: ". . . it must be clearly proved that, at the time of the committing of the act, the party accused was labouring under such a defect of reason, from disease of the mind, as not to know the nature and quality of the act he was doing; or if he did know it, that he did not know he was doing what was wrong."

McNaughtan's Rule has largely been followed in both English and American law since then. An alternative way of formulating the defense—one that stressed the ability to control one's actions in addition to understanding them, as in McNaughtan—is the American Law Institute's code, adopted in 1962, which reads: "A person is not responsible for criminal conduct if at the time of such conduct as a result of mental disease or defect he lacks substantial capacity either to appreciate the criminality (wrongfulness) of his conduct or to conform his conduct to the requirements of the law."

Underlying the concept that a certain group of people—those who cannot understand or appreciate the wrongfulness of their acts—should be spared punishment is the belief that mental illness is real, that it can be diagnosed and treated, and that it can affect the capacity for free will. In this view, law is closely intertwined with medicine, and the testimony of psychiatrists and other mental health professionals carries much weight. This reliance of the justice system on the expertise of medicine has been considered humane and compassionate by some, and misguided and unwarranted by others.

The two selections that follow present opposing views of the insanity defense. Stephen Cohen says that the Hinckley jury reached the only verdict it could and that the law must be changed to restore public confidence in the principle of moral responsibility. Richard J. Bonnie disagrees, claiming that the insanity defense is essential to the moral integrity of the criminal law. He does, however, agree that the burden of proof in using the defense should be shifted to the defendant.

YES

Stephen Cohen

IT'S A MAD, MAD VERDICT

If the law truly means what it says, then John W. Hinckley Jr. had to be found not guilty of the attempted murder of the President of the United States. Not because he didn't do it—and not even because the defense proved that mental illness caused his acts—but because the jury could not help entertaining a reasonable doubt about Hinckley's sanity at the time of the shooting. As a matter of logic, that reasonable doubt left no lawful choice but to acquit the man who shot President Reagan and three other people in full view of hundreds of millions of television watchers.

Yet as the jury began to deliberate, few observers expected that kind of strict legal logic to prevail. Hinckley would certainly be convicted, the experts thought, if only because the idea that someone can shoot the President and not be punished for it is so abhorrent to both common sense and civil order. And if the initial reactions of ordinary people are any indication, the verdict has deeply outraged the sense of justice of most Americans.

Moreover, the verdict in this case seems to damage the stated purpose of the insanity defense, which is to affirm that most individuals are responsible for their actions, and, at the same time, to identify the very few who are utterly—and, in a moral sense, blamelessly—unable to control their conduct. In short, what the Hinckley case shows is that the insanity defense needs to be radically changed—in its definition of insanity, its allocation of the burden of proof, or both—or even abolished.

Hinckley's lawyers portrayed him as living out a delusion based on the movie *Taxi Driver*, obsessed with frustrated love for Jodie Foster, and suffering from a severe mental illness that caused his acts. The government, conceding that Hinckley was somewhat disturbed, argued that he nonetheless plotted and carried out the shooting as an easy means to achieve instant fame, and that he could have chosen not to attack the President. With expert opinion so deeply divided, why was acquittal a logical necessity? The answer is in the law on burden of proof—that is, who must prove what to the jury.

That law varies from jurisdiction to jurisdiction; in the federal court where Hinckley was tried, it happens to be unusually favorable to the defense. At the start, Hinckley, like all criminal defendants, was presumed by the law to be sane and therefore responsible for his conduct. But as soon as the defense introduced some evidence of insanity, the burden shifted to the prosecution. The defense was not obliged to prove that Hinckley was insane; the prosecution, on the other hand, *was* obliged to prove that he was sane, and to do so beyond a reasonable doubt. So even if the government's psychiatrists convinced the jury that Hinckley was probably sane, the picture drawn by the defense was enough to create a nagging doubt—and that, it turned out, was all it took.

The choice of experts for the defense team was deliberately unorthodox. For most insanity trials, lawyers hire forensic psychiatrists, professional witnesses who make a career of testifying in court and who engage in little outside medical practice. According to Dr. Willard Gaylin, a noted authority on psychiatry and law, "If you drew up a list of the fifty, one hundred, or ten thousand most prominent psychiatrists in the country, the doctors that lawyers use would not be on the list." These same psychiatrists turn up again and again in criminal cases. Like pro football players, they specialize in offense or defense, and their beliefs on critical issues seem to be determined more by the side they represent than by a fair examination of the issues.

The defense—in a stroke of brilliance or perhaps just an act of desperation—picked, as two of its three expert psychiatrists, eminent researchers in schizophrenia, Dr. Michael Bear and Dr. William Carpenter, neither of whom had prior courtroom experience. During the trial, the "untried" experts seemed awkward on the witness stand, especially in comparison with the polished performances of the experts on the opposing side; and the government argued that experts without criminal trial experience could not accurately evaluate criminal patients. The jury evidently disagreed.

The doubts raised by the defense psychiatrists were reinforced by other evidence. While awaiting trial, Hinckley twice tried to commit suicide. In May 1981 he swallowed a large number of Tylenol tablets. Six months later he jammed his cell door with a cracker box and hanged himself from the window bars. By the time guards climbed to his window from the outside and cut down his noose, he was turning blue. The judge was clearly worried that there might be a violent outburst or even another suicide attempt at the trial. Two federal marshals were stationed directly behind Hinckley at all times, with orders to keep lead pencils and paper clips out of his reach.

Sophisticated medical technology introduced physical evidence suggesting that Hinckley was abnormal. A CAT scan (a computer-enhanced, three-dimensional X-ray) showed organic abnormalities in Hinckley's brain, and a defense expert testified that folds, or solci, showed signs of atrophy. The prosecution challenged this testimony with its own expert who saw no evidence of atrophy in the brain pictures. If the atrophy does exist, it by no means proves that Hinckley was mentally ill, even though atrophy occurs ten times more often in schizophrenics than in apparently normal adults (30 percent versus 3 percent). But the effect of this evidence was to plant additional seeds of doubt.

The jury's doubts may also have been

strengthened by the grave errors committed by psychiatrists who treated Hinckley during the year before the shooting. Dr. Michael Hopper, who saw Hinckley about a dozen times, prescribed biofeedback and meditation exercises. He convinced Hinckley's father to banish Hinckley from home—despite the anguished protests of Hinckley's brother and sister, who felt that he could not cope in the outside world and wanted him committed to a mental hospital. Both Hopper and another psychiatrist, whom Hinckley saw while a student in Texas, treated him with valium for his complaints. Yet many doctors say that valium is "contraindicated" for schizophrenics, because it may cause violent behavior. According to the defense, to prescribe the drug for Hinckley was a medical disaster, or in the words of one of his lawyers, it was "like throwing gasoline on a lighted fire." Only hours before shooting Reagan, Hinckley says, he took twenty milligrams of valium, two to four times the usual dosage.

Survey the evidence of the defense on the issue of Hinckley's sanity: the suicide attempts, the CAT scan, the blunders of Dr. Hopper and other psychiatrists Hinckley was seeing, the experts' evaluations, and the emotional descriptions of Hinckley's troubles by his immediate family. Then consider the prosecution's case: the expert psychiatrists and the testimony of police and a physician who said Hinckley was calm and rational immediately after his arrest. And finally, recall the prosecution's very heavy burden of proof: to show decisively that Hinckley was sane.

Yet the announcement of the verdict had an extraordinary impact. Seasoned courtroom observers present during the entire trial were shocked. Why were they so certain that the jury would reject the insanity defense and convict Hinckley?

The first and greatest obstacle to acquittal was the undisputed fact that Hinckley had fired a bullet into the body of the President of the United States. During the past two decades, there have been eight attempts to murder Presidents, Presidential candidates, and other national leaders. Four victims died (John and Robert Kennedy, Martin Luther King, and Allard Lowenstein), one was crippled for life (George Wallace), one was seriously wounded (Ronald Reagan), and one emerged unscathed from two separate attempts (Jerry Ford). How, it was asked, could the jury possibly find Hinckley not guilty, knowing the message that it would send to potential assassins?

The second obstacle was the well-established reluctance of juries to acquit by reason of insanity except in the most extreme and obvious cases of mental disturbance. In federal court, where Hinckley was tried, the test for insanity is met if the defendant engages in criminal conduct either because he "lacks substantial capacity to appreciate the wrongfulness of his conduct or to conform his conduct to the requirements of law." But experienced trial lawyers know that this or any other legal formula has little impact on jurors, who tend to follow their own intuitive judgments regardless of what they are told by the judge. One criminal attorney calls it the "fireplug rule." He explains, "Jurors think you're sane unless you're a fireplug or swinging from the trees"—that is, unless you're stark staring mad or stark raving mad—and Hinckley is neither." Empirical studies bear out this impression. Juries in mock trials tend to reach the same results whether the definition of insanity they are given is broad or narrow, and they acquit only the most extremely and obviously mentally ill.

Prosecutor Roger Adelman certainly tried to appeal to the fireplug rule. Cross-examining defense expert William Carpenter, who claimed that Hinckley had suffered from schizophrenia for a number of years, Adelman demanded: "Didn't the defendant attend a Texas college and receive an A-minus on a book report? Didn't he manage to make plane reservations? Didn't he find his way in and out of New York City? And wasn't this during the same time you say he was suffering from schizophrenia?"

The third obstacle was the reluctance of juries to acquit if it leads to early release of the defendant. An informal poll I conducted of spectators queued up to enter the trial illustrates the point. Everyone in line agreed on two points: first, that Hinckley was absolutely loony, and second, that he should be convicted so that he'd be off the streets. What was the jury told about the consequences of a successful insanity defense? The judge answered for them in terms of abstract legal principles. Hinckley would be automatically committed to a mental hospital for fifty days, and he would then be entitled to a hearing to determine his eligibility for release. After that, he could seek a review in six months. This made it sound as if Hinckley could very well get out in a few years or even months.

In fact, Hinckley's future prospects are far less promising. Despite the acquittal, it seems certain that he will be confined for decades, if not for the rest of his life. He could be released only if a judge, after hearing from psychiatrists, finds that he is no longer dangerous. But what psychiatrist, even for hire, would risk such a prediction? And, if such a psychiatrist could be found, what judge would accept the prediction and order Hinckley's release? The jury, however, almost certainly could not learn these practical aspects from the theoretical cast of the instructions. The law does not require further explanation, and Judge Barrington Parker did not offer it on his own.

When these three obstacles are considered, it seems inconceivable that all twelve jurors could have found Hinckley not guilty. If ever there were a case in which the jury could be expected to suppress its "reasonable doubt," this was it. The overwhelming sentiment against the verdict indicates that the insanity defense is in need of substantial modification or, better, outright abolition.

One possibility is to lighten the government's burden of proof. Had Hinckley not been tried in a federal court—in a local District of Columbia court, for example—he could have faced an entirely different rule. The District of Columbia requires the defendant to carry the burden and to show "by a preponderance of the evidence" that he was insane. The case ended up in a federal rather than a local court, by the way, because of the recently enacted federal anti-assassination law. One of the ironies of this case is that a law designed expressly to protect Presidents made it easier to acquit someone who actually shot one.

But this does not mean that the federal burden of proof was necessarily the cause of the jury's failure to convict Hinckley. It does make it possible to say that acquittal was logically required. But in light of the jury's unanimous insanity verdict, it is doubtful that all twelve members would have convicted Hinckley even under a tougher burden of proof. At most, the result might have been a hung jury rather than a verdict of not guilty by reason of insanity.

A second possibility is to return to the narrow definition of insanity that existed in the nineteenth century, which called for acquittal only if the defendant could not tell right from wrong and this was the cause of the criminal act. In recent weeks there have been serious proposals to adopt the narrowest definition. But these efforts to reshape the boundaries of the legal definition of insanity are problematic, since jurors will continue to apply their own judgments of what is mentally aberrant.

Does, then, the insanity defense achieve its stated purposes? One argument is that it serves an important symbolic function: by excluding from blame those who commit crimes due to mental disease, we affirm that most will be held morally responsible. But instead of affirming moral responsibility, in the Hinckley case acquittal negates it. Particularly because the victim was the President, much of the public believes that Hinckley has duped the system and evaded responsibility for his acts.

And suppose that despite the very long odds against Hinckley's release, his attorneys contest his civil commitment at some point in the near future. Then the public will see positions flip-flop. The defense argued that Hinckley was sick; now it must contend that he is well. The government argues that he was well; now it must say that he is sick. As a matter of strict logic, neither side is being inconsistent, since the insanity defense is concerned with the moment when the crime was commited, and the focus of civil commitment is on future conduct. But this distinction is lost on the public, and the unseemly switch in positions will not do much for the principle of moral responsibility.

A second argument for the insanity defense is that it's wrong to punish someone who does not have the capacity for free choice. A six-year-old child, for example, who finds a loaded gun and pulls the trigger is not held criminally responsible for murder. By analogy, it is said, crimes caused by mental illness should not be punished. But the analogy is flawed. Although no one can pinpoint the precise moment when a child is sufficiently mature to be held responsible, the law uses age to draw a rough and ready, but distinct, line. But how do you tell whether an adult has free will?

Psychiatrists have tried to apply the concept of mental illness in determining who does and does not have free will. This approach mistakenly suggests that the process of detecting psychological disturbances closely resembles diagnosis of physical disease. Tuberculosis, for example, can be diagnosed according to reasonably objective criteria — the reaction to a skin test or the pattern on a chest X-ray—and has an established physical cause, the tuberculin bacillus. But the diagnostic criteria for schizophrenia are highly subjective. One person's delusions may be another's religion. As Lily Tomlin says, "If you speak to God, it's prayer; if God speaks to you, it's schizophrenia." The inherent vagueness in the concept of mental illness was illustrated in the furious debate between psychiatrists for the defense and the prosecution in the Hinckley case. And even if psychiatric detection of mental illness were reliable, there is a further issue: has the mental issue seriously impaired the defendant's free will? This is a question for a moral philosopher, not a medical psychiatrist.

For these reasons the insanity defense as it now exists should be abolished. It would, of course, be inhumane to find someone like Hinckley guilty and send him to prison without doing more. However heinous his acts and however much he deserves to be convicted, Hinckley is still terribly sick and needs psychiatric help for the period of his confinement. In this context, the analogy to physical illness is much more persuasive. Would we deny a convict treatment for TB, simply because he has been found guilty of a crime? Ideally, then, insanity should be relevant, not for the jury on the issue of guilt or innocence, but for the judge on sentencing. It should be reflected in the conditions under which the defendant is confined after conviction, and not in the jury's verdict on criminal responsibility.

The modern insanity standard evolved from an earlier political assassination case. In the 1840s, Daniel M'Naghten killed the private secretary of Sir Robert Peel, the British Prime Minister, in a bungled attempt on Peel's life. Although M'Naghten's acquittal by reason of insanity outraged the public at the time and seriously affronted Queen Victoria, the House of Lords upheld the verdict on appeal. If Hinckley's trial causes the insanity defense to be abolished, we will have come full circle. Political assassinations will have established and then abolished the insanity defense.

● ● ●

NO

Richard J. Bonnie

THE MORAL BASIS OF THE INSANITY DEFENSE

Two fundamentally distinct questions are intertwined in discussions of the insanity defense. One concerns the moral issue of responsibility, a question looking backward to the offender's mental condition at the time of the offense. The other is essentially dispositional and looks forward in time: what should be done with mentally disordered offenders, including those who are acquitted by reason of insanity, to minimize the risk of future recidivism?

This article addresses the issue of responsibility. Sweeping proposals to abolish the insanity defense should be rejected in favor of proposals to narrow it and shift the burden of proof to the defendant. The moral core of the defense must be retained, in my opinion, because some defendants afflicted by severe mental disorder who are out of touch with reality and are unable to appreciate the wrongfulness of their acts cannot justly be blamed and do not therefore deserve to be punished. The insanity defense, in short, is essential to the moral integrity of the criminal law.

But there are several observations to be made about the dispositional issues now receiving legislative attention.

First, the present dissatisfaction with the insanity defense is largely rooted in public concern about the premature release of dangerous persons acquitted by reason of insanity. Increased danger to the public, however, is not a necessary consequence of the insanity defense. The public can be better protected than is now the case in many states by a properly designed dispositional statute that assures that violent offenders acquitted by reason of insanity are committed for long-term treatment, including a period of postdischarge supervision or "hospital parole."

Second, a separate verdict of "guilty but mentally ill," which has been enacted in several states, is an ill-conceived way of identifying prisoners who are amenable to psychiatric treatment. It surely makes no sense for commitment procedures to be triggered by a jury verdict based on evidence

From "The Moral Basis of the Insanity Defense," *American Bar Association Journal,* 69, February 1983.

:oncerning the defendant's past rather :han present mental condition and need 'or treatment. Decisions concerning the oroper placement of incarcerated offend-ers should be made by correctional and nental health authorities, not by juries or :rial judges. Of course, the "guilty but nentally ill verdict" may not reflect dis-oositional objectives so much as it does a lesire to afford juries a "compromise" verdict in cases involving insanity pleas. If so, it should be rejected as nothing more :han moral sleight of hand.

Third, it is often said that the participa-:ion of mental health professionals in :riminal proceedings should be confined :o the sentencing stage. Clinical expertise s likely to be most useful on dispositional 'ather than on responsibility questions, and, indeed, most clinical participation in he criminal process now occurs at the sentencing stage. Expert witnesses, how-ever, cannot be excluded from the guilt stage so long as the defendant's mental condition is regarded as morally relevant o his criminal liability.

This brings the inquiry back to the issue of criminal responsibility.

The historical evolution of the insanity lefense has been influenced by the ebb and flow of informed opinion concerning scientific understanding of mental illness and its relation to criminal behavior. But it s well to remember that, at bottom, the lebate about the insanity defense and the dea of criminal responsibility raises fun-lamentally moral questions, not scientific ones. As Lord Hale observed three cen-uries ago, in *History of Pleas of the Crown,* the ethical foundations of the :riminal law are rooted in beliefs about human rationality, deterrability, and free will. But these are articles of moral faith ather than scientific fact.

Some critics of the insanity defense believe that mentally ill persons are not substantially less able to control their be-havior than normal persons and that, in any case, a decent respect for the dignity of those persons requires that they be held accountable for their wrong-doing on the same terms as everyone else. On the other hand, proponents of the defense, among whom I count myself, believe that it is fundamentally wrong to condemn and punish a person whose rational control over his or her behavior was impaired by the incapacitating effects of severe mental illness.

Few would dispute this as a moral claim. The question is how best to describe the moral criterion of irresponsibility and to minimize the number of cases in which the defense is successfully invoked by persons who should properly be punished.

CRIMINAL RESPONSIBILITY: THE OPTIONS

Putting aside details concerning the drafting of various tests, there are, in prin-ciple, three approaches to the insanity defense.

The Model Penal Code

One option is to leave the law as it now stands in a majority of the states and, by judicial ruling, in all of the federal courts. Apart from technical variations, this means the test proposed by the American Law Institute in its Model Penal Code. Under this approach, a person whose perceptual capacities were sufficiently intact that he had the criminal "intent" or mens rea required in the definition of the offense nonetheless can be found "not guilty by reason of insanity" if, by virtue of mental disease or defect, he lacked substantial capacity either to understand or appre-ciate the legal or moral significance of his actions, or to conform his conduct to the requirements of law. In other words, a person may be excused if his thinking was severely disordered—the so-called cognitive prong of the defense—or if his ability to control his behavior was severely impaired—the so-called volitional prong of the defense.

Revival of M'Naghten

The second option is to retain the insanity defense as an independent exculpatory doctrine—independent, that is, of mens rea—but to restrict its scope by eliminating the volitional prong. This approach would revive the M'Naghten test as the sole basis for exculpation on ground of insanity. This is the approach I favor, although I would modify the language used by the House of Lords in 1843 in favor of modern terminology that is simpler and has more clinical meaning. M'Naghten is now distinctly the minority position in this country. Fewer than one third of the states use this approach, although it is still the law in England.

Abolition: The Mens Rea Approach

The third option is the "mens rea" approach, which has been adopted in two states and has been endorsed by the Reagan administration. Its essential substantive effect is to abolish any criterion of exculpation, based on mental disease, that is independent of the mens rea elements of particular crimes. Instead, mentally ill (or retarded) defendants would be treated like everyone else.

CASE AGAINST THE MENS REA APPROACH

If the insanity defense were abolished, the law would not take adequate account of the incapacitating effects of severe mental illness. Some mentally ill defendants who were psychotic and grossly out of touch with reality may be said to have "intended" to do what they did but nonetheless may have been so severely disturbed that they were unable to understand or appreciate the significance of their actions. These cases do not arise frequently, but when they do a criminal conviction, which signifies the societal judgment that the defendant deserves to be punished, would offend the basic moral intuitions of the community. Judges and juries would be forced either to return a verdict of conviction, which they would regard as morally obtuse, or to acquit the defendant in defiance of the law. They should be spared that moral embarrassment.

The moral difficulty with the mens rea approach is illustrated by a case involving Joy Baker, a 31-year-old woman who shot and killed her aunt. According to her account—which no one has ever doubted—she became increasingly agitated and fearful during the days before the shooting; she was worried that her dogs, her children (ages eight and 11), and her neighbors were becoming possessed by the devil and that she was going to be "annihilated." On the morning of the shooting, after a sleepless night, she ran frantically around the house clutching a gun to her breast. Worried about what the children might do to her if they became demonically "possessed" and about what she might do to them to defend herself, she made them read and reread the 23d Psalm. Suddenly her aunt arrived unexpectedly. Unable to open the locked front door, and ignoring Mrs. Baker's frantic pleas to go away, the aunt came to the back door. When she reached through the broken screening to unlock the door, Mrs. Baker shot her.

The aunt then fell backward into the mud behind the porch, bleeding profusely.

"Why, Joy?" she asked. "Because you're the devil, and you came to hurt me," Joy answered. Her aunt said, "Honey, no, I came to help you." At this point, Mrs. Baker said, she became very confused and "I took the gun and shot her again just to relieve the pain she was having because she said she was hurt."

All the psychiatrists who examined Mrs. Baker concluded that she was acutely psychotic at the time she killed her aunt. The police who arrested her and others in the small rural community agreed that she must have been crazy because there was no rational explanation for her conduct. She was acquitted. Yet, had there been no insanity defense, she could have been acquitted only in defiance of the law. Although she was clearly out of touch with reality and unable to understand the wrongfulness of her conduct, she had the "criminal intent" or mens rea required for some form of criminal homicide. If we look only at her conscious motivation for the second shot and do not take into account her highly regressed and disorganized emotional condition, she was technically guilty of murder (euthanasia being no justification, of course). Moreover, even if the first shot had been fatal, she probably would have been guilty of manslaughter because her delusional belief that she was in imminent danger of demonic annihilation was, by definition, unreasonable.

These technical points, of course, may make little practical difference in the courtroom. If the expert testimony in Joy Baker's case were admitted to disprove mens rea, juries might ignore the law and decide, very bluntly, whether the defendant was "too crazy" to be convicted. The cause of rational criminal law reform, however, is not well served by designing rules of law in the expectation that they will be ignored or nullified when they appear unjust in individual cases.

THE CASE FOR NARROWING THE DEFENSE

While I do not favor abolition of the "cognitive" prong of the insanity defense, I agree with critics who believe the risks of fabrication and "moral mistakes" in administering the defense are greatest when the experts and the jury are asked to speculate whether the defendant had the capacity to "control" himself or whether he could have "resisted" the criminal impulse. I favor narrowing the defense by eliminating its so-called volitional prong or control test.

Few people would dispute the moral predicate for the control test—that a person who "cannot help" doing what he did is not blameworthy. Unfortunately, however, there is no scientific basis for measuring a person's capacity for self-control or for calibrating the impairment of that capacity. There is, in short, no objective basis for distinguishing between offenders who were undeterrable and those who were merely undeterred, between the impulse that was irresistable and the impulse not resisted, or between substantial impairment of capacity and some lesser impairment. Whatever the precise terms of the volitional test, the question is unanswerable, or it can be answered only by "moral guesses." To ask it at all invites fabricated claims, undermines equal administration of the penal law, and compromises its deterrent effect.

Sheldon Glueck of the Harvard Law School observed in *Mental Disorder and the Criminal Law* (1925) that the 19th century effort to establish irresistible impulse as a defense met judicial resistance because "much less than we know today was known of mental disease." He predicted "that with the advent of a more scientific administration of the law—especially with the placing of expert testimony upon a neutral, unbiased basis and in the hands of well-qualified experts—much of the opposition to judicial recognition of the effect of disorders of the . . . impulses should disappear." He added that "expert, unbiased study of the individual case will aid judge and jury to distinguish cases of pathological irresistible impulse from those in which the impulse was merely unresisted."

The opposition to the control test did not disappear in Professor Glueck's generation. In 1955, when the Model Penal Code was being drafted, *M'Naghten* still constituted the exclusive test of insanity in two thirds of the states. Advances in clinical understanding of mental illness in the 1940s and 1950s, however, inspired a new era of optimism about the potential contributions of psychiatry to a progressive and humane penal law. This renewed optimism was reflected in the model code's responsibility test that included "substantial" volitional impairment as an independent ground of exculpation.

The Model Penal Code has had an extraordinary impact on criminal law. For this we should be thankful, but I believe the code approach to criminal responsibility should be rejected. Psychiatric concepts of mental abnormality remain fluid and imprecise, and most academic commentary within the last ten years continues to question the scientific basis for assessment of volitional incapacity.

The volitional inquiry probably would be manageable if the insanity defense were permitted only in cases involving psychotic disorders. When the control test is combined with a loose or broad interpretation of the term "mental disease," however, the inevitable result is unstructured clinical speculation regarding the "causes" of criminal behavior in any case in which a defendant can be said to have a personality disorder, an impulse disorder, or any other diagnosable abnormality.

For example, it is clear enough in theory that the insanity defense is not supposed to be a ground for acquittal of persons with weak behavior controls who misbehave because of anger, jealousy, fear, or some other strong emotion. These emotions may account for a large proportion of all homicides and other assaultive crimes. Many crimes are committed by persons who are not acting "normally" and who are emotionally disturbed at the time. It is not uncommon to say that they are temporarily "out of their minds." But this is not what the law means or should mean by "insanity." Because the control test, as now construed in most states, entitles defendants to insanity instructions on the basis of these claims, I am convinced that the test involves an unacceptable risk of abuse and mistake.

It might be argued, of course, that the risk of mistake should be tolerated if the volitional prong of the defense is morally necessary. The question may be put this way: Are there clinically identifiable cases involving defendants whose behavior controls were so pathologically impaired that they ought to be acquitted although their ability to appreciate the wrongfulness of their actions was unimpaired? I do not think so. The most clinically compelling cases of volitional impairment involve the so-called impulse disorders—pyromania, kleptomania, and the like. These disorders involve severely abnormal compulsions that ought to be taken into account in sentencing, but the exculpation of pyromaniacs would be out of touch with commonly shared moral intuitions.

A PROPOSED TEST

The sole test of legal insanity should be whether the defendant, as a result of severe mental disease, was unable "to appreciate the wrongfulness of his conduct." My statute would read:

"Defense of [Insanity] [Nonresponsibility Due to Mental Disease].

"A. A person charged with a criminal offense shall be found [not guilty by reason of insanity] [not guilty only by reason of insanity] [not responsible due to mental disease] [guilty of a criminal act but not responsible due to mental disease] if he proves, by the greater weight of the evidence, that, as a result of mental disease or mental retardation, he was unable to appreciate the wrongfulness of his conduct at the time of the offense.

"B. As used in this section, the terms mental disease or mental retardation include only those severely abnormal mental conditions that grossly and demonstrably impair a person's perception or understanding of reality and that are not attributable primarily to the voluntary ingestion of alcohol or other psychoactive substances."

This language, drawn from the Model Penal Code, uses clinically meaningful terms to ask the same question posed by the House of Lords in *M'Naghten* 150 years ago. It is a necessary and sufficient test of criminal responsibility. During the past ten years we have evaluated hundreds of cases at our clinic. Only a handful have involved what I would regard as morally compelling claims of irresponsibility, and all of these would be comprehended by the proposed formulation. This test is fully compatible with the ethical premises of the penal law. Results reached by judges and juries in particular cases ordinarily would be congruent with the community's moral sense.

Some clinicians have argued that the volitional prong of the defense is morally necessary to take adequate account of psychotic deterioration, especially in cases involving affective disorders like manic-depressive illness. My view is that a test of insanity that focuses exclusively on the defendant's ability to "appreciate the wrongfulness of his conduct" is broad enough to encompass all cases of severe psychotic deterioration. This is because the term "appreciate" is designed to encompass "affective" dimensions of major mental illness.

BURDEN OF PERSUASION

Much has been said about the proper allocation of the burden of proof since the Hinckley trial. This issue does not arise under the mens rea option, because the prosecution clearly must bear the burden of proving all elements of the crime beyond a reasonable doubt. If the insanity defense is retained as an independent basis of exculpation, the argument may be put that the defendant should bear the burden of persuading the fact-finder of the truth or sufficiency of his claim.

Some commentators have argued that the prosecution should bear the burden of persuading the fact-finder, beyond a reasonable doubt, of all facts regarded as necessary to establish an ethically adequate predicate for criminal liability. When so-called defenses are concerned, the question is whether a just penal law could fail to give exculpatory effect to the claim. Consider entrapment and self-defense, for example. If the law need not recognize the defense at all—as is true for claims of entrapment, I submit—it is entirely proper to recognize it only if the defendant bears the risk of nonpersuasion. If exculpation is morally required if certain facts exist—as is true for claims of self-defense, I would argue—then, as a general rule, the prosecution should bear the risk and be required to negate the existence of those facts beyond a reasonable doubt.

The issue in the present context is whether the insanity defense presents any special considerations that warrant a departure from the general rule disfavoring burden shifting on ethically essential predicates for liability. This is a close question, but on balance, I think the answer is yes. In defenses of justification (self-defense) and situational excuses (duress), the defendant's claim must be linked to external realities and can be tested against ordinary experience, thereby reducing the likelihood of successful fabrication or jury confusion. A defendant's claim that he had a mental disorder that disabled him from functioning as a normal person, however, is not linked to the external world and by definition cannot be tested against ordinary experience. The concept of knowing, understanding, or appreciating the legal or moral significance of one's actions also is more fluid and less precise than many aspects of the elements of the penal law.

PUBLIC CONCERNS SATISFIED

The insanity defense, as I have defined it, should be narrowed, not abandoned, and the burden of persuasion may properly be shifted to the defendant. Like the mens rea proposal, this approach adequately responds to public concern about possible misuse of the insanity defense. Unlike the mens rea proposal, it is compatible with the basic doctrines and principles of Anglo-American penal law.

• • •

POSTSCRIPT

SHOULD THE INSANITY DEFENSE BE ABOLISHED?

Since the Hinckley verdict three states—Idaho, Montana, and Alabama—have abolished the insanity defense. Several other states—including Alaska, Connecticut, Georgia, Illinois, Indiana, Kentucky, Michigan, and New Mexico—have established verdicts of "Guilty but mentally ill." Others are considering similar revisions of their criminal law, and several different proposals have been introduced at the federal level.

Three major professional organizations—the American Bar Association (ABA), the American Psychiatric Association (APA), and the National Mental Health Association (NMHA)—speeded up already ongoing studies of the insanity defense and have issued reports. Both the ABA and the APA oppose abolition of the insanity defense and the establishment of "Guilty but mentally ill" statutes, which they consider the same as abolition, but they support revisions that would limit the use of the defense to grossly psychotic individuals. In effect, their proposals would return the standard to the McNaughtan Rule, which focused on the defendant's ability to understand the consequences of his action rather than his ability to control them. The NMHA, on the other hand, stressed that the public fear of the defense was based on "myths" rather than realities. Nevertheless, it acknowledged the public's concern and suggested an alternate defense called "Not responsible by reason of insanity."

For the texts of the ABA and APA proposals, see *Mental Disability Law Reporter* (March-April 1983); the NMHA's report was published in March 1983 by the association in Arlington, Virginia. Two books that favor revision of the insanity defense are Norval Morris, *Madness and the Criminal Law* (Chicago, 1982) and William Winslade and Judith Ross, *The Insanity Plea* (Scribner's, 1983). The relationship between law and psychiatry in a dramatic murder case is explored in Willard Gaylin, *Who Killed Bonnie Garland?* (Simon & Schuster, 1982). Also see *By Reason of Insanity*, edited by Lawrence Zelic Freedman (Scholarly Resources, 1983).

ISSUE 11

CAN THE PSYCHIATRIC WILL PREVENT INVOLUNTARY TREATMENT?

YES: Thomas S. Szasz, from "The Psychiatric Will: A New Mechanism for Protecting Persons Against 'Psychosis' and Psychiatry," *American Psychologist* 37:7 (July 1982)

NO: Paul Chodoff and Roger Peele, from "The Psychiatric Will of Dr. Szasz," *Hastings Center Report* 13:2 (April 1983)

ISSUE SUMMARY

YES: Psychiatrist Thomas S. Szasz believes that a "psychiatric will" offers protection from involuntary institutionalization to people who believe that mental illness is a myth and that psychiatry does not offer any benefits to those whose behavior is deviant.

NO: Psychiatrists Paul Chodoff and Roger Peel argue that the "psychiatric will" is only a rhetorical device that will deprive many severely disturbed people of the possibility of treatment.

In every society, some people behave in odd and nonconforming ways, though what is considered abnormal may vary considerably. Throughout history explanations of why some people are "crazy" or "mad" have varied: The moon was the cause (hence "lunatic"), thought some early peoples; the devil or spirits did it, thought others. Some of these deviant people were kept in chains and displayed publicly for the amusement of the crowds; others were loaded onto "ships of fools" and set free to wander. Still others were tolerated within their community or even respected because they were thought to have special powers. As early as 1400 in England a special institution designed to house the outcasts—Bethlehem Royal Hospital, or "Bedlam"—was established. One can only imagine what it was like, since "bedlam" now means a place of great confusion and disorder.

In our own times, the most prevalent view is that people whose behavior is strange and often self-destructive are "sick" and need treatment. They are, it is said, "mentally ill." The medical model of deviant behavior developed in the nineteenth century as part of the growth of scientific knowledge, the belief in rationality, and a sense of social responsibility about the helpless. Laws permitting people to be hospitalized in mental institutions against their will are based on the assumption, inherent in the medical model, that the state has a right—even an obligation—to provide treatment for those whose condition has impaired their capacity for rational thought.

Against the conventional view is the philosophy of an influential group of "anti-psychiatrists." Two of the most prominent—R.D. Laing of Scotland and Thomas S. Szasz of the United States—were themselves trained as psychiatrists. But they reject the notion that there is such a thing as "mental illness"; it is, they say, only a label that society has placed on those whose behavior it rejects, for social, ethical, political, aesthetic, or other reasons. Beginning in the 1960s, Szasz has vigorously protested the detention of people in mental institutions against their will. He calls it a form of imprisonment, a violation of basic human rights and the Constitution of the United States, and a "crime against humanity." People ought to be held responsible for their actions, Szasz says, and if they commit crimes, they should be tried and punished, not committed to mental institutions. If they hurt only themselves, they should be allowed to do it, since the liberty to control one's body is the most basic principle.

An important limitation on the state's right to commit people to mental institutions was set forth in the 1975 Supreme Court decision of *Donaldson* v. *O'Connor.* That case involved Kenneth Donaldson, a forty-five-year-old man whose parents had committed him to a Florida mental hospital fifteen years earlier because they believed that he had a "persecution complex." The court ruled that the state cannot constitutionally confine a "nondangerous individual who is capable of surviving safely in freedom by himself or with the help of willing and responsible family members or friends."

The following selections represent the most recent exchange in the longstanding debate between those who believe that involuntary hospitalization is totally unwarranted ethically and legally and those who believe that the state and the medical profession have a positive obligation to care for, and try to alleviate the anguish of, those whose capacities for rational decision making are diminished. Thomas S. Szasz presents a new legal mechanism—the "psychiatric will"—that he believes will protect those who do not want the conventional psychiatric approach, including involuntary hospitalization, to determine their fate should others feel that their behavior is irrational. Paul Chodoff and Roger Peele present a wary view of Szasz's "new testament," which they see as a vague and legally problematic measure that will only make it more difficult for psychiatry to treat the small segment of severely disturbed individuals for whom a caring society must take responsibility.

YES

Thomas S. Szasz

THE PSYCHIATRIC WILL

THE LAST WILL AND THE LIVING WILL

. . . Many of us are eager to exercise our desires over the distribution of our property after we die. It is the purpose of the last will to assure this by extending our control into a situation in which, once it has occurred, we can no longer exercise any control at all.

Although the use of the last will is an ancient practice, the anticipation of a lingering, painful, and absurdly expensive terminal illness and the desire to control its management (in advance, as it were) are of much more recent origin. The so-called living will now meets this contingency (Riffolo, 1978; Veatch, 1976). Executed while the person is not disabled by illness, a living will directs those responsible for caring for its author to abstain, under certain circumstances, from administering life-sustaining measures to him or her. The legal philosophy underlying this practice is illustrated by the following opinion of a Kansas court in the case of *Natanson v. Kline:* "Anglo-American law starts with the premise of thorough-going self-determination. It follows that each man is considered to be the master of his own body, and he may, if he be of sound mind, expressly prohibit the performance of life-saving surgery."[1]

After reviewing the literature on "Compulsory Lifesaving Treatment for the Competent Adult," Robert M. Byrn (1975) concludes that "Every competent adult is free to reject life-saving medical treatment. This freedom is grounded, depending upon the patient's claim, either on the right to determine what shall be done with one's body or the right of free religious exercise—both fundamental rights in the American scheme of personal liberty" (p. 33).

The psychiatric will I propose rests on the same principle and seeks to extend it to "mental treatment." It asserts, in effect, that competent American adults should have a recognized right to reject involuntary psychiatric interventions that they may be deemed to require *in the future,* when they are

From "The Psychiatric Will: A New Mechanism for Protecting Persons Against 'Psychosis and Psychiatry,'" *American Psychologist* 37:7, July 1982.

not competent to make decisions concerning their own welfare. My model for the psychiatric will is the so-called living will; and, more specifically, the rejection by Jehovah's Witnesses of blood transfusion as a medical treatment (Foley & McGinn, 1973).

A frequently cited opinion concerning the constitutionality of allowing Jehovah's Witnesses to reject blood transfusion, even when the transfusion may be lifesaving, was formulated in 1964 by Chief Justice (then Circuit Judge) Warren Burger. In this opinion, Burger recalled Justice Brandeis' famous words about our "right to be let alone." "The makers of our Constitution," wrote Brandeis, "... sought to protect Americans in their beliefs, their thoughts, their emotions, and their sensations. They conferred, as against the Government, the right to be let alone—the most comprehensive of rights, and the right most valued by civilized man."[2] To which, Chief Justice Burger added these (for my present purposes, decisive) words: "Nothing in this utterance suggests that Justice Brandeis thought an individual possessed these rights only as to *sensible* beliefs, *valid* thoughts, *reasonable* emotions, or *well-founded* sensations. I suggest he intended to include a great many foolish, unreasonable, and even absurd ideas which do not conform, such as refusing medical treatment even at great risk."[3]

Since the First Amendment to the Constitution bars the government equally from imposing special burdens on or extending special privileges to members of one or another religious group, it follows that if Jehovah's Witnesses possess such far-reaching rights to reject what they consider to be unwanted medical interventions, so do we all.

Actually, the position of Jehovah's Witnesses toward blood transfusion constitutes a special case in a much larger class of instances in which individuals want to reject medical treatment, even when such treatment may be lifesaving (or life-prolonging, a distinction that may sometimes be difficult to make). The paradigm here is the case of the aged or incurably ill person who does not want his or her life prolonged by means of extraordinarily complex, invasive, or expensive medical measures (Raber, 1980). Several groups are now lobbying on behalf of gaining for such persons a recognized "right to die." One of them, the "Society for the Right to Die,"[4] has drafted a model "living will." I shall cite a few lines of it to suggest its thrust and to indicate the form that a "psychiatric will" might take.

> Declaration made this ______ day of ______ month/year. I, ______, being of sound mind, willfully and voluntarily make known my desire that my dying shall not be artificially prolonged under the circumstances set forth below, do hereby declare: If at any time I should have an incurable injury, disease ... I direct that such [life sustaining] procedures be withheld or withdrawn and that I be permitted to die naturally.... In the absence of my ability to give directions regarding the use of such life-sustaining procedures, it is my intention that this declaration shall be honored by my family and physician(s) as the final expression of my legal right to refuse medical or surgical treatment. (Raber, 1980, p. 30)

Where the person is conscious and rational, the courts have, as we have seen, tended to accept the principle that an individual has a right to refuse medical treatment even if the result is death. *"Even in an emergency situation,"* explains Lappe (1978), "where death would ensue if treatment were not administered, the court, in *In re Estate of Brooks,* upheld a patient's refusal of treatment" (p. 196). Since involuntary psychiatric interventions are rarely lifesaving (and even if they were, in conformity with the foregoing ethical-legal principles, that would not be enough to justify their forcible imposition on unwilling clients), the *parens patriae* rationale for psychiatric coercions is gravely undermined by the evidence I have adduced. Indeed, since the psychiatric will I propose would bestow the right to reject psychiatric treatment on persons deemed (even by courts and psychiatrists) to be fully competent and rational at the time of their making their decision against *involuntary* psychiatry, it is difficult to see on what constitutional, moral, or political grounds Americans could be denied this right.

THE PSYCHIATRIC WILL

An impasse between the protagonists of two positions, each basing their policies on different premises, is thus not unique to the conflict about psychiatric commitment. As the example of the dilemma concerning giving blood transfusions to Jehovah's Witnesses illustrates, American law has resolved this conflict by decreeing that no adult should undergo a blood transfusion who doesn't want to and that no adult who wants to receive blood should be denied the benefits of this treatment (assuming that he or she has access to medical care).

It is surprising that a similar tactic of conflict-resolution has apparently never been proposed for dealing with the conflict between the proponents and opponents of coercive psychiatry. I shall restate the conflict about commitment so that the differing premises of the two protagonists are clearly articulated.

Many people (and virtually all psychiatrists and other mental health experts) fear the danger of a "nervous breakdown" or "psychotic illness." These persons believe that mental illness exists, that it is "like any other illness," that it is amenable to modern psychiatric treatment, and that the effectiveness and legitimacy of such treatment are independent of the patient's consent to it. Accordingly, such persons seek protection from "life-threatening" mental illness and support the use of involuntary psychiatric interventions.

On the other hand, some people (including a few psychiatrists and other mental health experts) fear the literal danger of psychiatry more than the metaphoric danger of psychosis. Some of these persons also believe that mental illness does not exist and that psychiatric coercions are tortures rather than treatments. Accordingly, such persons seek protection from the powers of psychiatry and advocate the abolition of involuntary psychiatric interventions.

Let me now apply the principles underlying the last testament and the living will to the psychiatric contingency some people might want to anticipate and control. The imagery of "sudden madness" or "acute psychosis" sketched earlier represents the dreaded situation that some persons may want to anticipate and plan for. Since involuntary psychiatric confinement is a tradition-honored custom in modern societies, the situation such persons need to anticipate must be *their own sudden madness managed by others by means of commitment and coerced treatment.* To forestall such an event, we need a mechanism enabling anyone reaching the age of maturity, who so desires, to execute a "psychiatric will" prohibiting his or her confinement in a mental hospital or his or her involuntary treatment for mental illness. Those failing to execute such a document before an actual encounter with coercive psychiatry would, of course, have the opportunity to do so as soon as they have "recovered" from their first episode of "mental illness" or otherwise regained their competence.

Since commitment entails the loss of liberty, the foregoing mechanism for its protection is relatively weak, requiring as it does the affirmative assertion of a desire to do without involuntary psychiatric care. In the absence of such a declaration, the person would remain a potentially defenseless subject for psychiatric coercion. Although such an arrangement would be a great improvement over the present situation, a more powerful psychiatric will could easily be fashioned by inverting the right to be asserted in it. In this "strong" version of the psychiatric will, people would have to assert their rights to be the beneficiaries of psychiatric coercion should the "need" for it arise. This would leave everyone who has not executed a psychiatric will free from psychiatric coercion, much as we are free, without having to go to such troubles, of theological coercion.[5]

The use of psychiatric wills might thus put an end to the dispute about involuntary psychiatric interventions. Earnestly applied, such a policy should satisfy the demands of both psychiatric protectionists and psychiatric voluntarists. Surely, the psychiatric protectionists could not, in good faith, object to being frustrated in their therapeutic efforts by persons competent to make binding decisions about their future—specifically, decisions to prohibit personally unauthorized psychiatric assistance. Nor could the psychiatric abolitionists object, in good faith, to being frustrated in their libertarian efforts by persons competent to make binding decisions about their future—specifically, to authorize, under certain circumstances, their own temporary (or not-so-temporary) psychiatric "enslavement."[6]

WHAT THE PSYCHIATRIC WILL WOULD DO

Although in the compass of a brief article it would be impossible to anticipate and to articulate all of the consequences that might result from adopting the use of a psychiatric will such as I have proposed, some of its effects (including certain new problems it would generate and how we might cope with them) deserve to be mentioned.

To begin with, although my main purpose in proposing a psychiatric will is to protect potential patients from unwanted psychiatric interventions, such a document would also protect would-be therapists from the risks they now face in their relations with involuntary mental patients. This dual function of the psychiatric will is inherent in its being an instrument for transforming a status relationship into a contractual relationship (Alexander & Szasz, 1973). As matters now stand, psychiatrists faced with the task of having to care for "seriously ill mental patients" often find themselves in a Catch-22 type of situation: They are in danger of being sued both for confining and for failing to confine the "patient," for using coercive treatment as well as for failing to use it. The psychiatric will, prospectively requesting or refusing involuntary psychiatric interventions, would constitute a contract between potential future psychiatrists. Hence, while it would protect the former from psychiatric coercion or psychiatric neglect (as the case may be), it would protect the latter from charges of unauthorized treatment or unprofessional neglect.

The situation of the "psychiatric patients" would briefly be this. For those who choose (whether actively or passively) to accept involuntary psychiatric interventions, the psychiatric will is unlikely to make much difference, except as noted above. For those who choose to reject such interventions, the consequences would depend on specific circumstances.

One large group of individuals who would have to be treated differently than they are at present is comprised of persons charged with serious crimes. Such persons are now routinely subjected to pretrial psychiatric examinations to determine their competence to stand trial. With the use of psychiatric wills, this tactic could be used only with the permission of the accused. As in times past, such individuals would be *presumed* to be rational and competent.[7] The principle that a defendant is presumed to be competent to stand trial, like the principle that he or she is presumed to be innocent until proved guilty, would thus be restored to the American criminal law. *Mutatis mutandis*, persons who commit crimes would have to be tried, and if guilty, punished, instead of being diverted into the psychiatric system (Szasz, 1963).

Finally, individuals innocent of lawbreaking but deemed to be in need of psychiatric care would have to be persuaded that receiving such care serves *their* best interests. If that option fails, they would, in Justice Louis Brandeis' words, have to be granted their "right to be let alone." Such a situation, in which both presumably helpless individuals and the individuals ostensibly desirous of helping them are each deprived of the option of forcibly coercing the other, would generate a powerful stimulus for creating new ways of dealing with the diverse dimensions of the problems now mislabeled as "mental illnesses" and mismanaged as "psychiatric treatments."

NOTES

1 Natanson v. Kline, 186 Kan. 393. 406-07, 350 P.2d., 1093, 1104 (1960) (dictum), cited with approval in Woods v. Brumlop, 71 N.M. 221, 227, 377 P.2d., 520, 524 (1962) (dictum).

2 Olmstead v. United States, 277 U.S. 438, 479. (1928).

3 Application of President and Directors of Georgetown College, 331 F. 2n, 1010 (D.C. Cir. 1964).

4 250 West 57th Street, New York, New York 10019.

5 As a concession to current social practices, I have listed the two versions of the psychiatric will in what I consider to be, from a point of view of political philosophy, an inverse order. Although the stronger version of the psychiatric will is theoretically more attractive, because the paternalistic perspective on involuntary psychiatric interventions is now so prevalent, the weaker version may be practically more acceptable. Of course, the rejection of psychiatric interventions need not be total in either version of such a will. For example, some persons might wish to authorize coerced hospitalization and to forbid treatment by drugs or electroshock, while others might wish to authorize coerced drug therapy and to forbid confinement. Only through a mechanism such as this could the responsibilities as well as the rights of the "severely mentally ill" be expanded.

6 A report about a recent law in Spain suggests that the mechanism exemplified by the living will and the psychiatric will may be increasingly important as the power of the therapeutic state keeps expanding over the body and mind of citizens regarded mainly as medical cannon fodder (Szasz, 1963, pp. 212-222). The report is self-explanatory:

> A new Spanish law has decreed that the bodies of deceased Spanish citizens belong to the state. Under this law the bodies may be used immediately upon death by hospitals for transplants without consultation with relatives. The only exemptions will be those who carried a card stating that they did not wish their bodies to be used in such a way. ("Habeas Corpus," 1980, p. 181)

7 "It is," wrote Thomas Jefferson (1814/1944) to Nicholas Dufief, "an insult to our citizens to question whether they are rational beings or not" (p. 636).

REFERENCE NOTE

1 Szasz, T.S. *Therapy by the judiciary*. Book in preparation, 1982.

REFERENCES

Alexander, G.J., & Szasz, T.S. From contract to status via psychiatry. *Santa Clara Lawyer*, 1973, *13*, 537-559.

Byrn, R.M. Compulsory lifesaving treatment for the competent adult. *Fordham Law Review*, 1975, *44*, 1-36.

Foley, J.W., & McGinn, T.J. Jehovah's Witnesses and the question of blood transfusion. *Postgraduate Medicine*, 1973, *53*, 109-113.

Lappé, M. Dying while living: A critique of allowing-to-die legislation. *Journal of Medical Ethics*, 1978, *4*, 195-199.

Raber, P.E. Ethical and legal problems of the living will. *Geriatrics*, 1980, *35*, 27-30.

Riffolo, P.J. The living will. *Journal of Family Practice*, 1978, *6*, 881-885.

Szasz, T.S. *Law, liberty, and psychiatry: An inquiry into the social uses of mental health practices*. New York: Macmillan, 1963.

Veatch, R.M. *Death, dying, and the biological revolution. Our last quest for responsibility*. New Haven, Conn.: Yale University Press, 1976.

• • •

NO

Paul Chodoff and Roger Peele

THE PSYCHIATRIC WILL OF DR. SZASZ

In 1961 *The Myth of Mental Illness* proclaimed that the conditions psychiatrists treat are not illnesses and that psychiatrists are not physicians. Rather, Thomas S. Szasz maintained, these conditions fall within the realm of myth and metaphor; they are moral, not medical problems. Szasz's bold foray against the received wisdom of psychiatry was greeted with protest and indignation, but he was not deterred. Since that time he has become the guru of a movement aiming to destroy the power of psychiatrists to hospitalize anyone involuntarily, or, as he puts it, to subject them to psychiatric slavery, because of "mental illness."

The latest Szaszian contribution is "The Psychiatric Will—A New Mechanism for Protecting Persons Against 'Psychosis' and Psychiatry." In this paper Szasz the intransigent appears in a softer light. As the leader of the abolitionist school (now labeled voluntarist), he extends the olive branch to his opponents, the psychiatric protectionists. He offers them the psychiatric will, whereby individuals of sound mind can express their wishes with regard to involuntary psychiatric hospitalization should they ever become "psychotic." Ought the so-called protectionists accept this gesture or treat it with the kind of caution that has been counseled toward Greeks bearing gifts?

SZASZ'S PROPOSAL

To summarize this proposal, according to Szasz, psychiatrists have justified involuntary hospitalization ("psychiatric coercion") on three grounds:

1. Mental illnesses are like bodily illnesses with the unique exception that by their very nature mental illnesses deprive their victims of the capacity to make informed judgments about the need for treatment; thus the need to hospitalize them against their will for the purpose of treatment. Szasz's answer in the paper is brief and uncompromising. "Since there are no mental diseases, there can be no treatments for them."

2. Some "mentally ill" people are dangerous to themselves; therefore, under the doctrine of parens patriae, hospitalization is required. For Szasz this justification also rests upon the untenable assumption of mental illness. Furthermore, it violates the principle of bodily self-ownership. It is wrong to force help on troubled people; such help should only be offered.

3. Some "mentally ill" persons are dangerous to others and therefore subject to the police power of the state. Szasz sees no reason (certainly not the fiction of mental

illness) to treat such actual or potential malefactors differently from anyone else: they should be prosecuted and punished.

Szasz acknowledges that the differences between the voluntarists and the psychiatric protectionists are profound and cannot be resolved through ill-considered and ineffective "therapy by the judiciary" as enunciated in recent judicial opinions. The protectionists and the voluntarists don't speak the same language; therefore, the side with the power prevails. Szasz believes that this power is now in the hands of the protectionists; but he acknowledges, in accordance with his libertarian principles, that it would be equally unjust for the voluntarists to impose their will on those who wish to be protected from the consequences of their "illnesses."

Some of his psychiatric opponents argue that if they themselves were to become acutely psychotic, they would hope to receive appropriate psychiatric treatment even without their consent. He is skeptical of this argument and dismisses as mere anecdotes accounts of the gratitude of patients who have recovered after involuntary hospitalization. However, taking these psychiatric statements as a base, he suggests a device to reconcile the two sides: the use of a mechanism analogous to others developed by society to anticipate situations in which the individual's capacity to act competently is destroyed. The obvious instance is the last will and testament whereby the individual controls the distribution of personal property after death. Another recent application of this principle is the "living will," expressing the individual's wish not to be subjected to treatment for a painful and intractable terminal illness. Szasz now proposes a further extension of the same "Ulysses" principle* through what he calls the psychiatric will; he claims that this is an original idea based on the suggestion of a law professor. Just as the refusal of a competent Jehovah's Witness to receive a blood transfusion deemed medically necessary has been sanctioned by court decision, so any competent individual should be permitted either to refuse or permit involuntary hospitalization should he become psychotic.

*A reference to the instruction of Ulysses that his crew lash him to the mast and refuse to release him when the ship sailed past the island of the Sirens, lest he succumb to their blandishments.

Two versions of a psychiatric will are possible. In the weak version present public policy would prevail unless the individual had executed a psychiatric will stating his or her refusal to be subjected to involuntary psychiatric interventions should these ever be considered. In the strong version, these policy assumptions would be reversed. Involuntary psychiatric hospitalizations could be carried out only on people who had executed a will authorizing such a procedure.

For Szasz the psychiatric will is a useful, beneficent, and logically irrefutable mechanism. Neither the protectionists nor the voluntarists could in good conscience object to it. Not only would it be right, it would have the additional virtue of protecting psychiatrists from the potential legal risks of hospitalizing someone involuntarily. A previously executed psychiatric will would give persons charged with serious crime the choice of invoking or refusing the insanity defense.

Thus for Szasz the psychiatric will justly and ingeniously solves most of the problems that now arise in connection with the psychiatric and legal status of those considered to be mentally ill.

IS IT LOGICAL?

How sound is the reasoning that underlies the proposal? The unmistakable keystone of the Szaszian theoretical arch is his denial that mental illness falls into the same categorical niche as bodily illness. For if mentally ill individuals have a sickness similar to those, say, with pneumonia, and, if sick, need treatment, and if their sickness prevents them from accepting treatment, then it is medically necessary and morally right to find ways to treat them even if this involves coercion. Szasz rejects the sickness label for the mentally disturbed; suffering and sorrow, he declares, cannot of themselves define a medical disease. A disease entity is defined by signs and symptoms generated by objective—that is, organic—determinants. Thus for him illness is organic. Since mental disturbances are not organic, mental illness is not illness. Without this syllogism, there would be no justification for converting psychiatric disorders from the medical realm to the realm of civil rights.

But Szasz's equation of illness with an organic base is stifingly narrow. In the considerable literature on the concept of illness, there is no consensus on its definition and limits. One widely accepted view stems from the work of Talcott Parsons, for whom the sick role or the medical model is defined by a number of characteristics, only one of which is an organic base. Certainly the clinical practices of most nonpsychiatric physicians would be severely truncated if they took as patients only those specifically and solely afflicted with organic disease. Furthermore and to the extent that we accept the importance of an organic base in defining sickness, organic etiological elements are by no means absent in individuals with psychiatric disturbances who are considered for involuntary hospitalization. Most such patients fall into three categories—those with brain disease like alcohol withdrawal delirium (delirium tremens)—clearly organic; those with schizophrenia; or with major affective disorders. Without going into detail, an organic determinant of these psychoses as measured by genetic evidence and suggestive biochemical data is becoming increasingly accepted.

We also take issue with Szasz that the gratitude of those who have been subjected to involuntary hospitalization after they have recovered is based only on "anecdotes." At least two studies indicate the reality of this phenomenon in a significant number of such patients. Szasz is also mistaken in claiming that his concept of the psychiatric will is original. The essential idea, if not precisely in this form, has already been put forward by R.E. Reinert, and by Charles Culver and Bernard Gert.

IS IT MORALLY AND LEGALLY USEFUL?

Whatever its parentage, will such a document alleviate the difficulties, legal and moral, now attendant on the decision to invoke coercive hospitalization? Szasz's argument for the legitimacy of his proposal lays great stress on the analogy between a "living will" and a "psychiatric will." The analogy, however, is only an analogy. Actually there are many more differences than similarities between the two. The narrow and exclusive purpose of the living will is to prevent treatment that prolongs dying. The broad purpose of the psychiatric will not only permits the individual to die unnecessarily but also to be harmed in other ways or even to harm others. The consequences of a living will will be felt principally by the person who signs it. The psychiatric will is much more likely to affect others around the signer and the general public. Carrying out a psychiatric will could mean death for someone other than the signer if the latter is, say, under the influence of a dangerous drug or is a paranoid schizophrenic; thus it seems extremely unlikely that the public would allow immunity from treatment which might prevent such a disaster. The living will is specific about what is being proscribed: "life-sustaining procedures." What is prohibited by the psychiatric will—"involuntary psychiatric interventions"—is extraordinarily vague.

With regard to legal implications, on close inspection Szasz's olive branch turns into a thorny thicket. He has crusaded for medicine and law to go their separate ways but the psychiatric will would inextricably entwine the two and provide a feast of litigation for lawyers. The validity of both testamentary and living wills depends inescapably on the competency of the maker. Would not this requirement apply as well to psychiatric wills? Thus a declarant wishing to avoid "involuntary psychiatric interventions" would appear to be inviting a psychiatric examination to determine his or her competency to make such a declaration!

Other legal problems can be imagined. Where would the dividing line be between involuntary psychiatric and involuntary medical interventions? Would the physician treating an infection in a delirious, depressed patient who had previously executed such a will be prohibited from prescribing penicillin? Could the physician who denied such treatment be sued by the patient's family for abandonment? If the person who signs a psychiatric will should become mentally disabled due to lack of treatment, would he or she lose legal disability entitlements? Would the will have to include provisos recognizing that psychiatric illnesses may lead to incompetency to hold a job, to marry, to divorce, to make a will, to agree to a contract, or to conduct one's business?

If the will also attempted to mandate the signer's future right to plead not guilty by reason of insanity if he or she should commit a crime, as Szasz approvingly suggests, the already complex legal questions could become even more hideously tangled. Incidentally, Szasz is incorrect when he says that with the use of psychiatric wills pre-trial psychiatric examinations to determine competency to stand trial could be used only with the permission of the accused. The Supreme Court has twice in recent decades made clear that it is unconstitutional to try a person who is incompetent to stand trial, and the Court's interpretation of the Constitution in this regard is hardly likely to be changed by a psychiatric will of either the strong or the weak variety.

At a practical level it is most unlikely that many patients who are involuntarily hospitalized—for instance the 2,000 who are committed at St. Elizabeth's Hospital in Washington each year—have the knowledge or the resources or the motivation to execute such a will. If the psychiatric will is intended as a real solution, even if the legal difficulties were overcome it could, at best, be available only to a very small segment of educated persons of particular ideological bent. If Dr. Szasz intends his suggestion only as a rhetorical device, however, we should keep in mind that the Greek gift turned out to be the Trojan horse. The pseudoreasonableness of the psychiatric will would only further impair the already heavily compromised ability of psychiatrists to treat the small segment of severely disturbed individuals who lack the capacity to make a rational judgment in their own behalf and for whom a caring society must take responsibility.

● ● ●

POSTSCRIPT

CAN THE PSYCHIATRIC WILL PREVENT INVOLUNTARY TREATMENT?

As a result of the ideological power of the "anti-psychiatrists," the dreadful condition of many large state mental institutions in which patients had been "warehoused" for years, the development of antipsychotic medications to control overtly disruptive behavior, and the reduction of mental health budgets, a mass exodus of patients from institutions began in the 1970s. It was believed that many patients had been committed unjustifiably and that they could be better, more humanely, and more cheaply treated in community group homes. The promise of "deinstitutionalization," as this process is called, has not been fulfilled, and the streets of all major American cities are filled with homeless former mental patients who are both potential victims and potential victimizers. The debate over involuntary hospitalization that began two decades ago must now go on in a somewhat different context, for there are not as many institutions to which people can be confined, there is less optimism about patients' eventual restoration to normality, and there is, perhaps most important, less public money to support treatment.

Thomas Szasz's views are amplified in several books, among them *The Myth of Mental Illness*, revised edition (Harper & Row, 1974) and *Ideology and Insanity* (Doubleday, 1970). A supporting view is found in Nicholas Kittrie, *The Right to Be Different: Deviance and Enforced Therapy* (Johns Hopkins, 1971). The justifications for involuntary hospitalization are found in Charles M. Culver and Bernard Gert, "The Morality of Involuntary Hospitalization," in *The Law-Medicine Relation: A Philosophical Critique*, edited by H.T. Engelhardt, Jr., and Stuart Spicker (Reidel, 1981); and in Paul Chodoff, "The Case for Involuntary Hospitalization of the Mentally Ill," *American Journal of Psychiatry* (May, 1976). Also see George J. Annas, "*O'Connor* v. *Donaldson:* Insanity Inside Out," *Hastings Center Report* (August, 1976), and Michael A. Peszke, *Involuntary Treatment of the Mentally Ill: The Problem of Autonomy* (Thomas, 1975).

ISSUE 12

CAN DECEPTION IN RESEARCH BE JUSTIFIED?

YES: Stanley Milgram, from "Subject Reaction: The Neglected Factor in the Ethics of Experimentation," *Hastings Center Report* 7:5 (October 1977)

NO: Thomas H. Murray, from "Learning to Deceive," *Hastings Center Report* 10:2 (April 1980)

ISSUE SUMMARY

YES: Psychologist Stanley Milgram believes that the central moral justification for allowing deceptive experiments is that the vast majority of subjects who take part in them find them acceptable after the rationale is explained.

NO: Social psychologist Thomas H. Murray argues that deception research is not only bad for subjects, but also harmful to researchers and to the goals of science itself.

Imagine the following situation: Two people come to a psychology laboratory to participate in a study about memory and learning—specifically, the researcher explains, about the effects of punishment on learning. One subject is a "teacher," and the other a "learner." The "learner" is strapped into a chair, and an electrode attached to his wrist. He is told to memorize a list of word pairs; whenever he makes an error he will be given electric shocks of increasing intensity. The "teacher" is then seated before an impressive shock generator, which has switches ranging from 15 volts to 450 volts. The researcher explains that when the "learner" gives a correct answer to a word pair, the "teacher" should move on to the next item. But when the answer is incorrect, the "teacher" must give him an electric shock—and at a higher voltage each time. As the experiment proceeds, the "learner" makes more and more mistakes and responds to the electric shocks with increasing protests, cries of pain, and finally screams of agony.

This experiment was real. It took place at Yale University in the early 1970s in Stanley Milgram's psychology laboratory. But the "learner" was an actor. He received no shocks and only pretended to be in pain. The "teacher" was the true subject of the experiment, which was not about learning at all but about obedience and authority. How far, Milgram wanted to know, would people go in following orders to inflict pain on someone who protests? A few people, he found, defied the researcher's orders. Most, despite obvious stress and discomfort, cooperated to a significant degree.

Much psychological and other social science research, particularly in the field of social psychology, is based on the use of deception to achieve its goals. Milgram's obedience experiments are particularly dramatic, but by no means rare. The moral dilemma posed by such research is: Is it justifiable to deceive subjects, thereby violating a basic ethical principle of truth-telling, in order to conduct a scientific experiment? Those who defend deception, such as Philip Zimbardo of Stanford University and Charles Smith of City University of New York, claim that deception produces beneficial knowledge that could not be obtained any other way. They point out that deception may be the only way to ensure that the subjects' responses are valid; that the only harms involved are temporary feelings of embarrassment or anger; and that after subjects are "debriefed" or told the true purpose of the experiment they do not object to it.

On the other side are those, such as Donald Warwick and Herbert Kelman of Harvard University and Diana Baumrind of the University of California at Berkeley, who believe that in principle it is unethical to deceive others, even for a scientific goal. Deception, they say, *wrongs* subjects (that is, it deprives them of the right to decide freely whether to participate in an experiment or not) even when it does not harm them physically or even psychologically. Research can be designed without deception to achieve the same answers, they argue. Furthermore, they believe that many subjects are reluctant to describe their true feelings about the research and in any case ought to be protected from what Baumrind calls "inflicted insights" (knowledge about oneself that one would rather not know—such as one's capacity to inflict pain on others). These opponents contend that deception research destroys trust in the researcher and in science itself, and makes it difficult to find truly "naive" or unsuspecting subjects.

The two selections that follow present the views of two social scientists with personal experience in deception research. Stanley Milgram describes the aftermath of his experiments and concludes that the main justification for his method was the subjects' own ultimate acceptance of it. Thomas Murray, on the other hand, describes why he stopped doing deception research: Not only did it harm the subjects, he says, but it also harmed him, and the larger enterprise of science itself.

YES

Stanley Milgram

SUBJECT REACTION: THE NEGLECTED FACTOR IN THE ETHICS OF EXPERIMENTATION

Social psychology is concerned with the way in which individual behavior, thoughts, and action are affected by the presence of other people. Although experimentation is not the only way of garnering knowledge in the discipline, it is a major tool of inquiry. As experiments in social psychology typically involve human subjects, they necessarily raise ethical issues, some of which I will discuss here.

INFORMED CONSENT

Many regard informed consent as the cornerstone of ethical practice in experimentation with human subjects. Yet social psychology has until now been unable to assimilate this principle into its routine experimental procedures. Typically, subjects are brought into an experiment without being informed of its true purpose. Indeed, sometimes subjects are misinformed. Is such a procedure ever justifiable?

Herbert Kelman[1] has distinguished two quite different explanations for not informing the potential subject of the nature of the experiment in which he is to take part. One might term the first the motivational explanation; that is, if one told the subject what the experiment was to be like, he might refuse to participate in it. Misinforming people to gain their participation appears a serious violation of the individual's rights, and cannot routinely constitute an ethical basis for subject recruitment.

The second, more typical, reason for not informing a subject is that many experiments in social psychology cannot be carried out if the subject knows about the experiment beforehand.

Consider in this connection Solomon Asch's classic study[2] of group pressure and conformity. The subject is told that he is to take part in a study on the perception of lines. He is asked to make a judgment as to which of three lines is equivalent in length to a standard line, but he does so in the presence of other individuals who, unknown to him, are working for the experimenter and

Reprinted by permission from the *Hastings Center Report*, 7:5, October 1977.

give wrong answers. The experimenter's purpose is to see whether the subject will go along with the erroneous group information or resist the group and give the correct answer.

Clearly the subject is misinformed in several respects. He is told that he is to take part in an experiment on perception rather than group pressure. He is not informed that the others present are working for the experimenter, but is led to believe that they have the same relationship to the experimenter as he. It is apparent that if a subject were informed of the true purpose before participating in the study, he could not experience the psychological conflict that is at the crux of Asch's study. The subject is not denied the information because the experimenter fears he would not participate in the study, but for strictly epistemological reasons, that is, for somewhat the same reason the author of a murder mystery does not reveal to the reader who the culprit is: to do so would undermine the psychological effects of the reading experience.

A majority of the experiments carried out in social psychology use some degree of misinformation. Such practices have been denounced as "deception" by critics, and the term "deception experiment" has come to be used routinely, particularly in the context of discussions concerning the ethics of such procedures. But in such a context, the term "deception" somewhat biases the issue. It is preferable to use morally neutral terms such as "masking," "staging," or "technical illusions" in describing such techniques, because it is not possible to make an objective ethical judgment on a practice unless it is described in terms that are not themselves condemnatory.

Is the use of technical illusions ever justified in experiments? The simplest response, and the one that is most socially and ethically comfortable, is to assert unequivocally that they are not. We all know that honesty and a fully informed relationship with the subject is highly desirable and should be implemented whenever possible. The problem is that many people also believe strongly in the value of inquiry into social psychology, of its potential to enlighten us about human social behavior, and ultimately to benefit us in important ways. Admittedly, this is a faith, but one which impels us to carefully examine whether the illusions and misinformation required by experiments have any claim to legitimacy. We know that illusions are accepted in other domains without affronting our moral sensibilities. To use a simple-minded example, on radio programs, sound-effects of prancing horses are typically created by a sound-effects man who uses split coconut shells; rainfall is created by sand falling on metal sheets, and so forth. A certain number of listeners know about this, some do not; but we do not accuse such programs of deceiving their listeners. Rather we accept the fact that these are technical illusions used in support of a dramatic effort.

Most experiments in social psychology, at least the good ones, also have a dramatic component. Indeed, in the best experiments the subjects are brought into a dramaturgical situation in which the script is only partially written: it is the subject's actions that complete the script, providing the information sought by the investigator. Is the use of technical illusions to be permitted in radio programs, but not scientific inquiry?

There are many instances in everyday life in which misinformation is tolerated or regarded as legitimate. We do not cringe at the idea of giving children misinformation about Santa Claus, because we feel it is a benign illusion, and common sense tells us it is not harmful. Furthermore, the practice is legitimized by tradition. We may give someone misinformation that takes him to a surprise party. The absolutists may say that this is an immoral act, that in doing so one has lied to another person. But it is more important to focus on the person who is the recipient of this information. Does he find it a demeaning experience, or a delightful treat?

One thing is clear: masking and technical illusions ought never to be used unless they are indispensable to the conduct of an inquiry. Honesty and openness are the only desirable basis of transaction with people generally. This still leaves open the question of whether such devices are permissible when they cannot be avoided in a scientific inquiry.

There is another side to this issue. In the exercise of virtually every profession there may be some exemption from general moral practice which permits the profession to function. For example, although a citizen who has witnessed a murder has a moral obligation to come forth with this information, lawyers have a right—indeed an obligation—of "privileged communication." A lawyer may know that his client has committed a murder, and is obligated not to tell the authorities. In other words, a generally accepted moral obligation is suspended and transformed in the case of legal practice, because in the long run we consider this exemption beneficial to society.

Similarly, it is generally impermissible to examine the genitals of strange women. But it is a technical requirement for the practice of obstetrics and gynecology. Once again, for technical reasons, we suspend a general moral rule in the exercise of a profession, because we believe the profession is beneficial to society.

The question arises: is there any comparable exemption due the social scientist because of technical requirements in the kind of work he does, which in the long run, we believe will benefit society? It is true that most often the individual participant in an experiment is not the beneficiary. Rather it is society as a whole that benefits, or at least, that is the supposition of scientific inquiry.

Still another side to the staging by social psychologists is frequently overlooked. The illusions employed by most experiments are usually short-term. They are sustained only insofar as they are required for the purpose of the experiment. Typically, the subject is informed of the experiment's true character immediately after he has participated in it. If for thirty minutes the experimenter holds back on the truth, at the conclusion he reaffirms his confidence in the subject by extending his trust to him by a full revelation of the purpose and procedures of the experiment. It is odd how rarely critics of social psychology experiments mention this characteristic feature of the experimental hour.

From a formal ethical standpoint, the question of misinformation in social psychology experiments is important, because dissimulation subverts the possibility of informed consent. Indeed, the emphasis on "deception" has virtually preempted discussion of ethics among social psychologists. Some feel it is a misplaced emphasis. Support is given to this view by a recent study by Elinor Mannucci.[3] She questioned 192 laymen concerning their reaction to ethical aspects of psychology experiments, and found that they regarded deception as a relatively minor issue.

THE OBEDIENCE EXPERIMENTS

In order to take a close look at the act of obeying, I set up a simple experiment at Yale University. Eventually, the experiment was to involve more than a thousand participants and would be repeated at several universities, but at the beginning, the conception was simple. A person comes to a psychological laboratory and is told to carry out a series of acts that come increasingly into conflict with conscience. The main question is how far the participant will comply with the experimenter's instructions before refusing to carry out the actions required of him.

But the reader needs to know a little more detail about the experiment. Two people come to a psychology laboratory to take part in a study of memory and learning. One of them is designated as a "teacher" and the other a "learner." The experimenter explains that the study is concerned with the effects of punishment on learning. The learner is conducted into a room, seated in a chair, his arms strapped to prevent excessive movement, and an electrode attached to his wrist. He is told that he is to learn a list of word pairs; whenever he makes an error, he will receive electric shocks of increasing intensity.

The real focus of the experiment is the teacher. After watching the learner being strapped into place, he is taken into the main experimental room and seated before an impressive shock generator. Its main feature is a horizontal line of thirty switches, ranging from 15 volts to 450 volts, in 15-volt increments. There are also verbal designations which range from SLIGHT SHOCK to DANGER—SEVERE SHOCK. The teacher is told that he is to administer the learning test to the man in the other room. When the learner responds correctly, the teacher moves on to the next item; when the other man gives an incorrect answer, the teacher is to give him an electric shock. He is to start at the lowest shock level (15 volts) and to increase the level each time the man makes an error, going through 30 volts, 45 volts, and so on.

The "teacher" is a genuinely naive subject who has come to the laboratory to participate in an experiment. The "learner," or victim, is an actor who actually receives no shock at all. The point of the experiment is to see how far a person will proceed in a concrete and measurable situation in which he is ordered to inflict increasing pain on a protesting victim. At what point will the subject refuse to obey the experimenter?

Conflict arises when the man receiving the shock begins to indicate that he is experiencing discomfort. At 75 volts, the "learner" grunts. At 120 volts he complains verbally; at 150 he demands to be released from the experiment. His protests continue as the shocks escalate, growing increasingly vehement and emotional. At 285 volts his response can only be described as an agonized scream.

Observers of the experiment agree that its gripping quality is somewhat obscured in print. For the subject, the situation is not a game; conflict is intense and obvious. On the one hand, the manifest suffering of the learner presses him to quit. On the other, the experimenter, a legitimate authority to whom the subject feels some commitment, enjoins him to continue. Each time the subject hesitates to administer shock, the experimenter orders him to continue. To extricate himself from the situation, the subject must make a clear break with authority. The aim of this investigation was to find when and how people would defy authority in the face of a clear moral imperative.

From Obedience to Authority: An Experimental View
by Stanley Milgram
(New York: Harper & Row, 1974), pp. 3-4.

They were far more concerned with the quality of the experience they would undergo as subjects. For example, despite the "deceptive" elements in the Asch experiment the great majority of respondents in Mannucci's study were enthusiastic about it, and expressed admiration for its elegance and significance. Of course, the layman's view need not be the final word, but it cannot be disregarded, and my general argument is that far more attention needs to be given to the experiences and views of those who actually serve as subjects in experiments.

NEGATIVE EFFECTS

Is an experiment that produces some sort of negative, aversive, or stressful effect in the subject ever justified? In this matter, two parameters seem critical: first, the intensity of the negative experience, and second, its duration. Clearly, the discussion that follows refers to effects that do not permanently damage a subject, and which most typically do not exceed in intensity experiences which the subject might encounter in ordinary life.

One thing is clear. If we assert categorically that negative emotions can never ethically be created in the laboratory, then it follows that highly significant domains of human experience are excluded from experimental study. For example, we would never be able to study stress by experimental means; nor could we implicate human subjects in experiments involving conflict. In other words, only experiments that aroused neutral or positive emotions would be considered ethical topics for experimental investigation. Clearly, such a stricture would lead to a very lopsided psychology, one that caricatured rather than accurately reflected human experience.

Moreover, historically, among the most deeply informative experiments in social psychology are those that examine how subjects resolve conflicts, for example: Asch's study of group pressure studies the conflict between truth and conformity; Bibb Latané and John Darley's bystander studies[4] create a conflict as to whether the subject should implicate himself in other peoples' troubles or not get involved; my studies of obedience[5] create a conflict between conscience and authority. If the experience of conflict is categorically to be excluded from social psychology, then we are automatically denying the possibility of studying such core human issues by experimental means. I believe that this would be an irreparable loss to any science of human behavior.

My own studies of obedience were criticized because they created conflict and stress in some of the subjects. Let me make a few comments about this. First, in this experiment I was interested in seeing to what degree a person would comply with an experimental authority who gave orders to act with increasing harshness against a third person. I wanted to see when the subject would refuse to go on with the experiment. The results of the experiment showed first that it is more difficult for many people to defy the experimenter's authority than was generally supposed. The second finding is that the experiment often places a person in considerable conflict. In the course of the experiment subjects sometimes fidget, sweat, and break out in nervous fits of laughter. I have dealt with some of the ethical issues of this experiment at length elsewhere,[6] but let me make a few additional remarks here.

SUBJECT REACTION: A NEGLECTED FACTOR

To my mind, the central moral jusitification for allowing my experiment is that it was judged acceptable by those who took part in it. Criticism of the experiment that does not take account of the tolerant reaction of the participants has always seemed to me hollow. I collected a considerable amount of data on this issue, which shows that the great majority of subjects accept this experiment, and call for further experiments of this sort. The table below shows the overall reaction of participants to this study, as indicated in responses to a questionnaire. On the whole, these data have been ignored by critics or even turned against the experimenter, as when critics claim that "this is simply cognitive dissonance. The more subjects hated the experiment, the more likely they are to say they enjoyed it." It becomes a "damned-if-they-like-it and damned-if-they-don't" situation. Critics of the experiment fail to come to grips with what the subject himself says. Yet, I believe that the subject's viewpoint is of extreme importance, perhaps even paramount. Below I shall present some approaches to ethical problems that derive from this view.

Some critics assert that an experiment such as mine may inflict a negative insight on the subject. He or she may have diminished self-esteem because he has learned he is more submissive to authority than he might have believed. First, I readily agree that the investigator's responsibility is to make the laboratory session as constructive an experience as possible, and to explain the experiment to the subject in a way that allows his performance to be integrated in an insightful way. But I am not at all certain that we should hide truths from subjects, even negative truths. Moreover, this would set experimentation completely apart from other life experiences. Life itself often teaches us things that are less than pleasant, as when we fail an examination or do not succeed in a job interview. And in my judgment, participation in the obedience experiment had less effect on a participant's self-esteem than the negative

EXCERPT FROM QUESTIONNAIRE USED IN A FOLLOW-UP STUDY OF THE OBEDIENCE RESEARCH

Now that I have read the report, and all things considered . . .	*Defiant*	*Obedient*	*All*
1. I am very glad to have been in the experiment	40.0%	47.8%	43.5%
2. I am glad to have been in the experiment	43.8%	35.7%	40.2%
3. I am neither sorry nor glad to have been in the experiment	15.3%	14.8%	15.1%
4. I am sorry to have been in the experiment	0.8%	0.7%	0.8%
5. I am very sorry to have been in the experiment	0.0%	1.0%	0.5%

emotions engendered by a routine school examination. This does not mean that the stress of taking an examination is good, any more than the negative effects of the obedience experiments are good. It does mean that these issues have to be placed in perspective.

I believe that it is extremely important to make a distinction between biomedical interventions and those that are of a purely psychological character, particularly the type of experiment I have been discussing. Intervention at the biological level *prima facie* places a subject "at risk." The ingestion of a minute dose of a chemical or the infliction of a tiny surgical incision has the potential to traumatize a subject. In contrast, in all of the social psychology experiments that have been carried out, there is no demonstrated case of resulting trauma. And there is no evidence whatsoever that when an individual makes a choice in a laboratory situation—even the difficult choices posed by the conformity or obedience experiments—any trauma, injury, or diminution of well-being results. I onced asked a government official, who favored highly restrictive measures on psychology experiments, how many cases of actual trauma or injury he had in his files that would call for such measures. He indicated that not a single such case was known to him. If this is true, then much of the discussion about the need to impose government restrictions on the conduct of psychology experiments is unrealistic.

Of course, one difficulty in dealing with negative effects is the impossibility of proving their nonexistence. This is particularly true of behavioral or psychological effects. It seems that no matter what procedures one follows—interviewing, questionnaires, or the like—there is always the possibility of unforeseen negative effects, even if these procedures do not uncover them. Therefore, in an absolute sense, one can never establish the absence of negative effects. While this is logically correct, we cannot use this as a basis for asserting that such effects necessarily follow from psychological experimentation. All we can do is rely on our best judgment and assessment procedures in trying to establish the facts, and to formulate our policies accordingly.

IS ROLE PLAYING A SOLUTION?

Given these problems and the particular requirements of experiments in social psychology, is there any way to resolve these issues so that the subject will be protected, while allowing experimentation to continue? A number of psychologists have suggested that role playing may be substituted for any experiment that requires misinformation. Instead of bringing the subject into a situation whose true purpose and nature were kept from him, the subject would be fully informed that he was about to enter a staged situation, but he would be told to act *as if it* were real. For example, in the obedience experiment subjects would be told: "pretend you are the subject performing an experiment and you are giving shocks to another person." The subject would enter the situation knowing the "victim" was not receiving shocks, and he would go through his paces.

I do not doubt that role playing has a certain utility. Indeed, every good experimenter employs such role playing when he is first setting up his laboratory situation. He and his assistants often go through a dry run to see how the procedure flows. Thus, such simulation is not new, but now it is being asked to serve as the end point, rather than the starting point of an experimental investigation. However, there is a major scientific problem. Even after one has had a subject role play his way through an experimental procedure, we still must wonder whether the observed behavior is the same as that which a genuine subject would produce. So we must still perform the crucial experiment to determine whether role-played behavior corresponds to nonrole-played behavior.

Nor is role playing free of ethical problems. A most striking simulation in social psychology was carried out by Philip Zimbardo at Stanford University.[7] Volunteers were asked to take part in a mock prison situation. They were to simulate either the role of prisoner or guard with the roles chosen by lot. They were picked up at their homes by local police cars, and delivered to Zimbardo's mock prison. Even in the role-playing version of prison, the situation became rather ugly and unpleasant, and mock guards acted cruelly toward the mock prisoners. The investigator called off the simulation after six days, instead of the two weeks for which it had been planned. Morever, the simulation came under very heavy ethical criticism. The ethical problems that simulation was designed to solve did not all disappear. The more closely role-playing behavior corresponds to real behavior, the more it generates real emotions, including aversive states, hostile behavior, and so on. The less real emotions are present, the less adequate the simulations. From the standpoint of the aversive emotions aroused in a successful simulation, ethical problems still exist.

Kelman aptly summarized the state of simulation research when he stated that simulation is not so useless a tool of investigation as its critics first asserted, nor as free of ethical problems as its proponents believed.[8]

PRESUMPTIVE CONSENT

Recall that the major technical problem for social psychology research is that if subjects have prior knowledge of the purposes and details of an experiment they are often, by this fact, disqualified from participating in it. Informed consent thus remains an ideal that cannot always be attained. As an alternative, some psychologists have attempted to develop the doctrine of *presumptive consent.* The procedure is to solicit the view of a large number of people on the acceptability of an experimental procedure. These respondents would not themselves serve in the experiment, having been "spoiled" in the very process of being told the details and purposes of the experiment. But we could use their expressed views about participation as evidence of how people in general would react to participation. Assuming the experiment is deemed acceptable, new subjects would be recruited for actual participation. Of course, this is, ethically, a far weaker doctrine than that which relies on informed consent of the participant. Even if a hundred people indicate that they would be willing to take part in an experiment, the person actually chosen for participation might find it objectionable. Still, the doctrine of the "presumed consent of a reasonable person" seems to me better than no consent at all. That is, when for epistemological purposes the nature of a study cannot be revealed beforehand, one would try to determine in advance whether a reasonable person would consent to being a subject in the study and use that as a warrant either for carrying out the investigation or as a basis for modifying it.

Perhaps a more promising solution is to obtain *prior general consent* from subjects in advance of their actual participation. This is a form of consent that would be based on subjects' knowing the general types of procedures used in psychological investigations, but without their knowing what specific manipulations would be employed in the particular experiment in which they would take part. The first step would be to create a pool of volunteers to serve in psychology experiments. Before volunteering to join the pool people would be told explicitly that sometimes subjects are misinformed about the purposes of an experiment, and that sometimes emotional stresses arise in the course of an experiment. They would be given a chance to exclude themselves from any study using deception or involving stress *if they so wished*. Only persons who had indicated a willingness to participate in experiments involving deception or stress would, in the course of the year, be recruited for experiments that involved these elements. Such a procedure might reconcile the technical need for misinformation with the ethical problem of informing subjects.

Finally, since I emphasize the experience of the person subjected to procedures as the ultimate basis for judging whether an experiment should continue or not, I wonder whether participants in such experiments might not routinely be given monitoring cards which they would fill out and submit to an independent monitoring source while an experiment is in progress. An appropriate monitoring source might be a special committee of the professional organization, or the human subjects' committee of the institution where the experiment is carried out. Such a procedure would have the advantage of allowing the subject to express reactions about an experiment in which he has just participated, and by his comments the subject himself would help determine whether the experiment is allowable or not. In the long run, I believe it is the subject's reaction and his experience that needs to be given its due weight in any discussion of ethics, and this mechanism will help achieve this aim.

NOTES

1 Herbert Kelman, "Remarks made at the American Psychological Association," New Orleans, 1974.

2 Solomon E. Asch, *Social Psychology* (New York: Prentice Hall, 1952).

3 Elinor Mannucci, *Potential Subjects View Psychology Experiments: An Ethical Inquiry.* Unpublished Doctoral Dissertation. The City University of New York, 1977.

4 Bibb Latané and John Darley, *The Unresponsive Bystander: Why Doesn't He Help?* (New York: Appleton, 1970).

5 Stanley Milgram, *Obedience to Authority: An Experimental View* (New York: Harper and Row, 1974).

6 Stanley Milgram, "Issues in the Study of Obedience: A Reply to Baumrind," *American Psychologist* 19 (1964), 848-52.

7 Philip Zimbardo, "The Mind is a Formidable Jailer: A Pirandellian Prison," *The New York Times Magazine* (April 8, 1973), p. 38.

8 Kelman, "Remarks."

• • •

NO

Thomas Murray

LEARNING TO DECEIVE

In 1968 Paul Goodman, the radical social critic, came to Temple University, introduced himself as a social psychologist, and spoke eloquently against the war in Vietnam. None of this is surprising except for Goodman's self-identification as a social psychologist. Perhaps it should have struck a discordant note in the minds of his audience, but to those of us whose image of social psychology came from the uncritical textbooks of the sixties, a person of Goodman's commitments fits our image of what a social psycholgist ought to be. To unsophisticated undergraduates social psychology seemed to be *the* relevant discipline. What other groups of scientists devoted their lives to research on prejudice, conformity, obedience to destructive authority, propaganda, conflict resolution, or any of a multitude of topics that seemed to penetrate to the heart of war, injustice, and other evils?

It was only natural for a college graduate in that same year, idealistic and naive, to enter a graduate program in social psychology as a way to honor simultaneously intellect and justice. I enrolled, filled with enthusiasm and hope. Enlightenment, in the form of disillusionment, came slowly. In a discipline like social psychology that values "hands-on" research, the real education takes place not in the seminar room but in the laboratory. There the skills of the profession are transmitted, the real work done, and the appropriate views learned. It is those practiced views, and their impact on those who adopt them, that I want to explore here.

THE GROWTH OF DISCIPLINE

The history of social psychology offers some clues as to how it reached its stance on laboratory work. The widely acknowledged founder of experimental social psychology was Kurt Lewin, whose career spanned the twenties to the fifties. In his vision of the science, social progress would advance hand in hand with social theory. His famous adage, "There is nothing so practical as a good theory," soon came to be translated into something more like "Take care of

Reprinted by permission from the *Hastings Center Report*, 10:2, April 1980.

theory and practical matters will take care of themselves." The emphasis was on doing good, respectable science; and the *sine qua non* of scientific respectability was the experimental method and its historical setting, the laboratory.

So dawned the age of the social laboratory and its pinnacle—the highly charged, dramatic, deception experiment.

An important part of the socialization of a professional is exposure to examples of excellence. Some of the examples offered to graduate students in my program (a representative one, I think) were Stanley Schachter's experiments on emotionality, Leonard Berkowitz on aggression, Bibb Latané and John Darley on helping in emergencies.[1] What these research programs and their kin had in common beside the fact that they were unusually well done were at least two things: the experiences of the subjects of the studies were intense and dramatic; and the deceptions employed were elaborate and skillfully managed.

By the sixties social psychologists had grown wary of Lewin's boundless faith in democracy, and were less worried about the immediate practicality of their research; but they remembered one lesson above all—whatever you do, do it with style and flair. Within the discipline the suspicion was growing that the acclaim a study received might have as much to do with the ingenuity and panache of the deception as with the importance of the scientific question. The tendency to choose flash over substance became so serious that a respected social psychologist, Kenneth Ring, took the discipline to task for what he called "frivolous values."[2] But these worries were largely ignored. Deception was securely entrenched as a methodology; not the only one certainly, but predominant in a number of research areas.* This was the state of the discipline in the mid-1960s, although one would not have known it from the typical undergraduate textbook.

Perhaps my description of the discipline suggests an image of the deception researcher as a cool manipulator, utterly insensitive to the feelings of his or her subjects. That description fits very few social psychologists. The individuals with whom I worked closely were principled and responsible people, concerned with doing the right things. Their behavior would be much easier to understand, and much less interesting, had they been callous and cynical. Certainly I met the latter type, but I never worked with them directly.

Consider the problem this way: explain how otherwise good people, at least no worse than the run of academics, come routinely to frighten, provoke, insult, depress, and generally lie to the subjects of their experiments. And what is the impact of their views in practice on themselves and on their conception of human nature outside of the laboratory? To my knowledge, there are no authoritative studies on the personalities of social psychologists, their values, or their beliefs about human nature—a curious gap for a discipline so interested in behavior and motivation.

The question then is: does deception research harm the researcher? All forms of work have their hazards. Are there any hazards unique to or especially acute for

*Studies of the incidence of deception research are difficult to interpret. They typically take a sample of journals known to publish mostly social psychological research and classify the studies into those that employ deception as a major part of the procedure, and those that do not. Results vary widely, depending on the journals sampled and the criteria for classifying a procedure as a "deception." For the sixties they range from 16 percent to 38 percent. But in some research areas—conformity and attitude change studies, for example—deception was used in 81 percent and 72 percent of the studies, respectively. These areas, and related ones, also carried with them the highest prestige within the discipline.

the scientist who routinely deceives as a part of his or her profession? Perhaps a "case history"—an autobiographical one in this instance—can illuminate the kinds of harms that arise in deception research, without of course testifying to their extent. As just this sort of "case history," I offer my own experience as a graduate student and neophyte deception researcher.

A STUDY IN HELPING BEHAVIOR

The first deception study in which I participated was on helping behavior in emergencies. We played out an elaborate scenario for each individual subject with minor variations. The variations allowed us to create five separate conditions or "treatments" within the experiment, varying in the likelihood that they would inhibit helping responses. Our subjects were greeted by a phony "experimenter," taken through an elaborate cover story (one that by all the usual criteria worked very well), and asked to sit in a tiny booth watching a TV monitor. Within a very few minutes, they witnessed the "experimenter," apparently alone in another room, receive what looked like a severe electric shock and collapse on the floor, out of camera range. My job was to time the subjects—how long would it take them to call for help or otherwise come to the 'experimenter's" aid? If they made no move to seek help within six minutes, I retrieved them from their booths. Then, with the study essentially over, I began my real work—"debriefing" the subject.

Whether or not the person "helped"—in the vernacular of the research report—I "revealed the true purpose of the study, answered all questions honestly, and remained with the subject until all negative effects of participation had been removed." Not quite. While I did reveal the true purpose of the study, I did not always answer all questions honestly; and I seriously doubt that I, or anyone else, could have removed all negative effects of participation.

Those people who offered help—almost always in the first two minutes—were a pleasure to talk with afterwards. They praised the experiment, my cleverness, and social psychology in general. But why shouldn't they? They had been put to the test, and they had passed! When another human being was in need, they responded. They left the debriefing confident.

However, my experiences with subjects who did not respond within six minutes was another matter. I quickly began to dread the movement of the stopwatch hands. I knew that when the six minutes had passed I would have to face someone who might be trembling, who might have trouble talking, and who would probably have fabricated some fantastic explanation of what had happened to the "victim." Among the 99 subjects I put through the procedure, I saw individuals whose faces were drained of color, who were reduced to stuttering, or who could barely force words through their clenched teeth. These subjects had many versions of what had happened: the "victim" had sneezed, or tripped, or just maybe there was something wrong. Virtually every subject who had not responded showed some anxiety.

Of course, I had to explain the study. What do you tell people who sat idly by, or at least who felt that they had done so, while another human being was in possible danger? When I told many of the people who did not help that they were in an experimental condition designed to inhibit helping, it seemed to make them feel better. However, when I debriefed subjects who had failed to help even though they were *not* in a condition designed to inhibit helping, I found myself lying, saying that they were in a help-inhibiting situation.

When they congratulate you for running such an ingenious and significant experiment, as they invariably do, you try to forget the queasiness in their smiles, and the uncertainty in their handshakes. You try to convince yourself that, yes, all harmful effects have been removed. But I did not believe it then, and I do not today. If your experiment is good, according to the canons of experimental design in social psychology, it is realistic. If you are not getting people's "real" responses to your simulations of reality, then you have no claim to be doing good science. The more skillful you are at simulating reality, the more accurately your subjects can infer how they are likely to act in the larger social world from the way they have acted in your laboratory. To the extent that my simulated emergency was realistic, my nonresponding subjects could make the inference that they were *not* the sort of person who acts courageously to help others in a crisis. And I doubt that my attempts to reassure them, including my willingness to encourage their rationalizations, could really undo all the damage to their self-esteem.

The social psychologist who wants to study some humanly significant area of human behavior with a deception paradigm comes squarely up against a paradox: the more "real"—hence, valuable—the study, the greater the likelihood that someone's self-image will be altered unfavorably. This paradox appears as a moral problem only if you believe that there is something ethically objectionable about social scientists, in Diana Baumrind's phrase, "inflicting insight" on their unwitting subjects. Others, Stanley Milgram for one, see this as merely telling subjects some truth about themselves.[3] But this already presumes that the scientist knows in just what respects the study *is* "real," and can explain it fully to the subjects, so that the subjects do not assume better—or worse—of themselves than is warranted. The first presumption is virtually impossible to satisfy; and there is evidence that the second may be wrong. That I might be making some individuals, volunteers in innocence and ignorance, judge themselves cowardly or callous, troubled me deeply. Before I began the work, I was warned that debriefing subjects after a procedure like the one we used would be like six weeks of psychotherapy packed into a half-hour. I had no idea how appropriate the warning would be.

One further incident brought home to me the potential effects of deception manipulations on subjects. Sometime after the helping research, I attended a meeting to discuss a proposed research project which was to use the now notorious "self-esteem manipulation." It is an extremely clever use of a principle well known to fortune-tellers—that within very wide limits, people will believe almost anything reported to them about themselves, as long as it comes from an "authoritative" source with some special claim to knowledge. Subjects take a phony personality test supposedly in the final stage of validation. When they return a couple of weeks later, they are handed an envelope containing a report of their "results." There are only two reports—one favorable, one unfavorable—and they are handed out on a random basis. What you do on the "test" has absolutely no relationship to the profile you receive. If you receive the positive profile, you read a flattering set of comments on the warmth of your personality, the depth of your friendships, your sincerity, honesty, maturity, and integrity. It ends with a sentence like: "On the whole, this is one of the most favorable profiles we have ever encountered." If, by chance, you receive the negative profile, you read about your coldness, shallowness, insincerity, lack of principle, immaturity, and lack of integration. It concludes with: "On the whole, this is one of the most unfavorable profiles we have ever encountered."

The purpose of this charade is to manipulate the individual's self-esteem in a controlled fashion, so that the effects of high vs. low self-esteem on some other variables can be systematically studied. To my knowledge, this manipulation is no longer in use, but a decade ago it was popular. At that time I protested. I argued that its scientific validity was suspect: it was at least plausible that the sort of "self-esteem" affected by the manipulation was different in action from the normal underlying level of self-esteem; that what was really being studied by the "self-esteem manipulation" was the effect of being told you were a complete loser. No wonder that people with experimentally induced "low self-esteem" then performed poorly on a wide range of tasks! My methodological objections carried little weight. My ethical objection—that it was wrong to fraudulently alter, even temporarily, a person's self-perception—carried no weight at all. It was irrelevant.

For years I felt my misgivings about deception research were the product of an overly scrupulous mind. The weight of opinion in my profession rested clearly on the side of deception research, though there were notable exceptions even then.[4] But deception research has come under increasingly strong attack in recent years. And I now find myself not so alone.

My case is undoubtedly extreme. But it is not unprecedented. There are examples of virulent attacks on deception research by former social psychologists, for example, Thorne Shipley[5] and Donald Warwick.[6] There are also an unknown number of would-be social psychologists who quietly retired from the field because they were unable to put their wholehearted efforts into deception research, and unwilling or unable to develop other research methods. Even though Alan Elms, a graduate student who assisted Milgram in his now famous research on "obedience," defends the use of deception, he has foresworn it in his own research.[7] How many young and idealistic graduate students have found themselves choosing between lying to a subject and adding to the anxiety caused by a deception, between becoming a professional liar and taking up a new profession? And what compromises must be made to allow a person to deceive in the name of science?

It should not be hard for the reader to empathize with the social psychologist contemplating the use of deception. You want to study some pressing problem; you believe that the controlled laboratory setting is the best place to disentangle the complex threads of social phenomena and get at the truth; and the only way you know of duplicating the real world in your laboratory is through elaborate deceptions. Nowhere in your reasoning does callousness or cynicism appear; nowhere do you think of your subjects as "marks" or dupes. You want to do good, science is the surest road to knowledge; therefore, you are doing good. Since the problem you want to study is likely some socially troublesome issue, by studying it, and thereby contributing to its resolution, you are doing doubly good. How could anyone have the temerity to accuse you of harming your subjects, when your intentions are so obviously laudable?

Social psychologists, like psychoanalysts, have specialized in the study of rationalization and self-justification. They, more than anyone, ought to be able to recognize the powerful pressures on them to justify deception research. To adjure deception research now would be tantamount to confessing to past sins; it would be abandoning the tool many know best; it would make impossible many of the most interesting and impressive (and most highly rewarded) studies. It would require surrender of the singularly unique contribution of social psychology to the catalogue of social research methods.

The argument over the future of deception research must begin with a clear-headed assessment of the reality and importance of intrusions on subjects' well-being and substantive rights. Ultimately, the victor will be decided by government regulations. But beyond that we need to consider the costs of deception research to the individual scientist and his or her professional community.

To begin with the latter, I find it difficult to believe that social psychologists are proud of their image as the tricksters of science. (There is even a tape of selected vignettes from the "Candid Camera" show especially designed to illustrate social psychological principles. Both the television show and the discipline have specialized in getting people to reveal their foibles through elaborately staged and carefully recorded scenarios.) The word has certainly gotten around on campuses so that a large percentage of students *expect* to be deceived in psychology experiments, although they do not necessarily consider deception bad.[8] Some regard that appraisal as a warrant for the continued use of deception; others, myself included, as a warning. I have heard social psychology spoken of scornfully by other scientists and by humanists. But these are all externalities. What psychic price does the individual social psychologist pay?

I know too many principled people who are social psychologists to make any hasty generalizations. And perhaps the mild cynicism they exhibit is no worse than the typical academic's. But do any of the values and presumptions they live with in their identity as researcher spill over into the rest of their lives? In trying to make our laboratory so much like the world, do we sometimes succeed in making our world like the laboratory? When we learn to stage events and manage impressions, are we led to do the same with our other relationships? Do we eventually come to see people as so easily duped outside the laboratory as inside it? And if our research induces people to behave inhumanely, do we come to believe that that is indeed the way people are? Because so much of social psychological research leads people to behave irrationally (if they behaved reasonably and rationally, what need would there be for the science?), do we come to see people as fundamentally irrational? In short, do we come to see people in general as easily manipulable, foolish, and not especially nice, as a result of our characteristic procedures?

The deception researcher's personal dilemma is this: either one successfully dissociates the carefully crafted manipulativeness that characterizes the relationship with research subjects from relationships with people outside the laboratory, or one does not. In the first case, we should worry about the impact of the inauthentic relationship on the subject, and about the researcher's learning to systematically shut off ethically central aspects of his or her personality, as for example, learning to lie with a completely straight face *and* a clear conscience. The very ability to dissociate completely parts of one's life would seem to threaten one's psychological integration as well as one's personal integrity. In the second case, it follows analytically that one's relationships outside the laboratory are colored by the way one treats subjects. Neither option looks morally attractive.

It could be said that I have misrepresented the nature of the subject-experimenter relationship; specifically, I have left out the debriefing where the two people face each other honestly, and try to confront the feelings aroused by what each has done. Indeed, I suspect this does happen with some extraordinary researchers, deepening their humanity and their strength as moral actors. But I think it is the rare exception to the discouraging rule. The vast majority of social psychologists receive only the most superficial training on how to conduct a compassionate debriefing. Debriefings are more often viewed as discharging a responsibility (often an unpleasant one), an opportunity to collect additional data, or even as a chance for a further manipulation! Deception researchers are not trained to recognize signs of anxiety in their subjects, nor to deal with them should they appear. Any special sensitivity of researcher to subject is likely to be the result of individual talent, or of clinical training which is *not* routinely part of a social psychologist's graduate experience.

One final cost of deception research requires discussion. What kind of science can grow from a discipline that relies on systematically deceiving its subjects? Here I am not questioning its moral value but rather its scientific value. Defenders of deception research regularly argue that if you were to tell subjects what you were really studying, then their responses would be somehow "unnatural." It is a point well taken, although the realm to which it is applicable may be smaller than originally thought. But, implicit in that very argument is the understanding that human subjects are not the passive recipients of external manipulations; that their responses are mediated by meanings and expectations.

And if, as is demonstrably the case, many, perhaps the majority, of our subjects expect to be deceived, do we have a science of "how-people-behave-when-they-don't-trust-the-authority-figure-who-is-telling-them-what-is-what" and no more? The people who become our "subjects" do not surrender their curiosity when they enter the lab. Nor do they lose their interest in interpersonal relationships, including that potential one with the experimenter. To assume that they do either, or that by employing deception we are somehow escaping the complex task of understanding the role of setting, expectations, and other persons, is naive and in the long run destructive to our goal of developing a robust science.

How might social psychology adapt were its practitioners to abandon or severely curtail the use of deception, or if we were to accept more complex models of persons-as-subjects? I believe the results would be intellectually invigorating as well as morally defensible. In my criticism of the received wisdom I am certainly not suggesting that we don rose-colored spectacles. Rather I am arguing that we may now be wearing dark glasses. Deception research may be neither good for the science nor good for the scientist.

NOTES

1 For Schachter's early work on emotionality see S. Schachter and J.E. Singer, "Cognitive, Social, and Physiological Determinants of Emotional State," *Psychological Review* 69 (1962), 379-99; and S. Schachter and L.

Wheeler, "Epinephrine, Chlorpromazine and Amusement," *Journal of Abnormal and Social Psychology* 65 (1962), 121-28. An influential work by Berkowitz was L. Berkowitz, *Aggression: A Social Psychological Analysis* (New York: McGraw-Hill, 1962). Latané and Darley's work is summarized in B. Latané and J.M. Darley, *The Unresponsive Bystander: Why Doesn't He Help?* (New York: Appleton-Century-Crofts, 1970).
2 Kenneth Ring, "Experimental Social Psychology: Some Sober Questions About Some Frivolous Values," *Journal of Experimental Social Psychology* 3 (1967), 113-23.
3 For Baumrind's latest thoughts on the matter see Diana Baumrind, "IRBs and Social Science Research: The Costs of Deception," *IRB: A Review of Human Subjects Research* 1 (October 1979), 1-4. For a recent statement of Milgram's views see Stanley Milgram, "Subject Reaction: The Neglected Factor in the Ethics of Experimentation," *Hastings Center Report* 7 (October 1977), 19-23.
4 Herbert Kelman, "The Human Use of Human Subjects," *Psychological Bulletin* 67 (1967), 1-11.
5 Thorne Shipley, "Misinformed Consent: An Enigma in Modern Social Science Research," *Ethics in Science and Medicine* 4 (1977), 93-106.
6 Donald P. Warwick, "Deceptive Research: Social Scientists Ought to Stop Lying," *Psychology Today* (February 1975), pp. 38, 40, 105.
7 Alan Elms, "Deception in Social Science Research: Under What Conditions Is It Justifiable?" Paper presented at a conference on "Ethical Issues in Social Science Research" at the Joseph and Rose Kennedy Institute of Ethics, Georgetown University, Washington, D.C., September 27-29, 1979.
8 Y.M. Epstein, P. Suedfeld, and S.J. Silverstein, "Subjects' Expectations of and Reactions to Some Behaviors of Experimenters," *American Psychologist* 28 (1973), 212-21.

• • •

POSTSCRIPT

CAN DECEPTION IN RESEARCH BE JUSTIFIED?

The American Psychological Association's Ethical Principles, as revised in 1979, permit deception in research but only under certain conditions: The research problem must be important; deception must be necessary in order to carry out the study; subjects must consider it reasonable after they have been debriefed; subjects must have the right to withdraw freely; and the after-effects must be minimized by the researcher. The latest (1981) federal regulations governing research with human subjects do not specifically mention deception. However, they do state that the requirements for informed consent can be waived or altered "if the research could not practicably be carried out without the waiver or alteration." This provision has been widely interpreted as a way of permitting deception research to be approved by an institutional review board, a committee that considers the ethical aspects of research conducted at the institution.

The results of Stanley Milgram's experiments and a fuller description of his method can be found in his book *Obedience to Authority: An Experimental View* (Harper & Row, 1974). For another controversial case of deception research involving clandestine observations of homosexual activity in a public restroom, see Laud Humphrey's, *Tearoom Trade* (Aldine, 1970). A generally sympathetic account is "Research through Deception" by Morton Hunt, *New York Times Magazine* (September 12, 1982). For a critique of deception by a social scientist, see Donald Warwick, "Social Scientists Ought to Stop Lying," *Psychology Today* (February 1975). Also see Joan E. Sieber, editor, *The Ethics of Social Research: Surveys and Experiments* (Springer-Verlag, 1982); and Tom L. Beauchamp et al., editors, *Ethical Issues in Social Science Research* (Johns Hopkins, 1982).

ISSUE 13

SHOULD PRISONERS BE BARRED FROM VOLUNTEERING FOR RESEARCH?

YES: National Commission for the Protection of Human Subjects of Biomedical and Behavioral Research, from *Report and Recommendations: Research Involving Prisoners* (Washington, D.C.: DHEW Publication No. (OS) 76-131, 1976)

NO: Carl Cohen, from "Medical Experimentation on Prisoners," *Perspectives in Biology and Medicine* 21:3 (Spring 1978)

ISSUE SUMMARY

YES: The National Commission, a federal advisory body, concludes that the conditions of prison life are inherently coercive and that prisoners can be allowed to volunteer for research only under very restricted conditions.

NO: Philosopher Carl Cohen argues that prisoners are not necessarily coerced into volunteering for research; if they are treated fairly they can be as free to choose whether or not to participate as anyone else.

In 1945 the Nuremberg trials of Nazi war criminals revealed a pattern of "crimes against humanity" committed against non-German nationals, both prisoners of war and civilians—among them Jews and what the Nazis considered "asocial" persons. What made these crimes particularly shocking was that many of them were carried out under the name of "medical research" and were conducted by medical professionals. Instead of using their skills to heal and comfort people, these Nazi doctors inflicted pain, torture, and often death. Following the trials, the Nuremburg Code established a series of ethical principles to govern the conduct of medical research. Among its main provisions was a requirement that the "voluntary consent of the human subject is absolutely essential." That principle has since been incorporated into all laws and regulations governing research involving human subjects.

In this country, the revelations of Nuremberg made many people reconsider research involving prisoners, which during World War II had been considered a patriotic and praiseworthy endeavor to help develop drugs that would save the lives of American soldiers. Research ethics came under intense scrutiny in the 1960s and 1970s, as scandals came to light about unethical research conducted in prisons and elsewhere. Although no one has ever claimed that abuses in American prisons were anything like the abysmal record of the Nazis, many asked: Can it *ever* be ethical to use prisoners as research subjects?

In 1974, partly to answer this question, Congress established the National Commission for the Protection of Human Subjects of Biomedical and Behavioral Research. It was charged with issuing recommendations to the then-Department of Health, Education and Welfare about federal policy in this area. The commission learned that at that time at least 3,600 prisoners were being used each year to test the safety of new drugs. The tests themselves were not particularly risky, but they offered no benefit to the prisoners' health. Virtually no other country outside the United States conducted clinical pharmacological studies on prisoners.

As part of its deliberations, the commissioners visited Jackson State Prison in Jackson, Michigan, where a special medical research unit had been set up. The commissioners expected to hear complaints of coercion to enter research, bad side effects, incomplete disclosure, and the like. Instead, as Dr. Robert J. Levine, a consultant to the Commission, recalls: "As one prisoner told us . . . : 'Ladies and gentlemen: You are in a place where death at random is a way of life. We have noticed that the only place in this prison that people don't die is in the research unit. Just what is it that you think you are protecting us from?' "

The Commission listened to both sides of the debate about the use of prisoners, which centers around two questions: Are prisoners able to exercise free choice in deciding whether to participate in research or not? And do they bear an unfair share of the burdens and receive an inadequate share of the benefits for their participation? As the excerpt from its final report indicates, it did not ban research in prisons entirely but recommended that research be permitted only in prisons in which the conditions are of such a high standard that there can be no question about the voluntariness of prisoner participation. In effect, the commission's recommendations would eliminate almost all research, since no existing prison could meet these standards.

The selection by Carl Cohen that follows presents the case for letting prisoners themselves decide whether to participate in experiments. He acknowledges that prison life is boring, controlled, and barren, but asserts that those realities do not make participation in research "coerced"—that is, compelled by physical or moral pressures. The argument against permitting prisoners to choose, he claims, confuses a broad sense of constraint (which characterizes the prison environment) with a narrow sense of constraint (the freedom to make a particular decision).

YES The National Commission for the Protection of Human Subjects of Biomedical and Behavioral Research

RESEARCH INVOLVING PRISONERS

INTRODUCTION

Prior to 1940, prisoners in the United States seldom participated in biomedical research that had no reasonable expectation of improving the health or well-being of the research subjects. During World War II, however, large numbers of prisoners participated in voluntary research programs to develop treatment for infectious diseases that afflicted our armed forces. This involvement of prisoners was considered to be not only acceptable, but praiseworthy. Following the war, the growth of biomedical research and the imposition of requirements for testing drugs as to safety led to the increased use of prisoners. Their participation in biomedical research not related to their health or well-being has continued in this country to the present time. This participation is now primarily in phase 1 drug and cosmetic testing, which is conducted or supported by pharmaceutical manufacturers in connection with applications to the Food and Drug Administration for licensing new drugs. Other research of this sort in which prisoners participate, or have participated, includes studies of normal metabolism and physiology, conducted by the Public Health Service (PHS); studies of the prevention or treatment of infectious diseases, conducted or supported by the PHS and the Department of Defense; a study of the effects of irradiation on the male reproductive function, supported by the Atomic Energy Commission; and testing of the addictive properties of new analgesics by giving them to prisoners with a history of narcotic abuse, conducted by the Addiction Research Center in Lexington, Kentucky. (The involvement of federal prisoners in the Lexington program is scheduled to be phased out.*)

Reprinted from *Report and Recommendations: Research Involving Prisoners*, National Commission for the Protection of Human Subjects of Biomedical and Behavioral Research, Department of Health, Education and Welfare, Washington, DC, 1976.

Prisoners also participate in research on practices that have the intent and reasonable probablity of improving their health or well-being. This research includes, for example, studies (supported by various components of DHEW* and the Federal Bureau of Prisons) to develop methods to reduce the spread of infections, improve dental care, help the subjects stop smoking and remove tatoos. A major focus of this sort of research involving federal prisoners has been the development of new treatments for narcotic addiction.

A third type of research in which prisoners participate includes studies of the possible causes, effects and process of incarceration, and studies of prisons as institutional structures or of prisoners as incarcerated persons. Components of DHEW have undertaken research of this sort for such purposes as learning the etiology of drug addiction and deviant or self-destructive behavior, and the factors relating to parole performance and recidivism.

Research is also conducted on the methods of treatment or "rehabilitation" of prisoners. The National Institute of Mental Health, the Federal Bureau of Prisons, and the Law Enforcement Assistance Administration have supported research on the experimental treatment of aggressive behavior with drugs and aversive conditioning techniques, as well as behavior modification based upon depriving inmates of basic amenities which they must then earn back as privileges. Rehabilitative practices have not always been based upon prior scientific design and evaluation, however, despite the fact that there are few, if any, approaches to the treatment or rehabilitation of prisoners for which effectiveness has been clearly demonstrated.

Outside the United States prisoners do not generally participate in biomedical research. This exclusion may be ascribed in part to continuing concern over experiments that were conducted on prisoners in Nazi concentration camps. Revelations of those experiments led to the enunciation of the Nuremberg Code (1946-1949), which required that human subjects of research "be so situated as to be able to exercise free power of choice" but did not expressly prohibit research involving civil prisoners. The Declaration of Helsinki, adopted by the World Medical Association in 1964 and endorsed by the American Medical Association in 1966, contained similar language that was subsequently deleted in 1975. Although little if any drug testing is conducted in foreign prisons, other kinds of research have been conducted in prisons throughout the world, such as studies dealing with the incidence and implications of chromosome abnormalities.

Since the 1960's, the ethical propriety of participation by prisoners in research has increasingly been questioned in this country. Among the events that have focused public attention on this issue was the publication of Jessica Mitford's book, *Kind and Usual Punishment*, in 1973. Eight states and the Federal Bureau of Prisons have formally moved to abandon research in prisons. The Health Subcommittee of the Senate Committee on Labor and Public Welfare held hearings (*Quality of Health Care - Human Experimentation*, 1973) on research involving prisoners in late 1973. Those speaking against the use of prisoners cited exploitation, secrecy, danger and the impossibility of obtaining informed consent as reasons to impose a prohibition or moratorium on the conduct of research

*The Department of Health, Education and Welfare, now known as the Department of Human Services.—ed.

in prisons. The advantages of using prisoners in research (*e.g.*, opportunity for close monitoring and controlled environment) and the procedures that are employed to protect prisoner participants were also described in the hearings. The Health Subcommittee held extensive hearings on other areas of human experimentation as well, and reported the bill establishing this Commission with a mandate that included a directive to study and make recommendations concerning the involvement of prisoners in research.

More recently, the House Subcommittee on Courts, Civil Liberties, and the Administration of Justice held hearings (*Prison Inmates in Medical Research,* 1975) on a bill (H.R. 3603) to prohibit "medical research" in federal prisons and prisons of states that receive certain federal support. Following these hearings, the Director of the Federal Bureau of Prisons determined that "continued use of prisoners in any medical experimentation should not be permitted," and he ordered that such participation by prisoners under federal jurisdiction be phased out.

Some of the more extreme behavioral programs have also raised questions. In her 1973 book, Jessica Mitford expressed concern about new approaches to "treatment" for offenders. Concurrently, others raised questions about the use of psychosurgery in prisons. In the early 1970's, the first challenges to behavior modification and aversive conditioning programs in prisons were argued in the courts, with mixed results. Most of the cases involved the right to refuse to participate in such programs, although prisoners have also petitioned for the right to be included in programs designed to alter sexually aggressive behavior.

Concern over behavior modification programs in prisons was expressed in a study, *Individual Rights and the Federal Role in Behavior Modification* (1974), prepared by the staff of the Constitutional Rights Subcommittee of the Senate Judiciary Committee. The study contained information on a number of such programs and suggested that this Commission make use of the information in attempting to resolve the issues that they raised. It should be noted that a number of the "treatment" programs mentioned in the study are reported to have been discontinued.

GENERAL CONCERNS

In conducting its investigations and studies, the Commission has noted and cannot ignore serious deficiencies in living conditions and health care that generally prevail in prisons. Nor can the Commission ignore the potential for arbitrary exercise of authority by prison officials and for unreasonable restriction of communication to and from prisoners. The Commission, although acknowledging that it has neither the expertise nor the mandate for prison reform, nevertheless urges that unjust and inhumane conditions be eliminated from all prisons, whether or not research activities are conducted or contemplated.

ETHICAL CONSIDERATIONS ABOUT USING PRISONERS AS RESEARCH SUBJECTS

There are two basic ethical dilemmas concerning the use of prisoners as research subjects: (1) whether prisoners bear a fair share of the burdens and receive a fair share of the benefits of research; and (2) whether prisoners are, in the words of the Nuremberg Code, "so situated as to be able to exercise free power of choice"—that is, whether prisoners can give truly voluntary consent to participate in research.

These two dilemmas relate to two basic ethical principles: the principle of *justice,* which requires that persons and groups be treated fairly, and the principle of *respect for persons,* which requires that the autonomy of persons be promoted and protected. Disproportionate use of prisoners in certain kinds of research (*e.g.,* phase 1 drug testing) would constitute a violation of the first principle; closed and coercive prison environments would compromise the second principle. It is within the context of a concern to implement these principles that the Commission has deliberated the question of use of prisoners as research subjects.

The Commission recognizes, however, that the application of these principles to the problem is not unambiguous. To respect a person is to allow that person to live in accord with his or her deliberate choices. Since the choices of prisoners in all matters except those explicitly withdrawn by law should be respected, as courts increasingly affirm, it seems at first glance that the principle of respect for persons requires that prisoners not be deprived of the opportunity to volunteer for research. Indeed, systematic deprivation of this freedom would also violate the principle of justice, since it would arbitrarily deprive one class of persons of benefits available to others—namely, the benefits of participation in research.

However, the application of the principles of respect and justice allows another interpretation, which the Commission favors. When persons seem regularly to engage in activities which, were they stronger or in better circumstances, they would avoid, respect dictates that they be protected against those forces that appear to compel their choices. It has become evident to the Commission that, although prisoners who participate in research affirm that they do so freely, the conditions of social and economic deprivation in which they live compromise their freedom. The Commission believes, therefore, that the appropriate expression of respect consists in protection from exploitation. Hence it calls for certain safeguards intended to reduce the elements of constraint under which prisoners give consent and suggests that certain kinds of research would not be permitted where such safeguards cannot be assured.

Further, a concern for justice raises the question whether social institutions are so arranged that particular persons or groups are burdened with marked disadvantages or deprived of certain benefits for reasons unrelated to their merit, contribution, deserts or need. While this principle can be interpreted, as above, to require that prisoners not be unjustly excluded from participation in research, it also requires attention to the possibility that prisoners as a group bear a disproportionate share of the burdens of research or bear those burdens without receiving a commensurate share of the benefits that ultimately derive from research. To the extent that participation in research may be a burden, the Commission is concerned to ensure that this burden not be unduly visited upon prisoners simply because of their captive status and administrative availability. Thus it specifies some conditions for the selection of prisoners as a subject pool for certain kinds of research. In so doing, the Commission is not primarily intending to protect prisoners from the risks of research; indeed, the Commission notes that the risks of research, as compared with other kinds of occupations, may be rather small. The Commission's concern, rather, is to ensure the equitable distribution of the burdens of research no matter how large or small those burdens may be. The Commission is concerned that the status of being a prisoner makes possible the perpetration of certain systemic injustices. For example, the availability of a population living in conditions of social and economic deprivation makes it possible for researchers to bring to these populations types of research which persons better situated would ordinarily refuse. It also establishes an enterprise whose fair administration can be readily corrupted by prisoner control or arbitrarily manipulated by prison authorities. And finally, it allows an inequitable distribution of burdens and benefits, in that those social classes from which prisoners often come are seldom full beneficiaries of improvements in medical care and other benefits accruing to society from the research enterprise.

Reflection upon these principles and upon the actual conditions of imprisonment in our society has led to the Commission to believe that prisoners are, as a consequence of being prisoners, more subject to coerced choice and more readily available for the imposition of burdens which others will not willingly bear. Thus, it has inclined toward protection as the most appropriate expression of respect for prisoners as persons and toward redistribution of those burdens of risk and inconvenience which are presently concentrated upon prisoners. At the same time, it admits that, should coercions be lessened and more equitable systems for the sharing of burdens and benefits be devised, respect for persons and concern for justice would suggest that prisoners not be deprived of the opportunity to participate in research. Concern for principles of respect and justice leads the Commission to encourage those forms of inquiry that could form a basis for improvement of current prison conditions and practices, such as studies of the effects of incarceration, of prisons as institutions and of prisoners as prisoners, and also to allow research on practices clearly intended to improve the health or well-being of individual prisoners.

The Commission has noted the concern, expressed by participants at the National Minority Conference and by others, that minorities bear a disproportionate share of the risks of research conducted in prisons. This concern is fostered, in part, by evidence that prison populations are disproportionately nonwhite. Evidence presented to the Commission indicates that where research is done in prison, those prisoners who participate tend to be predominantly white, even in institutions where the population as a whole is predominantly nonwhite; further, those who participate in research tend to be better educated and more frequently employed at better jobs than the prison population as a whole. This evidence suggests that nonwhites and poor or less educated persons in prison do not carry a greater share of the burdens of research.

However, the evidence is inconclusive for two reasons: first, because it does not fully satisfy questions related to the risks of research; and second, because it raises questions of justice with respect to the equitable distribution of benefits (as well as burdens) of research.

With respect to risks, the Commission notes that different research projects carry different risks; it is possible, though the Commission has no evidence to this effect, that one race or another may participate in more research of higher risk. And of course, the ratio of nonwhites to whites participating in research and hence bearing the burdens of research may still be disproportionate when compared to the ratio of the populations as a whole.

But the Commission also notes that those who participate in research consider the benefits sufficient to outweigh the burdens. Thus, the greater participation of whites may mean that there is an inequitable distribution of benefits between racial groups. Hence the greater participation by whites does not necessarily resolve the issue of distributive justice.

Similarly, the Commission notes that less research is conducted in women's prisons. While the reasons for this may well be the same reasons that women in general are used less frequently than men as research subjects (*e.g.*, the possibility of pregnancy), questions of distributive justice, similar to those raised above, may still need to be addressed with respect to participation in research by women prisoners.

DISCUSSION

Among the issues discussed by the Commission are two on which no specific recommendations are made, but concerning which the considerations of the Commission should be expressed: (1) remuneration, and (2) alternatives to conducting research in prisons. (1) Remuneration is a subject that should be analyzed by human subjects review committees, in consultation with prison grievance committees and prison authorities. There are at least two considerations that must be balanced in the determination of appropriate rates for participation in research not related to the subjects' health or well-being. On the other hand, the pay offered to prisoners should not be so high, compared to other opportunities for employment within the facility, as to constitute undue inducement to participate. On the other hand, those who sponsor the research should not take economic advantage of captive populations by paying significantly less than would be necessary if nonprisoner volunteers were recruited. Fair solutions to this problem are difficult to achieve. One suggestion is that those who sponsor research pay the same rate for prisoners as they pay other volunteers, but that the amount actually going to the research subjects be comparable to the rates of pay otherwise available within the facility. The difference between the two amounts could be paid into a general fund, either to subsidize the wages for all inmates within the prison, or for other purposes that benefit the prisoners or their families. Prisoners should participate in managing such a fund and in determining allocation of the monies. Another suggestion is that the difference be held in escrow and paid to each participant at the time of release or, alternatively, that it be paid directly to the prisoner's family.

A requirement related to the question of appropriate remuneration for participation in research is that prisoners should be able to obtain an adequate diet, the necessities of personal hygiene, medical attention and income without recourse to participation in research.

(2) Some of the Commission members endorse the alternative of permitting prisoners to participate in research provided it is conducted in a clinic or hospital outside the prison grounds, and provided also that nonprisoners participate in the same projects for the same wages. Other members of the Commission believe that such a mechanism would serve only to increase the disparity between the conditions within the prison and those within the research unit, thereby heightening the inducement to participate in research in order to escape from the constraints of the prison setting.

All of the members of the Commission endorse the suggestion that the use of alternative populations be explored and utilized more fully than is presently the case. This may be especially important to permit drugs to continue to be tested, as required by current law and regulations of the FDA, during any period in which prisons have not satisfied the conditions that are recommended for the conduct of such research. Increased utilization of alternative populations would have the added benefit of providing nonprisoner populations to participate in research projects along with prisoners, or in parallel with similar projects within prisons, in order to satisfy the general concern that prisoners not participate in experiments that nonprisoners would find unacceptable. The Commission also suggests that Congress and the FDA consider the advisability of undertaking a study and evaluation to determine whether present requirements for phase 1 drug testing in normal volunteers should be modified.

CONCLUSIONS

In the course of its investigations and review of evidence presented to it, the Commission did not find in prisons the conditions requisite for a sufficiently high degree of voluntariness and openness, notwithstanding that prisoners currently participating in research consider, in nearly all instances, that they do so voluntarily and want the research to continue. The Commission recognizes the role that research involving prisoners has played. It does not consider, however, that administrative convenience or availability of subjects is, in itself, sufficient justification for selecting prisoners as subjects.

Throughout lengthy deliberations, the strong evidence of poor conditions generally prevailing in prisons and the paucity of evidence of any necessity to conduct research in prisons have been significant considerations of the Commission. An equally important consideration has been the closed nature of prisons, with the resulting potential for abuse of authority. Some of the Commission members, who are opposed to research not related to the health or well-being of prisoner-participants, have, however, agreed to permit it to be conducted, but only under the following standards: adequate living conditions, separation of research participation from any appearance of parole consideration, effective grievance procedures and public scrutiny at the prison where research will be conducted or from which prospective subjects will be taken; importance of the research; compelling reasons to involve prisoners; and fairness of such involvement. Compliance with these requirements must be certified by the highest responsible federal official, assisted by a national ethical review body. The Commission has concluded that the burden of proof that all the requirements are satisfied should be on those who wish to conduct the research.

• • •

NO

Carl Cohen

MEDICAL EXPERIMENTATION ON PRISONERS

PROLOGUE

Ought we to permit medical experimentation on prisoners? The issue is both practically important and morally complex. Some argue as follows: No human subject may be used in a medical experiment without his informed and freely given consent. But prisoners, by virtue of their total custody, cannot give free and uncoerced consent. Hence prisoners—no matter how valuable experimentation with their cooperation may prove—must be excluded from all populations of subjects in medical experimentation.

This argument, when expanded and reinforced, is very persuasive, as I shall show. I aim also to show that its key premise is simply mistaken, and the argument unsound.

Government agencies (HEW, NIH, the National Commission for the Protection of Human Subjects) and the human subject review committees all provide assorted rules and guidelines for prison experimentation. It is not my aim to report these. My question is this: *Should* we adopt the rule, now proposed by some, excluding all or almost all experimentation involving prison volunteers?[1]

Some clarifications first. The principle that informed consent must be got from every human subject in a medical experiment is well established. . . . But "informed consent" involves more than information. Better thought of as "full consent" what is demanded in fact entails three elements; information, competency, and voluntariness. Where the consent received is defective in any one of these respects, we will rightly think the subject to have been improperly used.

Problematic defects of information arise when experiments are proposed in which the subjects may not be told the truth, or the whole truth, about the investigation of which they are part—because their knowing what the investigator is after will have the effect of his not getting it. Deception is not uncommon in behavioral research, but I bypass the problem here. Problematic defects of competency arise when experiments call for subjects who are not (in fact or in law) competent to give their consent—infant children, the mentally disabled, the comatose, and so on. Some experiments with persons in these categories is essential, obviously, if care for them is to be improved; hence principles must be devised for determining who may give third-party consent ("proxy consent") for the incompetent, and under what restrictions it may be given. These issues of competency are sorely vexed, but here I bypass them also. . . .

13. SHOULD PRISONERS BE BARRED FROM VOLUNTEERING?

CAN A PRISONER GIVE VOLUNTARY CONSENT?

Voluntariness, the third element of full consent, is most difficult to specify. We insist that a subject's consent be freely given and uncoerced. What does that entail? Clear cases of "volunteers" who did not give their consent freely are not hard to recall or imagine. The archetype—which reality often approximates—is the army platoon, lined up before the first sergeant who asks sternly for volunteers, and orders those who do not volunteer to take two steps forward. At the other extreme, cases of honest volunteering, genuinely autonomous, are legion. But very many cases fall between the extremes, and that of the prison volunteer is one of these.

It may well seem that, by virtue of the complete custody of their persons, prisoners lack the capacity to act with the kind of uncoerced voluntariness required. If they do lack it, they ought not be subjects. So I want now to put, more carefully than I have found it put anywhere, what precisely it is about the prisoner's condition that might render him or her unfit to be a consenting subject in a medical experiment.

The argument goes like this. The prison environment, both in fact and in principle, is such that consent without coercion is not possible there. This is not because of any defect in prisoners; it flows from the deeply intrusive, literally totalitarian character of prisons. One may take this as a condemnation of prisons, or simply as an unpleasant but unavoidable fact about them. Attitudes about prisons are not in contention here. Prisons being what they are, their inmates are in a state of constant coercion, from which there is no escape within the walls. No matter what the prisoner says, or we say to him, coercion is the essence of his condition. In that condition no consent to put oneself at risk should be accepted as full consent. Hence medical experimentation on prisoners should be forbidden flatly.

This is the general thrust. Now, more concretely and specifically, see how this coercive spirit permeates the prison environment.

First. The body of the prisoner is simply not under his own control. Orders committing persons to prison are very blunt about this, generally containing the phrase: "the body of the defendant shall be delivered" to the custodial institution appropriately identified. No system of criminal punishment that relies upon prisons, however humane its intent, can evade this fact. . . .

Second. Not only is the prisoner's person unfree, but the control of that person, and the secure incarceration of his body, are his keepers' chief and overriding concerns. Prisons are closed, tightly guarded places. Anyone who has not visited a medium or maxiumum security prison can hardly imagine the impact of omnipresent locks, bars, and armed guards. Supervision of hour-by-hour conduct is close; inspection is constant; privacy is nil; coercion is the flavor of every moment.

Third. Most prisoners are very poor, and have tightly limited opportunity to earn the most puny wages. Some states pay no wages for prison labor; most states pay less than one dollar per day; only six states pay more than that. And even where wages are paid, not all prisoners have the chance to earn them. From this poverty any decent payment for service is partial rescue.

Fourth. Boredom, killing monotony, is that feature which, next to control, most pervades prison life. The state tells every prisoner when to sleep, when to rise, when to eat and what, when to work and when to play, what to do and how to do it—all with maddening sameness. From this barrenness, any change is relief.

Fifth, and finally. The dominant concern in every prisoner's life is release and the eventual date of it. In this country prison sentences of indeterminate length are very common. That single most important date is therefore subject to the judgment, even to the whim, of administrators whom the prisoner can rarely reach or even address. His behavior in prison—in ways he cannot be sure of—must affect, perhaps determine, his date of release. Even for those with determinate sentences, that date remains indeterminate if there is, as usually, a parole board to be pleased. The felt need to please officials—doing what (at least in their own minds) prisoners think might please those who might be in a position to effect a somewhat earlier release—is an unavoidable pressure upon the behavior or prisoners.

It is in this environment that voluntariness of consent to subjection to medical experimentation must be assessed. However freely it appears that he consents, the prisoner is coerced so fully by his circumstances that even asking him must be unfair. His service as subject must be seen by him as a precious opportunity to escape, if only for short or infrequent periods, from the drabness and routine of prison life. He will see new faces, talk to interesting people who are neither inmates or guards, leave his normal, grim surroundings on occasion for a setting that is lit by freedom and interest. And he is further coerced by the monetary rewards—dollars at a crack, even scores of dollars in a long experiment—promising opportunity for riches not possible otherwise. The risks run are overshadowed by the partial escape from state-imposed penury. Fifty dollars a month, say, for prison subjects in a malaria test—why, that is coercion turned green! And above all, what an opportunity to prove one's good will, one's eagerness to pay his debt to society, one's sincere intention to make up for past evils and be good! Surely they who have power in this sphere will note this evidence of good character. Surely it will not work against the prisoner when parole or release is being considered—and it may, it just *may* do some good. How can the rational prisoner not be coerced by such a concatenation of pressures? He cannot. It is not right (this argument concludes) even to ask the prisoner whether he wishes to put himself at risk when doing so is encouraged by his circumstances so strongly and so perniciously. No matter the circumspection and honest care of the investigator. If, as we have seen, full and uncoerced consent simply cannot be given by prisoners, the request for volunteers must not, in fairness, be made to them. . . .

A CLOSER LOOK AT COERCION

There is the case, and it is a strong one. But it is not strong enough. The argument is rightly cautionary. Its several considerations show, I submit, that medical experiments using prisoners as subjects must go forward, if at all, under rules more constraining, and supervision more strict, than such experimentation in more ordinary contexts. It has not been shown, I contend, that a prisoner cannot give full consent in the sense that being a voluntary subject requires full consent.

I begin by granting much of the factual description of the prison environment presented above—although that account was deliberately put in rather purple language. But it is so; prison life is controlled, barren, poor, monotonous. Coercion is the spirit of the prison. Regrettably, however, those who accept the argument above, or some variant of it, are led by their detestation of prisons to equivocate upon the word "coercion." When careful with it we find, reasonably enough, that there are respects in which the prisoner is coerced and respects in which he is not—and, indeed, that the same is true of everyone. We need to identify carefully that sense of coercion employed when we say that coercion vitiates an apparently free consent. Then we must decide whether, when given an opportunity to volunteer as subject, the prisoner is coerced in that sense. We will find upon reflection, I think, that another sense of coercion—looser and more suggestive, characterizing the flavor of prison activity—has been drawn upon. To make the argument work a transition is made, perhaps inadvertently, from that broad sense of coercion to a tighter, narrower sense that bears directly upon freedom in making choices.

By "coercion" our common meaning is compulsion by physical or moral pressures. Thus A coerces B when B is compelled or constrained to act as A wishes him to, as a result of measures taken by A to effect just that result. The bandit coerces me, with his revolver, into handing over my wallet. The threat of criminal prosecution if I do not file an income tax return is a coercive instrument designed to constrain my behavior. We are tempted—and too many yield—to leap from this to calling coercive whatever restrains or limits or influences behavior. I may be coerced into giving to the United Fund, say, by the threat of discharge or defamation; but I am not coerced into charitable giving by my strong desire to be admired as a public benefactor. Again, if my wealth were unlimited I should sail the seas in splendor; my means being what they are, I cast an admiring glance at every ocean racing yacht, and go on splashing about in my little sailing dinghy. It is an elastic use of English to say I am coerced into doing so. There are, too, desires of the utmost intensity which influence my conduct and with which I must come to terms. But these desires are not imposed (unless one holds a satanic view of the human condition) in order to bend my volition; they are the normal matrix of my life. It is facile or confused to suppose that I am coerced by my own wants. Even my most passionate wants, my sexual desires, cannot be said to coerce me into seduction.

We sometimes think powerful inducements, as well as threats, to be coercive. Sometimes they may be, but only when the subject in question is caused, by an extraordinary and deliberate temptation, to do what should not ever be done. If a poor person is tempted by a huge sum to accept a risk we think it not proper to urge upon anyone, the offer is there coercive. But if the reward be for conduct that is itself reasonable, the fact that one's condition renders that reward exceptionally attractive does not show that coercion has been applied. Professional football players are not coerced by huge salaries into risking their necks, nor are workers coerced into work by their need for earnings.

A definitive account of coercion I do not seek to provide here. No doubt any account, however refined, will leave some rough edges. But moderately thoughtful reflection will show, I believe, that the coercion that full consent precludes is the coercion flowing from the deliberate effort on the part of one who offers the choice (or his agent) to pressure the offeree into a particular decision. The pressure must be such that the offerer could have refrained from exerting it, but deliberately did not refrain.

If I seek admission to a research hospital specializing, say, in eye disease, desperate about my failing sight, and I am admitted upon the condition that I put myself at serious risk in an experiment having nothing to do with my condition, I have indeed been coerced improperly. Even in matters involving minor risks, if I am subjected to a moral barrage regarding the social value of medical research and the importance of the experiment at hand to all mankind, when asked for my consent to serve as subject, I am coerced, if mildly, by the deliberate pressures of the investigator. We do not permit such distortions of potential subjects' volitions, rightly. But if I suffer from a serious disease for which cure is unknown, it is quite reasonable that I should find serving as subject, in an experiment aimed at enlarging knowledge about that disease, attractive in a way that one who does not suffer from that disease does not find attractive. My diseased condition does not coerce me. Or if one insists upon the lingo in which such sickness inevitably renders me "coerced," then certainly that so-called coercion could not begin to establish that my freely expressed consent was really involuntary.

Our lives are led, and our decisions made, within a network of needs and wants, some natural, some arising from the acts of others, some aggravated by the acts of the state. We are all bored, or threatened, or tantalized in differing degrees by a perilous world, some hostile people, and a not very sensitive government. Sometimes, within that framework, we are coerced by the design of persons or institutions into choosing *X* rather than *Y*. Such design, introduced in order to manipulate our choosing, is the coercion here chiefly of concern to us. The Nuremberg code, in defining voluntary consent, puts the matter well. It insists that the person involved must in his situation be able to exercise free power of choice "without the intervention of any element of force, fraud, deceit, duress, over-reaching, or other ulterior form of constraint or coercion. . . .

Let us now apply this view of coercion to the case of the prisoner giving informed consent to serve as medical subject. The opportunity is given him, let us suppose, to respond by letter to a notice on a bulletin board, after which, if he proves a suitable subject, he is given full information about procedures, risks, pay, and the rest by a research investigator. Is he coerced into giving consent by the fact of his imprisonment? On reflection I think we will see that he is not.

The question is not, "Are prisoners coerced?"—for we agree that, in general, theirs is a condition in which many more choices are foreclosed, and decisions compelled, than in conditions of ordinary life. But the pervasive presence of restraints in the prison leaves open the question of whether, with respect to a particular option put before him, he is coerced. He has a chance, say, to participate as subject in a set of drug tests, requiring intermittent hospital visits, small to moderate risks, occasional days of complete bed rest, and paying $20 per month for the 6 months of the tests. Most experiments using human subjects involve less time, less money, and less risk. Some involve more. Take this one as a realistic illustration.

It is true that his participation may promise occasional release from boredom. Boredom, however, is not a condition over which the investigator has any control, or in which he has any interest. It is simply the condition that the potential prisoner-subjects (as well as a good many nonprisoner-subjects) were in when the choice of participating or not was encountered by them. They are no more coerced into consenting by their boredom than I am coerced into seducing by my lust. The conditions in which we find ourselves powerfully affect our responses to choices put before us. If the standard of noncoercion be that potential subjects be free of all conditions that may significantly influence their willingness to consent, we will have no subjects and no experiments.

"But," the critic may reply, "although we are, indeed, all in conditions that constrain us in some respects, there remain enormous differences of degree. The prisoner's conditions are unusually severe, and that severity is what we underscore. When, for example, he supposes that giving his consent may help him, somehow, achieve an earlier release, he is in the special condition of desperately wanting release, and blindly hoping that someone up there will be more moved to help him because he did consent. That is what is unusual about his condition."

This reply will not work; it does not serve to distinguish the prisoner's case from the case of others whom we do not regard as improperly coerced. It is not only prisoners who have desperate desires that they hope may come nearer to fulfillment because of participation in experiment. Indeed, while the prisoner's hopes along that line may be tenuous and largely the result of his own wishful thinking, many nonprisoners are faced with the opportunity to participate in experiments involving considerable risk, which offer more serious hope of fulfilling desperate wants. Consider the person with psoriasis covering much of his body, given the opportunity to participate in an experiment using a new and very powerful ultraviolet light that may increase the likelihood of his developing cancer and may injure his eyes. No pressure whatever is brought to bear on him by the researcher. But he or she must feel very great pressures from the intense longing to be rid of that disfiguring affliction. Is that potential subject coerced by virtue of the desperation of his desire? Not in any sense that precludes his consent, surely; and if we thought he and others like him were truly coerced, we should have to forbid the experiment. Again, it is not rare for persons suffering from what appear to be terminal cancers to be offered the opportunity to participate in a controlled experiment with a new, highly toxic, chemical therapy that offers only slight hope of remission. All else has failed. Will the patient give consent to be experimental subject? Very probably; he reaches for every chance to live. Is he coerced into being a guinea pig by the intensity of his desire? Not if the facts are presented to him truly and fairly. Indeed, we are likely to think that, though the new chemotherapy may have dreadful side effects, he is entitled, after being fully informed of the facts, to make up his own mind and, if given his circumstances he thinks it worth the risks, to consent to the desperate try.

If the researcher in this latter case had portrayed the patient's condition more grimly than the facts warranted, in order to get him to consent, we would think the patient to have been coerced, not by the intensity of his desire to live, but by that deceptive account. If the researcher had refrained deliberately from telling the patient of some alternative therapy offering equal hopes, in order to woo his participation, the patient would have been coerced, not by his needs or their grip on him, but by the manipulation of the investigator. Analogously, it is not the degree of boredom, or the passion of the desire for release, or the level of any condition that the prisoner is in, that can coerce him. It is only deliberate conduct, conduct designed to deceive, to pressure, to constrain, that would coerce in the sense required. Therefore the boredom, the desire for early release, the being under constant guard—these cannot in themselves constitute coercion of a potential subject.

The critic may take another tack. "I see now [he may say] that it is not the intensity of desire that marks off the prisoner's case, or renders him coerced. Yet the precariousness of his condition is the key to the immorality I've been driving at. It is the deliberate choosing of prison populations to do experiments we would not do with others, taking advantage of their desperation, that is coercive. This, I now see, is the root of my complaint. By using prisoners the researcher gets away with an exploitation of subjects that would be impossible elsewhere—and that calculated exploitation must not be allowed."

Here the critic gives a caution that deserves to be taken seriously; but its scope must not be overblown. If we do on prisoners experiments we would not do on others, believing that for ordinary persons the risks clearly outweigh the potential benefits, the calculated choice of a precariously placed population enabling us to get away with that would, indeed, be wrongful. What troubles so about it, however, is that experiments would then be done which ought not be done at all. In the same way, where great risk far outweighs potential benefit we would not tolerate huge sums used to inveigle the participation of indigent welfare recipients. To do with some, because we can get away with it, what we ought to do with no one is surely unconscionable. Some experiments in prisons, in the past, have been like that.

But this argument does not have the general force its advocates may suppose. When, for example, subject populations are enlisted both in and out of prisons on the same terms—as is often done—this objection has no place. When the judgment of experimental justifiability is made independently of the special circumstances of possible subject pools, an improper reliance upon those special circumstances cannot be complained of.

Moreover, the special circumstances of subjects may rightly enter when the experiment is of a kind that requires just that kind of subject for scientific reasons. Persons suffering from a given disease are reasonably chosen for experiments dealing with that disease, obviously, and any inclination they have to serve as subjects arising from that circumstance is neither avoidable nor pernicious. Again, some experiments have special requirements for long-term regularity and control, calling for subjects in unusually restricted circumstances. Seeking out those who fit the requirements of the investigation—an investigation whose worthiness is independently established—is equally reasonable, and no less so if those subjects be prisoners. It is a fact that for some scientific purposes prisoners are irreplaceable as subjects. Prisoners constitute extraordinarily stable populations, under constant and detailed observation. Diet, activity, whereabouts, and other factors possibly critical to the experiment are thoroughly known and dependable. And all of this is the case not as an imposed demand of the investigator, but as a consequence of the incarceration with which he had nothing to do. For experiments requiring repeated trials, over long periods, rigorously free of perturbing variables, there are no populations like these. One can imagine the sequestering of a nonprison subject pool for months or years, but there is no practical likelihood of it. Very few other persons, identifiable and accessible, are so situated that the time they must devote as subjects to lengthy experiments does not impose heavy burdens in removing them from what would be their alternate activities. The short of it is that, for reasons having nothing to do with manipulative intent but everything to do with scientific reliability, prison populations serve medicine as no other populations can. The critic rightly insists that prisoners should not be preyed upon, that we must not do in prisons what should not be done. This is a long way from showing that no experiments ought be conducted in prisons, or that prisoners ought not be allowed to volunteer as subjects.

What shall we say of payment to prisoners? That, after all, clearly is a factor under the researcher's full control. Moderate remuneration, of course, is widely given to subjects, in and out of prison. Insofar as those sums are deliberately offered to allure and tempt they are, in every case, manipulative. And of course their manipulative force is the greater as the potential subject is the poorer. This argues against payment to subjects in any context, and I think that is an alternative worthy of serious consideration. On the other hand, the prospect of a small money reward (which does serve as a major motivating force in prisons) neither threatens nor pressures nor tempts to do what should not be done. The very moderate sums involved—$20 or $40 or so—are also viewed by many not so much as lures as compensation for inconvenience. Some who would be pleased to volunteer cannot otherwise afford the time. In that spirit the sums involved do not coerce anyone. We ought no more permit large sums to tempt prisoners into undue hazards than we ought permit that among nonprisoners. Neither should we withhold from prisoners the minor compensations that serving as subject normally provides. One principle we surely wish to maintain is that prisoners not be in any way special targets for exploitation, and their not being special targets entails their being treated, in the matter of payment, just as nonprisoners are treated. They should be paid no more, no less.

How "more" or "less" ought to be calculated is a nice question. Is it equality of the absolute sum that is required? Or is it the same relative proportion of regular income that is called for? This is arguable. In my judgment it is the same dollar sum that should be used, both to be fair and to avoid the appearance of unfairness. The sums are in any event small; and adjusting them relatively entails the supposition of an "average regular income" of nonprisoner-subjects that must be wholly arbitrary.

It should be seen that even these small sums will be more alluring to prisoners than to most nonprisoners. If the payment be set at a regular standard, however, its allure is not the result of any deliberate effort by the researcher to twist the volition of the prisoner. Such twisting would be coercive. Given reasonable restrictions that twisting can be avoided in the case of prisoners as it is in the case of nonprisoners.

I conclude that the argument against permitting prisoners to choose in this sphere, by virtue of their necessarily coerced condition, is simply mistaken. It confuses a wide sense of constraint (rightly characterizing the prison environment) with a different, narrow sense of constraint in the decision at hand—of which the prisoner can, with care, be entirely free. In the sense that one's condition coerces him, we are all coerced, and many of us as severely or more severely than prisoners. In the sense that choices before us, given our condition, may be made by us without ulterior manipulation in view of the merits of the case, the prisoner can, if fairly treated, be as free to choose as the rest of us. . . .

1 The report and recommendations of the National Commission for the Protection of Human Subjects of Biomedical and Behavioral Research (*Research Involving Prisoners* [Washington, D.C., 1976]) is an important example.

● ● ●

POSTSCRIPT

SHOULD PRISONERS BE BARRED FROM VOLUNTEERING FOR RESEARCH?

The National Commission's recommendations did not settle the issue. Final regulations issued in 1978 by DHEW and the Food and Drug Administration omitted most of the very stringent standards and simply banned research in federal prisons, unless it was related to the health and well-being of particular individuals or to conditions affecting prisoners as a class. Several states followed suit. But in the spring of 1981 four prisoners at Jackson State Prison—joined by the Upjohn Company, which maintains a research unit at the prison—filed a lawsuit contending that the ban denied them their constitutional right to choose to participate in research. Instead of arguing its case in court, the FDA withdrew its regulations and in December 1981 proposed new ones, which provide that research not relevant to the well-being of prisoners either as individuals or as a class can be permitted only for "compelling" reasons. The debate will now undoubtedly focus on what, if any, circumstances can be called "compelling."

Meanwhile, all except two major drug companies have been discouraged by the erratic state of regulation and have taken their drug testing out of prisons and into the "free-living" population—primarily their own employees.

For a summary of all the arguments, see Robert J. Levine, *Ethics and Regulation of Clinical Research* (Urban & Schwarzenberg, 1981), Chapter 11. Jessica Mitford's book *Kind and Usual Punishment* (Random House, 1974) was an influential exposé of abuses in prison research. Two positive views of research from a current and former prisoner are: Daniel E. Travitzky, "Volunteering at Vacaville" and Frank Hatfield, "Prison Research: The View from Inside," *Hastings Center Report* (February 1977).

ISSUE 14

SHOULD ANIMAL EXPERIMENTATION BE STOPPED?

YES: Peter Singer, from "Tools for Research, or What the Public Doesn't Know It Is Paying For," *Animal Liberation* (New York: The New York Review, 1975)

NO: Maurice B. Visscher, from "The Ethics of the Use of Lower Animals in Scientific Study," *Ethical Constraints and Imperatives in Medical Research* (Springfield, Ill.: Charles C. Thomas Publisher, 1975)

ISSUE SUMMARY

YES: Philosopher Peter Singer claims that much experimentation involving animals is brutal and serves no direct or urgent purpose for the benefit of humans and that alternative scientific methods can be used to achieve the same knowledge.

NO: The late philosopher and physician Maurice B. Visscher holds that man, by virtue of his superior capacity for rational thinking, has the opportunity to mold his environment and that it is totally impossible to advance scientific knowledge about the control or cure of disease without the use of living animals as research subjects.

In 1865 the great French physiologist Claude Bernard wrote: "Physicians already make too many dangerous experiments on man before carefully studying them in animals." In his insistence on adequate animal research before trying a new therapy on human beings, Bernard established a principle of research ethics that is still considered valid. But in the past few decades this principle has been challenged by another view—one that sees animals not as tools for human use and consumption but as moral agents in their own right. Animal experimentation, according to this theory, cannot be taken for granted but must be justified by ethical criteria at least as stringent as those that apply to research involving humans.

Philosophers traditionally have not ascribed any moral status to animals. Like St. Thomas Aquinas before him, Rene Descartes, a seventeenth-century

French physiologist and philosopher, saw no ethical problem in experimentation on animals. Descartes approved of cutting open a fully conscious animal because it was, he said, a machine more complex than a clock but no more capable of feeling pain. Immanuel Kant argued that animals need not be treated as ends in themselves because they lacked rationality.

Beginning in England in the nineteenth century, "anti-vivisectionists" or people who advocated the abolition of animal experimentation campaigned, with varying success, for laws to control scientific research. But the internal dissensions in the movement and its frequent lapses into sentimentality made it only partially effective. At most the vivisectionists achieved some legislation that mandated more humane treatment of animals used for research, but they never succeeded in abolishing the research (in fact such experimentation increased enormously in recent years) or even in establishing the need for justification of particular research projects.

The more recent movement to ban animal research, however, is both better organized politically and rests on a more rigorous philosophical basis. The movement, often called "animal liberation" or "animal rights," is similar in principle to the civil rights movement of the 1960s. Just as blacks, women, and other minorities sought recognition of their equal status, animal advocates have built a case for the equal status of animals.

Peter Singer, one of the leaders of this movement, has presented an eloquent case that we not only practice racism and sexism in our society—we practice "speciesism." That is, we assume that human beings are superior to other animals; we are prejudiced in favor of our own kind. Experimenting on animals and eating their flesh are the two major forms of speciesism in our society. Singer points out that some categories of human beings—infants and mentally retarded people—rate lower on a scale of intelligence, awareness, and self-consciousness than some animals. Yet we would not treat these individuals in the way we do animals. He argues that "all animals are equal" and the suffering of an animal is morally equal to the suffering of a human being.

Proponents of animal research counter that such views are fundamentally misguided, that human beings, with the capacity for rational thought and action, are indeed a superior species. They contend that, while animals deserve humane treatment, the good consequences of animal research (i.e., knowledge that will benefit human beings) outweigh the suffering of individual animals. No other research techniques can substitute for the reactions of live animals, they declare.

The following exerpt from Peter Singer's book *Animal Liberation* presents a gripping recital of actual animal experiments. Singer uses these examples to bolster his claim that such experimentation is unnecessary for scientific reasons and ought to be stopped. Maurice B. Visscher, on the other hand, argues that the "reverence for life" espoused by people such as Albert Schweitzer has been taken to unjustifiable extremes. We need animal research, he says, because it will benefit human beings.

YES

Peter Singer

TOOLS FOR RESEARCH . . .
OR WHAT THE PUBLIC DOESN'T KNOW IT IS PAYING FOR

In July 1973 Congressman Les Aspin of Wisconsin learned through an advertisement in an obscure newspaper that the United States Air Force was planning to purchase 200 beagle puppies, with vocal chords tied to prevent normal barking, for tests of poisonous gases. Shortly afterward it became known that the army was also proposing to use beagles—400 this time—in similar tests.

Aspin began a vigorous protest, supported by antivivisection societies. Advertisements were placed in major newspapers across the country. Letters from an outraged public began pouring in. An aide from the House of Representatives Armed Services Committee said that the committee received more mail on the beagles than it had received on any other subject since Truman sacked General MacArthur, while an internal Department of Defense memo released by Aspin said that the volume of mail the department had received was the greatest ever for any single event, surpassing even the mail on the bombings of North Vietnam and Cambodia.[1] After defending the experiments initially, the Defense Department then announced that it was postponing them, and looking into the possibility of replacing the beagles with other experimental animals.

All this amounted to a rather curious incident; curious because the public furor over this particular experiment implied a remarkable ignorance of the nature of quite standard experiments performed by the armed services, research establishments, universities, and commercial firms of many different kinds. True, the proposed air force and army experiments were designed so that many animals would suffer and die without any certainty that this suffering and death would save a single human life, or benefit humans in any way at all; but the same can be said for tens of thousands of other experiments performed in the United States alone each year. For instance, limiting ourselves for the moment just to experiments done on beagles, the following should, one might think, have provoked as much protest as those planned by the air force and the army:

> At the Lovelace Foundation, Albuquerque, New Mexico, experimenters forced sixty-four beagles to inhale radioactive strontium 90 as part of a larger "Fission Product Inhalation Program" which began in 1961 and has been paid for by the US Atomic Energy Commission. In this particular experiment twenty-five of the dogs eventually died. One of the deaths occurred during an epileptic seizure; another from a brain hemorrhage. Other dogs, before death, became feverish and anemic, lost their appetites, had hemorrhages and bloody diarrhea.
>
> The experiments, in their published report, compared their results with the results of other experiments at the University of Utah and at Argonne National Laboratory, in Illinois, in which beagles were injected with strontium 90. They concluded that the various experiments had led to similar results on the dose of strontium 90 needed to produce "early deaths" in 50 percent of a sample group of beagles, but that there was a difference in the number of deaths occurring later, because dogs injected with strontium 90 retain more of the radioactive substance than dogs forced to inhale it.[2]

> At the University of Rochester School of Medicine a team of experimenters placed fifty beagles in wooden boxes and irradiated them with different levels of radiation by X-rays. Twenty-one of the dogs died between the ninth and thirty-ninth day after irradiation. The experimenters determined the dose at which 50 percent of the animals will die with "95 percent confidence." The irradiated dogs vomited, had diarrhea, and lost their appetites. Later they hemorrhaged from the mouth and the anus. In their report these experimenters summarized nine other experiments in which more than 700 beagles and other dogs were irradiated with X-rays, and they said that the injuries produced in their own experiments were "typical of those described for the dog."[3]
>
> Experimenters working for the US Food and Drug Administration gave thirty beagles and thirty pigs large amounts of methoxychlor (a pesticide) in their food, seven days a week for six months, "in order to ensure tissue damage." Within eight weeks, eleven dogs showed signs of "abnormal behavior" including nervousness, salivation, muscle tremors, spasms, and convulsions. Dogs in convulsions breathed as rapidly as 200 times a minute before lack of oxygen caused them to collapse. Upon recovery from an episode of convulsion and collapse, the dogs were uncoordinated, apparently blind, and "any stimulus such as dropping a feed pan, squirting water, or touching the animals initiated another convulsion." After further experiments on an additional twenty beagles, the experimenters concluded that massive daily doses of methoxychlor produce different effects in dogs from those produced in pigs.[4]

These three examples should be enough to show that the air force beagle experiments were in no way exceptional. Note that all of these experiments, according to the experimenters' own reports, obviously caused the animals to suffer considerably before dying. No steps were taken to prevent this suffering, even when it was clear that the radiation or poison had made the animals extremely sick. Note, too, that these experiments are parts of series of similar experiments, repeated with only minor variations, that are being carried out all over the country. Note, finally, that these experiments do not save human lives. We already knew that strontium 90 was unhealthy before the beagles died; and the experimenters who poisoned dogs and pigs with methoxychlor knew beforehand that the large amounts they were feeding the animals (amounts no human would ever consume) would cause damage. In any case, as the differing results they obtained on dogs and pigs make clear, it is not possible to reach any firm conclusions about the effects of a substance on humans from tests on other species. The same is true of radioactive substances, and so the precision with which experimenters determine the dose necessary to make 50 percent of a sample group of beagles die has no application to humans.

Nor should we limit ourselves to dogs. People tend to care about dogs because they have dogs as pets; but other animals are as capable of suffering as dogs are. Dogs are only one species of many that are used in experiments. In Britain sentimental attachment to dogs and cats has gone so far that the law regulating experiments on animals requires an experimenter to obtain a special certificate for performing an experiment on unanesthetized dogs and cats; apes and monkeys, however, receive no such protection; nor, of course, does the common laboratory rate. Few people feel sympathy for rats. Yet the laboratory rat is an intelligent, gentle animal, the result of many generations of special breeding, and there can be no doubt that the rats are capable of suffering, and do suffer from the countless painful experiments performed on them.

The practice of experimenting on nonhuman animals as it exists today throughout the world reveals the brutal consequences of speciesism. Experiments are performed on animals that inflict severe pain without the remotest prospect of significant benefits for humans or any other animals. These are not isolated instances, but part of a major industry. In Britain, where experimenters are required to report the number of experiments performed, official government figures show that around 5 million experiments on animals are now performed each year. In the United States there are no figures of comparable accuracy....

An official of the US Department of Agriculture has stated that the number of rats and mice used annually for research purposes is estimated at 40 million.[5] In testimony before congressional committees in 1966, the Laboratory Animal Breeders Association estimated that the number of mice, rats, guinea pigs, hamsters, and rabbits used for experimental purposes in 1965 had totaled around 60 million; and they projected a figure of 97 million for these species by 1970. They estimated the number of dogs and cats used in 1965 as between 500,000 and 1 million.[6] A 1971 survey carried out by Rutgers University College of Agriculture and Environmental Sciences produced the following estimates of the number of animals used each year in U.S. laboratories: 85,000 primates, 500,000 dogs, 200,000 cats, 700,000 rabbits, 46,000 pigs, 23,000 sheep, 1.7 million birds, 45 million rodents, 15-20 million frogs, and 200,000 turtles, snakes, and lizards; a total of more than 63 million animals.[7]

These estimates are somewhat lower than the Laboratory Animal Breeders Association estimates for the species included in their survey for 1965; and much lower than their projections for 1970. These projections may, of course, have been over-optimistic expectations about the continued growth of the animal breeding industry, which had grown phenomenally in preceding years. Assuming then that the Rutgers University figures are a reasonable, and certainly not exaggerated, estimate, it is still clear that the official Animal Welfare Act report covers only a very small fraction of the animals experimented upon in the United States.

Of this vast number of experiments, only a few contribute to important medical research. Huge numbers of animals are used in university departments from Forestry to Psychology, and many more are used for commercial purposes, to test new cosmetics, shampoos, food coloring agents and other inessential items. All this can go on only because of our prejudice against taking seriously the suffering of a being that is not a member of our own species. The typical defender of experiments on animals does not deny that animals suffer. He cannot use this argument because he needs to stress the similarities between humans and other animals in order to claim that his experiment may have some relevance for human purposes. The researcher who forces rats to choose between starvation and electric shock to see if they develop ulcers (they do) does so because he knows that the rat has a nervous system very similar to man's, and presumably feels an electric shock in a similar way.

There has been opposition to experimenting on animals for a long time. This opposition has made little headway because experimenters, backed by commercial firms who profit by supplying laboratory animals and equipment, have been able to convince legislators and the public that opposition comes from sentimental cranks who consider the interests of animals more important than the interests of human beings. But to be opposed to what is going on now it is not necessary to insist that all experiments stop immediately. All that we need to say is that experiments serving no direct and urgent purpose should stop immediately, and in the remaining areas of research, methods involving animals should be replaced as soon as possible by alternative methods not involving animals. . . .

In Britain almost 100 new cosmetics and toiletries come onto the market every *week*, and it has been estimated that up to a million animals die annually in research connected with cosmetics alone.[8] The figure for the United States is not known, but could well be much higher. To this must be added the enormous numbers of animals used to test inessential foodstuffs—new coloring agents, new sweeteners or other flavoring agents, new preservatives, and so on. Any company that wants permission to market such a new substance must lodge with the Food and Drug Administration evidence of the product's safety. This evidence consists of a thick file full of reports of the experimental poisoning of animals.

It is not only products intended for consumption that are tested. All kinds of industrial and household goods are fed to animals and tested on their eyes. A reference book, *Clinical Toxicology of Commercial Products*, provides data, mostly from animal experiments, on how poisonous hundreds of commercial products are. The products include: insecticides, antifreeze, brake fluids, bleaches, Christmas-tree sprays, church candles, oven-cleaners, deodorants, skin fresheners, bubble baths, depilatories, eye make-up, fire extinguishers, inks, suntan oils, nail polish, mascara, hair sprays, paints, and zipper lubricants.[9]

Whenever the testing on animals of products intended for human use is criticized, someone brings up the tragic "thalidomide babies" in support of the claim that thorough testing is needed to protect the general public. This example is worth investigating. The lesson to be learned from it is not what most people expect.

The first thing to remember is that thalidomide was not an essential, life-saving substance. It was a new kind of sleeping tablet, and while sleeping tablets may be more important than cosmetics, the animal suffering involved in testing a substance is in any case a high price to pay for the avoidance of sleeplessness. So doing without animal testing would not mean releasing substances like thalidomide untested; it would mean doing without it, and trying to become less dependent on drugs.

Second, and more important, is the fact that thalidomide *was* extensively tested on animals before it was released. These tests failed to show any abnormalities. Indeed, as the editor of a recent book on toxicology has stated: "the toxicity tests that had been carefully carried out on thalidomide without exception had demonstrated it to be an almost uniquely safe compound."[10] Even after the drug was suspected of causing deformities in human babies, tests on pregnant laboratory dogs, cats, rats, monkeys, hamsters, and chickens all failed to produce deformities. Only when a particular strain of rabbit was tried were deformities produced.[11]

The thalidomide story underlines something that toxicologists have known for a long time: species vary. Extrapolation from one species to another is a highly risky venture. Thalidomide is harmless to most animals. Insulin, on the other hand, can produce deformities in infant rabbits and mice, but not in humans.[12] And as another toxicologist has said: "If penicillin had been judged by its toxicity on guinea pigs it might never have been used on man."[13]

What we should learn from thalidomide, then, is not that animal testing is necessary, but that it is unreliable; not that we need to poison more animals, but that we need to find alternative methods of testing, and until then we should make do without new nonessential drugs.

When experiments can be brought under the heading "medical" we are inclined to think that any suffering they involve must be justifiable because the research is contributing to the alleviation of suffering. But the general label "medical research" can be used to cover research which is not directed toward the reduction of suffering, but is motivated by a general goalless curiosity that may be acceptable as part of a basic search for knowledge when it involves no suffering, but should not be tolerated if it causes pain. Very often this research has been going on for decades and much of it, in the long run, turns out to have been quite pointless. . . .

How can these things happen? How can a man who is not a sadist spend his working day heating an unanesthetized dog to death, or driving a monkey into a lifelong depression, and then remove his white coat, wash his hands, and go home to dinner with his wife and children? How can taxpayers allow their money to be used to support experiments of this kind? And how can students go through a turbulent era of protest against injustice, discrimination, and oppression of all kinds, no matter how far from home, while ignoring the cruelties that are being carried out on their own campuses?

The answers to these questions stem from the unquestioned acceptance of speciesism. We tolerate cruelties inflicted on members of other species that would outrage us if performed on members of our own species. Speciesism allows researchers to regard the animals they experiment on as items of equipment, laboratory tools rather than living, suffering creatures. Sometimes they even refer to the animals in this way. Robert White of the Cleveland Metropolitan General Hospital, who has performed numerous experiments involving the transplanting of heads of monkeys, and the keeping alive of monkey brains in fluid, outside the body, has said in an interview that:

> Our main purpose here is to offer a living laboratory tool: a monkey "model" in which and by which we can design new operative techniques for the brain.

And the reporter who conducted the interview and observed White's experiments found his experience

> a rare and chilling glimpse into the cold, clinical world of the scientist, where the life of an animal has no meaning beyond the immediate purpose of experimentation.[14]

This "scientific" attitude to animals was exhibited to a large audience in December 1974 when the American public television network brought together Harvard philosopher Robert Nozick and three scientists whose work involves animals. The program was a follow-up to Fred Wiseman's controversial film *Primate,* which had taken viewers inside the Yerkes Primate Center, a research center in Atlanta, Georgia. Nozick asked the scientists whether the fact that an experiment will kill hundreds of animals is ever regarded, by scientists, as a reason for not performing it. One of the scientists answered: "Not that I know of." Nozick pressed his question: "Don't the animals count at all?" Dr. A. Perachio, of the Yerkes Center, replied: "Why should they?" while Dr. D. Baltimore, of the Massachusetts Institute of Technology, added that he did not think that experimenting on animals raised a moral issue at all.[15]

As well as the general attitude of speciesism which researchers share with other citizens there are some special factors operating to make possible the experiments I have described. Foremost among these is the immense respect that we still have for scientists. Although the advent of nuclear weapons and environmental pollution have made us realize that science and technology need to be controlled to some extent, we still tend to be in awe of anyone who wears a white coat and has a PhD. In a well known series of experiments Stanley Milgram, a Harvard psychologist, has demonstrated that ordinary people will obey the directions of a white-coated research worker to administer what appears to be (but in fact is not) electric shock to a human subject as "punishment" for failing to answer questions correctly; and they will continue to do this even when the human subject cries out and pretends to be in great pain.[16] If this can happen when the participant believes he is inflicting pain on a human, how much easier is it for a student to push aside his initial qualms when his professor instructs him to perform experiments on animals? What Alice Heim has rightly called the "indoctrination" of the student is a gradual process, beginning with the dissection of frogs in school biology classes. When the budding medical student, or psychology student, or veterinarian, reaches the university and finds that to complete the course of studies on which he has set his heart he must experiment on living animals, it is difficult for him to refuse to do so, especially since he knows that what he is being asked to do is standard practice in the field.

Individual students will often admit feeling uneasy about what they are asked to do, but public protests are very rare. An organized protest did occur in Britain recently, however, when students at the Welsh National School of Medicine in Cardiff complained publicly that a dog was unnecessarily injected with drugs more than 30 times to demonstrate a point during a lecture. The dog was then killed. One student said: "We learned nothing new. It could all have been looked up in textbooks. A film could be made so that only one dog dies and all this unnecessary suffering is stopped."[17] The student's comment was true; but such things happen routinely in every medical school. Why are protests so rare?

The pressure to conform does not let up when the student receives his degree. If he goes on to a graduate degree in fields in which experiments on animals are usual, he will be encouraged to devise his own experiments and write them up for his PhD dissertation.... Naturally, if this is how students are educated they will tend to continue in the same manner when they become professors, and they will, in turn, train their own students in the same manner.

It is not always easy for people outside the universities to understand the rationale for the research carried out under university auspices. Originally, perhaps, scholars and researchers just set out to solve the most important problems and did not allow themselves to be influenced by other considerations. Perhaps some are still motivated by these concerns. Too often, though, academic research gets bogged down in petty and insignificant details because the big questions have been studied already, and have either been solved or proven too difficult. So the researcher turns away from the well-ploughed fertile fields in search of virgin territory where whatever he learns will be new, although the connection with a major problem may be more remote....

To return to the question of when an experiment might be justifiable. It will not do to say: "Never!" In extreme circumstances, absolutist answers always break down. Torturing a human being is almost always wrong, but it is not absolutely wrong. If torture were the only way in which we could discover the location of a nuclear time bomb hidden in a New York City basement, then torture would be justifiable. Similarly, if a single experiment could cure a major disease, that experiment would be justifiable. But in actual life the benefits are always much, much more remote, and more often than not they are nonexistent. So how do we decide when an experiment is justifiable?

We have seen that the experimenter reveals a bias in favor of his own species whenever he carries out an experiment on a nonhuman for a purpose that he would not think justified him in using a human being, even a retarded human being. This principle gives us a guide toward an answer to our question. Since a speciesist bias, like a racist bias, is unjustifiable, an experiment cannot be justifiable unless the experiment is so important that the use of a retarded human being would also be justifiable.

This is not an absolutist principle. I do not believe that it could *never* be justifiable to experiment on a retarded human. If it really were possible to save many lives by an experiment that would take just one life, and there were *no other way* those lives could be saved, it might be right to do the experiment. But this would be an extremely rare case. Not one tenth of one percent of the experiments now being performed on animals would fall into this category. Certainly none of the experiments described in this chapter could pass this test....

NOTES

1 *Air Force Times*, 28 November 1973; *New York Times*, 14 November 1973.
2 From a paper by R. Maclellan, B. Boecher, and others in M. Goldman and L. Bustad, eds., *Biomedical Implications of Radio-Strontium Exposure*, Atomic Energy Commission Symposium, Series #25, CONF-710201 (April 1972). The source for the starting date of these experiments is *Laboratory Animal Care*, 20 (1) p. 61 (1970).
3 K. Woodward, S. Michaelson, T. Noonan, and J. Howland; *International Journal of Radiation Biology*, 12 (3) p. 265 (1967).
4 A. Tegeris, F. Earl, H. Smalley, and J. Curtis, *Archives of Environmental Health*, 13, p. 776 (1966).
5 Personal communication to the author, 8 October 1974.
6 Hearings before the Subcommittee on Livestock and Feed Grains of the Committee on Agriculture (US House of Representatives, 1966), p. 63.
7 *Christian Science Monitor*, 18 July 1973.
8 *Sunday Mirror* (London), 24 February 1974, p. 10.
9 M.N. Gleason et al., eds., *Clinical Toxicology of Commercial Products* (Baltimore: Williams and Wilkins, 1969).
10 S.F. Paget, ed., *Methods in Toxicology* (Blackwell Scientific Publications, 1970), p. 4.
11 Ibid., pp. 134-139.
12 Ibid., p. 132.
13 G.F. Somers, *Quantitative Method in Human Pharmacology and Therapeutics* (Elmsford, New York: Pergamon Press, 1959); quoted by Richard Ryder, *Victims of Science*, p. 153.
14 *Scope* (Durban, South Africa), 30 March 1973.
15 "The Price of Knowledge," broadcast in New York, 12 December 1974, WNET/13; transcript supplied courtesy WNET/13 and Henry Spira.
16 S. Milgram, *Obedience to Authority* (New York: Harper & Row, 1974). Incidentally, these experiments were widely criticized on ethical grounds because they involved human beings without their consent. It is indeed questionable whether Milgram should have deceived participants in his experiments as he did; but when we compare what was done to them with what is commonly done to nonhuman animals, we can appreciate the double standard with which critics of the experiment operate.
17 *South Wales Echo*, 21 January 1974.

● ● ●

NO

Maurice B. Visscher

THE ETHICS OF THE USE OF LOWER ANIMALS IN SCIENTIFIC STUDY

There is a minority of the human race who categorically deny the ethical propriety of the sacrifice of lower animal life under any conditions for the advancement of scientific knowledge. However, the numbers of these persons who call themselves antivivisectionists, and particularly their uncritical supporters, appear to be growing and consequently an analysis of the background of their positions seems to be essential. The analysis is also necessary today in view of the growing fraction of persons in the Western world who appear to have lost their bearings in ethical theory and practice.

In an earlier day in the Judeo-Christian world the authoritarian dogma that lower animals were created for the service of man provided an adequate justification for their use in scientific study. Today, however, for large segments of society the situation has changed. No documentation is needed to sustain the assertion that the authority of Judeo-Christian cosmology has lost much popular ground in the last several centuries, and opinions regarding the origin and the place of man and other animals in the universe have also changed. The explosion in scientific knowledge and particularly the popularization of crucial aspects of it in relation to both cosmology and the evolution of life on our planet have resulted in a major revolution in background thinking about literalism in interpretation of ancient stories about creation which were once accepted by most of the literates and illiterates alike in the Western World as authoritative and reliable accounts. Today, for example, after everyone with a television set has seen men walking on the moon, and with spaceships sending us information about the other planets in our solar system, it has become difficult or impossible for anyone with much logical capacity to believe that the planet Earth is the center of the universe. In connection with the origin of the human race, comparable great shifts in views have occurred. Even a quarter of a century ago, although the statistical facts about overall genetic inheritance were known, the genetic coding mechanism was still a mystery. Today it is difficult for anyone who puts trust in observation

From "The Ethics of the Use of Lower Animals in Scientific Study," by Maurice Visscher, in *Ethical Constraints and Imperatives in Medical Research.* Reprinted by permission of Charles C. Thomas, Publisher, Springfield, Illinois.

and logic to doubt that the same basic mechanisms which control human heredity were in operation billions of years ago in less elaborate form controlling morphogenesis in primitive organisms. The kinship of man with other forms of life can be doubted only by those who reject the methods of science as useful and ultimately reliable in unravelling the secrets of nature.

The superior place of the genus *Homo sapiens* in the hierarchy of living things has not been altered, however. Scientific study of man in comparison with other, presumably earlier, forms of animal life has shown that the mutations which produced a brain with a neocortex capable of verbal communication, projective and abstract logic and other attributes not found in other animals, provides a basis for a view which still puts man at the pinnacle of evolution of animal life on earth.

The problem of man today is how to survive healthily on this planet. It has been that problem in different forms and contexts since the first examples of the genus Homo appeared. But the problem today has a new dimension, introduced by the rise of science and technology. The greatest problems are perhaps those of how to feed and otherwise care for an exploding population, how to limit that population, and especially how to prevent the destruction of the human race, and perhaps all life on the planet, by thermonuclear war. But the prevention and cure of disease are also prime desiderata. Scientific study, including study of living lower animals has been and will be indispensible to human survival and happiness. Even to solve the problems of overpopulation, animal experimentation has been and still is of prime importance. Therefore, clarifying a consensus concerning the ethics of animal experimentation is an important issue.

Man has, by virtue of his superior capacity for abstract and projective logic, a chance to do something about molding his environment and controlling his own behavior in rational ways. He can consider what he ought to do. Ethics is obviously that aspect of mental activity which deals with what individuals and societies at large think that they ought to do.

What people think they ought to do depends, of course, on value systems. This is where controversy enters. A person who starts, as for example Albert Schweitzer[1] did, with a value system that begins by asserting the theoretical equivalence of value of all life, from the protista to man, and giving to the life of a mosquito or a daisy the same absolute value as to the life of a human, is bound to encounter a hard time in his logic. Schweitzer did. He spoke feelingly about never thoughtlessly crushing a flower or an earthworm, but he always ended up justifying the act of crushing countless plants and animals to meet a real human need, provided that one always cut a field of grain, for example, with a conscious sense of remorse that it had to be done. Likewise in his expressions about the sacrifice of lower animal life for medical research, he recognized the ethical propriety of such sacrifice but labored the need for conscious recognition that in each instance a judgment should be made. His exact words were, "Those who carry out scientific experiments with animals, in order to apply the knowledge gained to the alleviation of human ills, should never reassure themselves with the generality that their cruel acts serve a useful purpose. In each individual case they must ask themselves whether there is a real necessity for imposing such a sacrifice upon a living creature. They must try to reduce the suffering insofar as they are able."[2]

Schweitzer was a very complex personality who combined a broad philosophic grasp of the realities of the natural world with a rigid personal ethic which grew out of his contemplation of the consequences of the "universal will to live" ideas of earlier philosophers. Furthermore, he recognized the dilemma in which he found himself, as is evident when he wrote, "The world is a ghastly drama of will to live divided against itself. One existence makes its way at the cost of another; one destroys the other. One will to live merely exerts its will against the other, and has no knowledge of it. But in me the will to live has come to know about other wills to live. There is in it a yearning to arrive at unity with itself, to become universal."[3]

The philosophy of reverence for life became an overriding philosophic passion for Schweitzer in his later life, but his ideas about it began to appear as early as 1919. In a sermon he gave on February 23 of that year he expressed his conviction as to its great import for man while he detailed—with sorrow it would appear—the enormous gap between the facts of life in nature and his ideal. He said,

> Reverence for life and sympathy with other lives is of supreme importance for this world of ours. Nature knows no similar reverence for life. It produces life a thousandfold in the most meaningful way and destroys it a thousandfold in the most meaningless way. In every stage of life, right up to the level of man, terrible ignorance lies over all creatures. They have the will to live but no capacity for compassion toward other creatures. They cannot feel what happens inside others. They suffer but have no compassion. The great struggle for survival by which nature is maintained is in strange contradiction with itself. Creatures live at the expense of other creatures. Nature permits the most horrible cruelties to be committed. It impels insects by their instincts to bore holes into other insects, to lay their eggs in them so that maggots may grow there and live off the caterpillar, thus causing it a slow and painful death. Nature lets ants band together to attack poor little creatures and hound them to death. Look at the spider. How gruesome is the craft that nature taught it!
>
> Nature looks beautiful and marvelous when you view it from the outside. But when you read its pages like a book, it is horrible. And its cruelty is so senseless! The most precious form of life is sacrificed to the lowliest. A child breathes the germs of tuberculosis. He grows and flourishes but is destined to suffering and a premature death because these lowly creatures multiply in his vital organs. How often in Africa have I been overcome with horror when I examined the blood of a patient who was suffering from sleeping sickness. Why did this man, his face contorted in pain, have to sit in front of me, groaning, "Oh, my head, my head"? Why should he have to suffer night after night and die a wretched death? Because there, under the microscope were minute, pale corpuscles, one ten-thousandth of a millimeter long—not very many, sometimes such a very few that one had to look for hours to find them at all.[1]

Nevertheless Schweitzer was, in his way, a pragmatist. In another of his essays he wrote, "Proceeding along that way, I have led you to this conclusion: that rational processes, properly pursued, must lead to the true ethic.

"Another commentary: What of this ethic? Is it absolute?

"Kant defines absolute ethics as that which is not concerned with whether it can be achieved. The distinction is not one of *absolute* as opposed to *relative*, but *absolute* as distinct from *practicable* in the ethical field. An absolute ethic calls for the creating of perfection in this life. It cannot be completely achieved; but that fact does not really matter. In this sense, reverence for life is an absolute ethic. It does not lay down specific rules for each possible solution. It simply tells us that we are responsible for the lives about us. It does not set either maximum or minimum limits to what we must do."[4]

Schweitzer was a gentle soul, with an unfulfilled yearning for logical consistency, who devoted his great talents to a practical exemplification of a life of service to the less fortunate. But he did not, as some appear to believe, think that moral scruples should, for example, prevent an ethical person from sacrificing the lives of animals in scientific study. In fact, although he did not develop the theme himself, the reverence for life principle can easily lead one to the logical conclusion that one has a moral duty to sacrifice life, if necessary, in scientific study, in order that the conditions of life generally can be improved.

A more pragmatic and more rationally consistent philosopher, the late John Dewey, wrote a definitive essay in 1909 on "The Ethics of Animal Experimentation." It was prepared as a reasoned argument against then impending antivivisection legislation. He wrote,

> Scientific inquiry has been the chief instrumentality in bringing men from barbarism to civilization, from darkness to light, while it has incurred, at every step, determined opposition from the powers of ignorance, misunderstanding and jealousy. It is not so long ago, as years are reckoned, that a scientist in a physical or chemical laboratory was popularly regarded as a magician engaged in unlawful pursuits, or as in impious converse with evil spirits, about whom all sorts of detrimental stories were circulated and believed. Those days are gone. Generally speaking, the value of free scientific inquiry as an instrumentality of social progress and enlightenment is acknowledged. At the same time, it is still possible, by making irrelevant emotional appeals and obscuring the real issues to galvanize into life something of the old spirit of misunderstanding, envy and dread of science. The point at issue in the subjection of animal experimenters to special supervision and legislation is thus deeper than at first sight appears. In principle it involves the revival of the animosity to discovery and to the application to life of the fruits of discovery which, upon the whole, has been the chief foe of human progress, it behooves every thoughtful individual to be constantly on the alert against every revival of this spirit, in whatever guise it presents itself.[5]

Modern antivivisectionists have attempted to wrap the hallowed robes of Albert Schweitzer around themselves. They have taken his "reverence for life" philosophy out of context and are using it to justify new attacks upon animal experimentation. Recently a collection of essays edited by Stanley and Roslind Godlovitch and John Harris[6] has brought together the views of some British philosophers, novelists and humane society activists, along with one botanist, all of whom develop one or another aspect of the theme that the sacrifice of sentient animal life in biological, and particularly medical research is of very questionable ethical propriety. Their points of view can be summarized, as the philosopher Patrick Corbett did in the postscript to the volume, as follows: "Our conviction, for reasons we have given, is that *we* require *now* to extend the great principles of liberty, equality and fraternity over the lives of animals. Let animal slavery join human slavery in the graveyard of the past!" These viewpoints are not unique to the British. Catherine Roberts,[7] an American biologist, published in 1971 in the

American Scholar, the organ of the United Chapters of Phi Beta Kappa, a long article defending the viewpoint that the taking of life from any sentient lower animal should be abhorrent to the scheme of morality of any decent person. She said,

> Evolving life can therefore no longer tolerate the biological injustice of inflicting agony upon animals to ameliorate and prolong the physical existence of human lives. Brief respites from suffering and death made possible by the ruthlessness of scientists against lower life contribute nothing whatever to the spiritual ascent of mankind. Evolving life has need instead of gentle souls like Saint Francis and Gandhi to show us how to come together to live lives of nonviolence, in joy and peace with the whole of sentient creation. For the meek, strengthened and made wise in their decisions by divine sanction and their spiritual heritage, *shall* inherit the earth. The choice to abolish the sentient laboratory animal is an evolutionary inevitability and a moral imperative.

The range of the positions of the newer antivivisectionists is from advocacy of regulations which would put the onus of responsibility for proof upon the scientist in each case that important needed new knowledge could not be obtained by the use of cell or tissue cultures, or computers, or more sophisticated mathematics, to outright prohibition of the use of animals. Common sense appears to be a scarce commodity among activist opponents of the use of animals in scientific research. The generally omnivorous human race sacrifices the lives of many billions of animals yearly for food, not to mention fur, leather and feathers. In 1973 in the U.S. alone, 2.5 billion chickens were killed for food. Hundreds of millions of other species were also used for human food. There are, of course, some antivivisectionists who do not eat meat, fish or fowl, and refrain from wearing animal skins or fur. But the fraction of the human race that is consistent on such scores is small.

On strictly logical grounds it would appear that no one who condones any sacrifice of aquatic or terrestrial animal life for food or clothing has a leg to stand on in criticizing the humane sacrifice of animal life in relatively very small numbers for the control of disease. It is possible for adults, and probably for children after the nursing period, to live entirely on vegetable matter, but it is totally impossible to advance certain kinds of knowledge essential to the control of cure or amelioration of disease without the use of living animals of various sorts.

The outright antiscience, antirational small core of antivivisectionists would not be a great problem, except for the fact that they form the nucleus for the crystallization of much larger numbers of ordinary pet lovers who can be mobilized to press for extremely restrictive and unwise legislation. In an affluent society, especially one with an aging population of lonely people who frequently distrust other humans and become more attached to lower animal pets than to humanity, there is a danger that a dominating majority will one day put an end to the era of progress in medicine and the rest of biological science, out of ignorance and prejudice. How this could happen in a society devoted to carnivorous eating habits may be hard to envision, but the near success of the bill in the British Parliament aimed at hobbling their biomedical researchers, shows that fears on this score are not paranoid.

The relation of this issue to the safe use of human subjects for medical investigation can be made quite obvious. A new drug cannot be tested safely in man until it has been studied thoroughly in a variety of lower animals. Cell and tissue cultures are useful in analyzing some basic kinds of biochemical action, but drugs ordinarily do not act simply on one kind of cell or tissue, nor do they necessarily act the same way on isolated cells or even organs as they do when other cell types are present in an integrated system. Drug efficacy and safety must ordinarily be tested on numerous species of animal in order to be able to make reliable transferable predictions as to their actions in man. The majority of new drugs tested first in a number of species of animals have shown reliable transferability of information to man. Therefore, the U.S. Food and Drug Administration quite properly requires extensive animal testing before it will authorize even tentative small-scale tests on man. The same rule is applied in practically all countries in which a pharmaceutical industry exists.

The thalidomide tragedy is often brought up by antivivisectionists and their allies as an example of a case in which the toxic effects on embryos in the human were not predicted by prior animal study and that therefore animal study is futile. The facts are that the animal studies on thalidomide were inadequate, and the reason for the inadequacy was simply that no tests for teratogenicity were made. Obviously, too few animal studies were performed. Thalidomide is therefore a prime example of the need for more, not less, preliminary study on lower animals before applications are made in human use. The experience with that drug should point up the ethical necessity of large-scale toxicity testing on animals.

The same general principle applies in other types of medical research. No one would consider using an attenuated live virus vaccine without extensive study on lower animal models. Likewise with innumerable other innovations, very extensive investigation has preceded any human application. This is as it should be if humane ethics are to prevail. If there has been a defect in policy till recently, it is that too little rather than too much lower animal study has preceded trials on man.

An antivivisectionist today should be an anachronism. Most outright antivivisectionists are actually misanthropic zoophiles. Some of them, as already noted, are dressing up their opposition to the use of animals in scientific study with the wholly illustory claim that the use of animals in research is obsolete in an era of advanced computer technology and other powerful mathematical tools. But some of the critics of animal experimentation go on to suggest that, if empirical data are really necessary, they should be acquired by the use of human rather than subhuman subjects. Often the suggestion is made that the human experimenter himself, rather than a dog, cat, monkey or mouse, should be the subject. Actually many scientists have made themselves the first guinea pigs when scientific necessity has required the use of human subjects, but it would seem to approach the absurd, not to say the insane, to suggest seriously as some have done,[8] that human subjects be routinely employed in order to avoid the use of lower animals in scientific study for human welfare, as in drug toxicity studies in the instance cited.

More than a century ago Claude Bernard[9] summarized the problem when he said,

> Have we the right to make experiments on animals and vivisect them? As for me, I think we have this right, wholly and absolutely. It would be strange indeed if we recognized man's right to make use of animals in every walk of life, for domestic service, for food, and then forbade him to make use of them for his

own instruction in one of the sciences most useful to humanity. No hesitation is possible; the science of life can be established only through experiment, and we can save living beings from death only after sacrificing others. Experiments must be made either on man or on animals. Now I think that physicians already make too many dangerous experiments on man, before carefully studying them on animals. I do not admit that it is moral to try more or less dangerous or active remedies on patients in hospitals, without first experimenting with them on dogs; for I shall prove, further on, that results obtained on animals may all be conclusive for man when we know how to experiment properly. If it is immoral, then, to make an experiment on man when it is dangerous to him, even though the result may be useful to others, it is essentially moral to make experiments on an animal, even though painful and dangerous to him, if they may be useful to man.

NOTES

1 Schweitzer, Albert: *Reverence for Life,* trans. by R.H. Fuller. New York, Harper & Row, 1969, pp. 120-121.
2 Schweitzer, Albert: *The Teaching of Reverence for Life* trans. by R. and C. Winston. New York, Holt-Rinehart Winston, 1965, p. 48.
3 Schweitzer, Albert: *The Philosophy of Civilization,* trans by C.T. Campion. New York, Macmillan, 1950, p. 312.
4 Clark, Henry: *The Ethical Mysticism of Albert Schweitzer* Boston, Beacon Press, 1962, Appendix I, pp. 186-187.
5 Visscher, M.B.: In Dewey, John: Medical research and ethics. *JAMA, 199(9):*634, February 27, 1967.
6 Godlovitch, Stanley and Roslind, and Harris, John *Animals, Men and Morals.* New York, Taplinger, 1972.
7 Roberts, Catherine: Animal experimentation and evolution. *The American Scholar,* Summer 1971.
8 Advertisement placed by United Action for Animals, Inc *New York Times,* September 7, 1969.
9 Bernard, Claude: *Experimental Medicine,* trans. by Henry Copley Greene, U.S.A., Henry Schumann, 1949, p. 102.

• • •

POSTSCRIPT

SHOULD ANIMAL EXPERIMENTATION BE STOPPED?

In July 1983 animal welfare groups publicized the Defense Department's plans to shoot dogs and other animals so that medical students and other scientists could study the treatment of gunshot wounds. The public outcry was so great that the agency cancelled its planned experiments until it could investigate the matter.

Several legislative efforts are underway to alter the conduct of animal experimentation. One bill, introduced by Senator Robert Dole (R.-Kansas), would give the Secretary of Agriculture the power to issue "standards for research facilities, including proper requirements for animal care, treatment, and methodology in experimental procedures to ensure that animal pain and distress are minimized." The Association of American Medical Colleges opposes this bill. Another proposal, supported by the biomedical research community, would authorize the National Academy of Sciences to conduct an eighteen-month study evaluating the current use of animals in research. Eight states already have laws banning the use of pound animals in state-funded research, and similar legislation has been introduced in California. Although the future of particular bills is unclear, it is certain that political efforts to ban or limit animal research will continue, despite protests from the research community that such restrictions will disrupt research and drive up costs.

For views of the animal liberation movement, see Peter Singer, *Practical Ethics* (Cambridge, 1979); Tom Regan and Peter Singer, editors, *Animal Rights and Human Obligations* (Prentice-Hall, 1976); and Richard Knowles Morris and Michael W. Fox, editors, *On the Fifth Day: Animal Rights and Human Ethics* (Acropolis, 1978). Opposing views are found in R.G. Frey, *Interests and Rights: The Case Against Animals* (Clarendon, 1980); and Joseph Margolis, "Animals Have No Rights and Are Not the Equal of Humans," *Philosophic Exchange* 1 (Summer 1974). Also see *Ethics and Animals,* edited by Harlan B. Miller and William H. Williams (Humana, 1983).

ISSUE 15

SHOULD BLOOD BE A GIFT?

YES: Richard M. Titmuss, from "Why Give to Strangers?" *The Lancet,* January 16, 1971

NO: Harvey M. Sapolsky and Stan N. Finkelstein, from "Blood Policy Revisited—A New Look at 'The Gift Relationship,' " *The Public Interest* 46 (Winter 1977)

ISSUE SUMMARY

YES: The late Richard M. Titmuss, who was a British professor of social administration, believes that a system of voluntary blood donations is not only safer and more economical than a commercial system but fosters the important ethical ideal of altruism.

NO: Harvey M. Sapolsky, a physician, and Stan N. Finkelstein, a political scientist, challenge Titmuss's negative view of the free market system in blood, especially as it exists in America, calling it a more flexible and efficient method of allocating a vital resource.

The French anthropologist Claude Levi-Strauss has described a scene that he has often observed in modest restaurants in the south of France: The customers sit at a long communal table; before each person is a bottle of wine. Each patron, before eating, pours a glass of wine not into his own glass but into the glass of the person seated next to him. This seemingly trivial gift-giving ceremony, says Lévi-Strauss, establishes a sense of community among the diners where before they were only isolated individuals.

Every society has certain unifying rituals of gift-giving, from the "potlatch" feast of the American Indians along the North Pacific coast to marriage gifts in Africa to birthday presents in our own culture. Modern medical technology, which has made it possible to transfuse blood and transplant organs from one person to another, has created an even more significant possibility: One person can give to another the most precious gift of all, the "gift of life." Yet blood and transplantable organs are in scarce supply, and so far there are no fully acceptable artificial substitutes. The question is: How should their distribution be organized so that all who are in need are treated justly and so that a sense of community is fostered?

Although the problem arises in many areas of the health care system, the debate has centered around the blood supply. Blood has a particularly strong emotional meaning; it symbolizes unity, continuity, and life itself. Blood can be transfused for many medical purposes—to replace blood lost in hemorrhages, burns, and surgery, or to correct blood disorders such as anemia, leukemia, hemophilia, and immune deficiencies. Unlike a kidney donation, which is a permanent loss to the donor, blood renews itself in the healthy donor, so that blood donation is an act of altruism, or unselfishness, rather than a sacrifice. On the other hand, if not enough blood is available through voluntary donations, the supply must be augmented by paid contributions.

The debate began in full force in 1971, when Richard M. Titmuss published the article in this section, later expanded into a book called *The Gift Relationship: From Human Blood to Social Policy* (Random House). Titmuss pointed out that in countries such as Great Britain, Australia, France, Belgium, The Netherlands, Finland, and Japan, all the whole blood needed for patients comes from voluntary donations. In such a system donors contribute to a blood bank (even when they are responding to a call for blood for a particular patient). The patient's needs are met from the blood bank, and the donations are intended to replenish the general supply. No one is paid for giving blood; the only reward is the knowledge that one's blood will flow in the veins of another human being—a complete stranger—and that if the situation were reversed, blood would also be available for one's own needs.

Titmuss contrasted this situation with the one in America, where a commercial blood supply coexists with a voluntary one. Such a market system, he declared, will drive out the voluntary system because the volunteer will get less satisfaction knowing that someone else is getting paid for blood. Moreover, those who are at risk for supplying contaminated blood (hepatitis carriers, drug addicts, and the like) will be more likely to act selfishly and sell their blood.

Titmuss's arguments had a powerful effect in this country, and the National Blood Policy, announced in 1973, was intended to "accelerate the evolution to an all-voluntary supply of blood." The American Blood Commission was founded in 1975 as an association of agencies dedicated to promoting voluntary blood donations. Today about ninety percent of whole blood for transfusions comes from volunteer donors. However, as much as two-thirds of plasma and other blood parts (used, for example, to treat hemophilia) comes from commercial sources.

Recently, however, Titmuss's views have been challenged. The selection by Harvey M. Sapolsky and Stan N. Finkelstein argues that Titmuss underestimated the voluntary sector of the American blood supply and that blood collected in America is actually safer than that collected in Britain. They feel that market forces are more beneficial to society than Titmuss and his followers recognized.

YES

Richard M. Titmuss

WHY GIVE TO STRANGERS?

In Alexander Solzhenitsyn's novel *Cancer Ward* Shulubin is talking to Kostoglotov:

> "We have to show the world a society in which all relationships, fundamental principles and laws flow directly from moral ethics, and from them *alone*. Ethical demands would determine all calculations: how to bring up children, what to prepare them for, to what purpose the work of grown-ups should be directed, and how their leisure should be occupied. As for scientific research, it should be conducted where it doesn't damage ethical morality, in the first instance where it doesn't damage the researchers themselves."
>
> Kostoglotov then raises questions. "There has to be an economy after all doesn't there? That comes before everything else." "Does it?" said Shulubin. "That depends. For example, Vladimir Solovyov argues rather convincingly that an economy could and should be built on an ethical basis."
>
> "What's this? Ethics first and economics afterwards?" Kostoglotov looked bewildered.

The questions raised by Solzhenitsyn could as well be directed at social policy institutions. What, for example, are the connections between what we in Britain conventionally call the social services and the role of altruism in modern industrial societies? And have we a convenient model for studying such relationships? Blood as a living tissue and as a bond that links all men and women so closely that differences of colour, religious belief, and cultural heritage are insignificant beside it, may now constitute in Western societies one of the ultimate tests of where the "social" begins and the "economic" ends.

THE WORLD DEMAND FOR BLOOD

The transfer of blood and blood derivatives from one human being to another represents one of the greatest therapeutic instruments in the hands of modern medicine. But these developments have set in train social, economic, and ethical consequences which present society with issues of profound importance.

The demand for blood and blood products is increasing all over the world. In high-income countries, in particular, the rate of growth in demand has been rising so rapidly that shortages have begun to appear. In all Western countries, demand is growing faster than rates of growth in the population aged 18-65 from whom donors are drawn. And, despite a massive research effort in the United States to find alternatives, there is often no substitute for human blood.

Many factors are responsible for this increase in demand. Some surgical procedures call for massive transfusions of blood (as many as 60 donations may be needed for a single open-heart operation, and in one American heart-transplant case over 300 pints of blood were used); artificial kidneys require substantial volumes of blood; and developments in organ transplants could create immense additional demands. Furthermore, more routine surgery is now used more frequently and is made available to a larger proportion of the population than formerly. A more violent or accident-prone world insistently demands more blood for road casualties and for war injuries (in 1968 more than 300,000 pints of blood were shipped from the U.S.A. and elsewhere to treat victims of the Vietnam war).

There seems to be no predictable limit to the demand for blood supplies, especially when one remembers the as-yet unmet needs for surgical and medical treatment.

SUPPLY OF BLOOD

On the biological, technical, and administrative side, three factors limit the supply of blood.

Only about half of a population is medically eligible to donate blood. Furthermore, the amount any one person can give in a year is restricted—two donations in the British National Blood Transfusion Service (probably the lowest limit and the most rigorous standard in the world); five in the United States, a minimum often exceeded by paid donors, commercial blood-banks, and pharmaceutical companies using techniques such as plasmapheresis; in Japan, where 90% of blood is bought and sold, the standard is even lower. These differences can be analysed as a process of redistribution of life chances in terms of age, sex, social class, income, ethnic group, and so on.

Human blood deteriorates after three weeks in the refrigerator, and this perishability presents great technical and administrative problems to those running transfusion services. But it does mean that, by measuring wastage (i.e., the amount of blood that has to be thrown away) the efficiencies of different blood collection and distribution systems can be compared.

Blood can be more deadly than any drug. Quite apart from the problems of cross-matching, storage, labelling, and so on, there are serious risks of disease transmission and other hazards. In Western countries a major hazard is serum hepatitis transmitted from carrier donor to susceptible patient. Since carriers cannot yet be reliably detected, the patient becomes the laboratory for testing "the gift." Donors, therefore, have to be screened every time they come to give blood, and the donor's truthfulness in answering questions about health, medical history, and drug habits becomes vital. Upon the honesty of the donor depends the life of the recipient of his blood. In this context we need to ask what conditions and arrangements permit and encourage maximum truthfulness on the part of the donors. Can honesty be pursued regardless of the donor's motives for giving blood? What systems, structures, and social policies encourage honesty or discourage and destroy voluntary and truthful gift relationships?

TYPES OF DONORS

To give or not to give, to lend, repay, or even to buy and sell blood are choices which lead us, if we are to understand these transactions in the context of any society, to the fundamentals of social and economic life.

The forms and functions of giving embody moral, social, psychological, religious, legal, and aesthetic ideas. They may reflect, sustain, strengthen, or loosen the cultural bonds of the group, large or small. They may inspire the worst excesses of war and tribalism or the tolerances of community.

Customs and practices of non-economic giving—unilateral and multilateral social transfers—thus may tell us much, as Marcel Mauss so sensitively demonstrated in his book *The Gift*, about the texture of personal and group relationships in different cultures. In some societies, past and present, gifts to men aim to buy peace; to express affection, regard, or loyalty; to unify the group; to fulfil a contractual set of obligations and rights; to function as acts of penitence, shame, or degradation; and to symbolise many other human sentiments. When one reads the work of anthropologists and sociologists such as Mauss and Lévi-Strauss, who have studied the social functions of giving, a number of themes relevant to any attempt to delineate a typology of blood-donors may be discerned.

From these readings and from statistics for different countries a spectrum of blood-donor types can be constructed. At one extreme is the paid donor who sells his blood for what the market will bear: some are semi-salaried, some are long-term prisoner volunteers, some are organised in blood trade-unions. As a market transaction, information that might have a bearing on the quality of blood is withheld if possible from the buyer, since such information could affect the sale of the blood. Thus in the United States blood-group identification cards are loaned, at a price, to other sellers, and blood is illegally mislabelled and updated, and other devices are used which make it very difficult to screen out drug addicts, alcoholics and hepatitis carriers, and so on.

At the other extreme is the voluntary, unpaid donor. This type is the closest approximation in social reality to the abstract idea of a "free human gift." There are no tangible immediate rewards, monetary or non-monetary; there are no penalties; and donors know that their gifts are for unnamed strangers without distinction of age, sex, medical illness, income, class, religion, or ethnic group. No donor type can be characterised by complete disinterested spontaneous altruism. There must be some sense of obligation, approval, and interest; some awareness of the need for the gift; some expectation that a return gift may be needed and received at some future date. But the unpaid donation of blood is an act of free-will: there is no formal contract, legal bond, power situation; no sense of shame or guilt; no money and no explicit guarantee of or wish for reward or return gift.

Almost all the 1½ million registered donors in Britain and donors in some systems in European countries fall into this category. An analysis of blood-donor motives suggests that the main reason people give blood is most commonly a general desire to help people; almost a third of the

British donors studied said that their gift was in response to an appeal for blood; 7% said it was to repay a transfusion given to someone they knew.

By contrast, in the United States less than 10% of supplies come from the voluntary community donor. Proportionately more and more blood is being supplied by the poor, the unskilled, the unemployed, Negroes, and other low-income groups, and with the rise in plasmapheresis there is emerging a new class of exploited high blood yielders. Redistribution in terms of "the gift of blood and blood products" from the poor to the rich seems to be one of the dominant effects of the American blood-banking system.

WHICH SYSTEM?

When we compare the commerical blood-bank, such as that found in the United States, with the voluntary system functioning as an integral part of the National Health Service in Britain we find that the commercial bloodbank fails on each of four counts—economic efficiency, administrative efficiency, price, and quality. Commercial blood-bank systems waste blood, and shortages, acute and chronic, characterise the demand-and-supply position. Administratively, there is more paperwork and greater computing and accounting overheads. The cost varies between £10 and £20 per unit in the United States, compared with £1 16s, (£2 if processing costs are included) in Britain. And, as judged by statistics for post-transfusion hepatitis, the risk of transfusing contaminated blood is greater if the blood is obtained from a commercial source.

Paradoxically—or so it may seem to some—the more commercialised blood-distribution becomes (and hence more wasteful, inefficient, and dangerous) the more will gross national product be inflated. In part, and quite simply, this is the consequence of statistically "transferring" an unpaid service (voluntary donors, voluntary workers in the service, unpaid time), with much lower external costs, to a monetary and measurable paid activity involving costlier externalities. Similar effects on the gross national product would ensue if housewives were paid for housework or childless married couples were financially rewarded for adopting children or if hospital patients cooperating for teaching purposes charged medical students. The gross national product is also inflated when commercial markets accelerate "blood obsolescence"; the waste is counted because someone has paid for it.

What *The Economist* described in its 1969 survey of the American economy as the "efficiency gap" between that country and Britain clearly does not apply to the distribution of human blood. The voluntary, socialised system in Britain is economically, professionally, administratively, and qualitatively more efficient than the mixed, commercialised, and individualistic American system.

Another myth, the Paretian myth of consumer sovereignty, has also to be shattered. In the commercial blood market the consumer is not king. He has less freedom of choice to live unharmed; little choice in determining price; is more subject to scarcity; is less free from bureacratisation; has fewer opportunities to express altruism; and exercises fewer checks and controls in relation to consumption, quality, and external costs. Far from being sovereign, he is often exploited.

What also emerges from this case-study is the significance of the externalities (the values and disvalues external to but created by blood-distribution systems treated as entities) and the multiplier effects of such externalities on what we can only call "the quality of life." At one end of the spectrum of externalities is the individual affected by hepatitis; at the other end, the market behaviour of economically rich societies seeking to import blood from other societies who are thought to be too poor and economically decadent to pay their own blood-donors.

CONCLUSION

We started with blood as a model for examining how altruism and social policy might work together in a modern industrial society. We might equally have chosen eye banks, patients as teaching material, fostering, or even the whole concept of the community-based distribution of welfare to those in need. All these involve in some degree a gift relationship. The example chosen suggests, firstly, that gift exchange of a non-quantifiable nature has more important functions in a complex society than the writings of Lévi-Strauss and others might indicate. Secondly, the application of scientific and technological developments in such societies is further accelerating the spread of such complexity, and has increased rather than decreased the scientific as well as the social need for such relationships. Thirdly, for these and many other reasons, modern societies require more rather than less freedom of choice for the expression of altruism in the daily life of all social groups. This requirement can be argued for on social and ethical grounds, but, as we have seen for blood donors, it can also be argued for on scientific and economic criteria.

I believe that it is a responsibility of government, acting, for example, through social policy, to weaken market forces which put men in positions where they have little opportunity to make moral choices or to behave altruistically if they wish to do so. The voluntary blood-donor system is a practical example of a fellowship relationship operating on an institutional basis, in this instance the National Health Service. It shows how social policy decisions can foster such relationships between free and equal individuals. If we accept that man has a social and biological need to help then he should not be denied the chance to express this need by entering into a gift relationship.

● ● ●

NO

Harvey M. Sapolsky
and Stan N. Finkelstein

BLOOD POLICY REVISITED—A NEW LOOK AT "THE GIFT RELATIONSHIP"

The advocates of central planning and the supporters of free markets clash in nearly every field of public policy. But perhaps none of their confrontations is more emotionally based, or less useful for decision-making, than the current debate over blood policy. Emotionalism is inherent in the topic of the controversy. Blood is essential for life. It cannot be produced artificially. In order that some of those in need of transfusions may live, others must be persuaded to give their own blood. It is not surprising, then, that many would regard the system by which blood donations are induced and blood transfusions paid for as symbolic of the bonds of community—or lack thereof—in modern society, and as having moral qualities few other human transactions could. Only the barrenness of the debate needs to be explained.

Although there have been conflicts among the professionals involved since transfusions began to become common nearly 40 years ago, the current public debate stems from the publication in 1970 of a widely reviewed study of blood-banking practices by Richard M. Titmuss, the now deceased English social theorist. In *The Gift Relationship*, Titmuss compared the blood-banking system in the United States, where a market in blood is permitted, with those in other nations, especially Great Britain, where all blood donors are unpaid and blood is provided free to those in need of transfusions. According to Titmuss, because the United States allows blood to be bought and sold, it suffers from unnecessary shortages, unconscionable wastage, and avoidable illness and death caused by transfusion-induced hepatitis. The profit motive causes donors and procurers of blood to lie about the quality of their product, thus endangering the health of the recipients. Great Britain, by contrast, supposedly suffers from none of these problems. In Titmuss' view, the "gift of life" in America is an unhealthy one, medically and socially.

Titmuss acknowledged that not all of the blood supplied in the United States is collected by commercial sources. The American Red Cross, nonprofit hospital blood banks, and community blood centers (represented nationally by the American Association of Blood Banks and the Council of Community Blood Centers) are also active in the field. He claimed, however, that the commercial sector accounted for approximately one third of the supply, and that its share of blood collections was rapidly growing. Moreover—in contrast to the situation in Britain, where everyone is guaranteed blood without cost when they need it, and no one expects any personal gain for giving—even blood given to nonprofit agencies in the United States is often donated either under a kind of duress (with the donors trying to insure the availability of blood for themselves or their families, or to avoid the replacement fees that are charged for transfused blood) or on the delivery of some side payment (time off from work, or a ticket to a sporting event). Relatively few Americans give their blood, and among them only a small percentage (Titmuss estimated less than 10 per cent) are truly altruistic donors.

This devastating critique was accepted as accurate by American social scientists who commented on Titmuss' work. To be sure, not all of them were persuaded by every strand of the arguement. For instance, several challenged the contention that the mere knowledge of the existence of a market for blood would in itself cause potentially altruistic donors not to volunteer their blood. Personal experience, they knew, proved otherwise. Most, however, found no fault with the conclusion that blood services functioned best when they were centralized and the donations were exclusively voluntary. If a market produced the undesirable results Titmuss indicated, then it ought to be abolished: This was their general verdict.

The responsible officials in the Department of Health, Education, and Welfare (HEW) apparently shared this view, for they soon sought to bring the noncommercial elements in blood banking into a consortium to rationalize the blood-resources system in the United States. The result of this effort was the establishment in 1975 of the American Blood Commission, an organization composed of the major blood-collection agencies and representative consumer groups, and dedicated to a policy of promoting "volunteerism" in blood donations and the regionalization of blood services. Titmuss would think this policy deficient since it does not require that transfusions be provided free of charge, nor attempt to eliminate non-cash payments for blood donations. But he would not be displeased with the direction of change it indicates for American blood policy, since it is the direction preferred in *The Gift Relationship*.

NEEDLESS DEATH AND ILL HEALTH

The Gift Relationship, however, is not a very useful guide for policy. The American blood system, even unreformed, is much less than the disaster Timuss described, and the British system, as structurally different as it is, is much less than the model of virtue.

The most serious charge Titmuss made was that the American system promotes needless death and ill health. At least two and perhaps three or more types of hepatitis virus are transmitted through blood transfusions. Those who survive surgery or other medical procedures involving transfusions face the threat of debilitating and potentially fatal hepatitis infections. Because the available tests for the hepatitis antigens in blood fail to prevent completely the transmission of the disease—currently the best among them is less than 50 per cent effective—the safe operation of the blood-resources system requires that its participants act in a socially responsible manner. Individuals with a history of hepatitis infections must be banned from donating their blood for transfusions, and units of blood that are suspected of causing infections should be traced back to their source to prevent the spread of the disease through repeat donations. A trade in blood, Titmuss argued, creates incentives for socially irresponsible and medically dangerous behavior. When there is a market in blood, derelicts, drug addicts, and others with both a high risk of being hepatitis carriers and a need for money have an interest in concealing their poor health. Those who pay them and resell their blood have the same interest. In the United States, where blood is exchanged for money, transfusion hepatitis is an important medical problem. (Though precise figures are not available, the official estimates are 1,000 to 3,700 deaths and 90,000 to 120,000 hospitalizations each year—or an infection rate of approximately 4.3 cases per 100 transfusions.) In Great Britain, where a cup of tea or a glass of stout is about all you can get for a blood donation, transfusion hepatitis is considered rare, with an infection rate perhaps a seventh of the American rate. Money, it would seem, is the root of at least one evil.

The hepatitis problem, however, is more complicated than Titmuss would have us believe. Commercially procured blood (that is, blood collected by profit-making enterprises) does, to be sure, carry a higher than average risk of infection. Studies of hospitals that have switched from commercial to voluntary sources for their blood show large, often dramatic, drops in their rates of transfusion-related hepatitis. But not all paid blood is commercial. Some nonprofit hospitals pay their donors. And volunteer blood is not always less risky than paid blood, commercially or otherwise procured. The Mayo Clinic and the Massachusetts General Hospital, two of the nation's most prestigious medical institutions, pay some of their donors, and they both have lower rates of transfusion hepatitis than is the experience with volunteer blood available in their areas.

A recent study conducted by the General Accounting Office (GAO) supports this point. The GAO examined positive hepatitis-B-antigen rates of donor groups at a number of blood collection agencies, some of which paid donors and some of which did not.*

*Hepatitis screening tests such as the B-antigen test are not perfect indicators, since some infectious blood does pass the screens, and the rates found are likely to be related to the number of first-time donors in the group tested. Agencies that pay their donors tend to have more repeat givers than those that rely on volunteers. Nevertheless, the B-antigen test results are used because they represent the measure of hepatitis infectivity of blood that is most readily available.

15. SHOULD BLOOD BE A GIFT?

The GAO found that some paid groups, particularly at hospitals, had test rates nearly equal to the best of the volunteer groups, and that some volunteer groups had rates ranking with the worst of the paid groups, which were almost exclusively commercial. The variance in the rankings among the groups was better explained by socioeconomic factors, most particularly by the poverty rate of the area from which the donors were drawn, than by whether the donors were paid.

Race and ethnicity also seem to be important correlates of the risk of hepatitis infection. A study conducted by the Greater New York Blood Program found that orientals had positive test rates four times higher than blacks, and blacks had rates four times higher than whites. Among whites, those of Northern European origin had lower rates than those of Southern European origin.

These findings help explain the variation in national transfusion-hepatitis rates. Sweden, which pays all of its blood donors, has a very low transfusion-hepatitis rate; Japan, which switched from a largely paid blood-donor system to an essentially all-volunteer system in the late 1960's, still has a very high rate. The low rate in England relative to the United States is probably due more to the fact that British blood is used than to the fact that all British donors are volunteers.

The National Transfusion Service, the government agency which manages the blood system in Great Britain, apparently agrees, for it discreetly discriminates against new immigrants in its collection procedures. The regional units of the Transfusion Service avoid scheduling collection visits at factories and other sites where there are large concentrations of Pakistanis, Indians, Jamaicans, or other immigrant groups. Blood collected from donors born in Asian, African, and Caribbean countries (and certain other countries, but not the United States) is labeled as high-hepatitis-risk (in code) and is then not used, if possible, for direct transfusions. A very rational policy perhaps, but not one that the British advertise. When asked recently by the press about the sorting of blood by national origin, some regional directors of the Transfusion Service denied ever having followed the practice, even though their colleagues at the other regional centers knew they had and thought they were continuing to do so.

EFFICIENCY IN BLOOD BANKING

Titmuss also accused the American system of gross inefficiency. He noted that while in some American cities there are severe shortages of blood, in others blood is literally thrown away. Blood emergencies are continually being declared, and yet upwards of 30 per cent of the collections are supposedly not used. In contrast, he reported that the British Transfusion Service has always managed to meet the expanding blood needs of the National Health Service and British medicine as a whole without encountering shortages or wastage.

Given the inventory problems involved in blood banking, however, such a perfect record is difficult to imagine. Whole blood becomes "outdated" in 21 days.* Blood must be biologically cross-matched for each patient. Blood and blood components

*Whole blood has a liquid component, plasma, and cellular components, red and white cells and platelets. After 21 days, whole blood ceases to be usable as whole blood, though blood products can still be processed.

must be stocked at all times for emergencies. The least effort at investigation will discover that blood is often in short supply, not only in Newark but also in South London, and that donors are reluctant to give during vacation periods and holidays, in both Great Britain and the United States.

From a theoretical perspective one might expect that shortages would be less likely here than in Britain, since we do rely, after all, largely on an entrepreneurial system for our health services. An operation postponed by the unavailability of blood means a postponed surgical fee. Given that hospitals are structured to serve physician demands, a chronic local shortage of blood would certainly result in the search for alternative sources of supply, commercial or otherwise, and perhaps also in the replacement of the hospital blood-bank director. Since there are no indications that surgeons are dissatisfied with the blood supply, and the growth in the national surgical rate seems unimpaired, it is doubtful that serious shortages do exist.

Perceptions of shortage in the United States result largely from the competition that prevails for donors and the existence of systems that link the availability of blood to individual and group donations. Exaggerations of need and of the consequences of the failure to donate are bound to occur under such arrangements. In some instances, the declaration of emergencies is part of the regular advertising campaign of particular collection agencies. In others it is the product of the organizational practices of the media. For example, a call for donors during a disaster is likely to be repeated automatically on each newscast, and well beyond the time when the emergency need is fulfilled. Even the government agencies that set blood policy find it difficult to resist exaggeration. When the GAO sought to cite, as an example of the effects of switching from paid to volunteer blood, the claims made by the Clinical Center Blood Bank of the National Institutes of Health (NIH) that coverage for NIH employees and their families would be threatened if donations did not increase, HEW, the parent organization of NIH, replied that these claims could not be taken seriously as indicating a shortage—they were merely an advertising technique to keep the level of donations high, and bore no relationship to actual blood availability!

American blood-banking statistics are invariably incomplete since there is no single agency, public or private, to which the thousands of organizations involved in blood collection and usage must report their activities. The data that have been available are based on the voluntary completion of questionnaires distributed irregularly by public and private groups. In *The Gift Relationship,* Titmuss notes that surveys conducted during the 1960's could not account for the use of up to 30 per cent of the blood collected, and he argued that much if not all of this "missing" blood was wasted through "out-dating." In Britain, he claimed, wasted blood represents only one or two per cent of the collections. The most recent national survey of blood banking in the United States was done for 1971 by Booz Allen Hamilton, under the sponsorship of the National Heart and Lung Institute. This survey reported the "outdating" rate for blood as 12.9 per cent of the 1971 collections, a figure quite close to the rate of 11.8 per cent for the same year reported recently by the British Transfusion Service to the Council of Europe's Public Health Committee.*

*The use of another 13.1 per cent of the American supply was not accounted for in the Booz Allen Hamilton survey, but there is no way to determine whether this represents additional "outdating," unreported transfusions, or both.

Titmuss thought that the most efficient manager of blood resources would be a monopoly supplier, which, for example, could prevent the waste of blood by restricting or promoting the availability of particular blood-bank products. One measure of blood-banking efficiency is the degree of production of "packed" red cells used to substitute for whole blood in transfusions. By this measure, at least, the fragmented American system is more efficient than the more centralized British system. In 1971, "packed" red cells accounted for approximately 22 per cent of red cells supplied in the United States, while the British Transfusion Service's production of "packed" cells for the same year amounted to only 5.4 per cent of its total red-cell output. Even allowing for the looseness of the American data, the progressiveness and efficiency of the British system is in doubt.

The Transfusion Service, however, is not quite the monopolist that Titmuss would have us believe. To begin with, the regional units of the Transfusion Service (there is a blood service for each of the 14 Regional Authorities of the National Health Service) operate independently of one another, thus sacrificing the economies of scale that a coordinated national processing of blood products might achieve. There is even some difficulty in shipping blood between regions. Each shipment is made not according to a standard procedure, but rather at the discretion of the Regional Director supplying the blood. In addition, British hospitals are permitted alternative sources of supply for some of their blood needs, the major restriction being that no donors are paid. Most large British hospitals, for example, maintain panels of blood donors separate from those maintained by the Transfusion Service; in London, the British Red Cross operates a donor service to provide hospitals with fresh whole blood, a product that many practitioners prefer to use for special needs, although the Transfusion Service is said to find it both inconvenient and medically unnecessary to supply. While the amount of blood obtained from the alternative sources is probably not large relative to the collections of the Transfusion Service, the existence of the alternative sources of supply is an indication that British hospitals are unwilling to commit themselves completely to the preferences of a single supplier, even one that is (like the hospitals themselves) an arm of the Health Service. Perhaps the hospitals in Britain seek the flexibility and the responsiveness of a more decentralized system.

THE REAL MARKET AND THE REAL SHORTAGE

No matter what the supply source, paid blood is unavailable in Great Britain, and this may soon be the case in the United States as well. Urged on by their national associations, the hospitals and community blood banks that have been paying donors are increasingly relying on voluntary giving. And commercial blood banks, always the major source of paid blood, are apparently withdrawing from the market in whole blood. While estimates made in the 1960's of the commercial-blood-sector's share of the total whole-blood supply were in the range of 15 to 30 per cent, the 1971 national survey found that its share was approximately 11 per cent of the total collections. Government officials believe that the commercial share is still dropping, some say it is now as low as five per cent of the total.

Commercial firms, however, have not

entirely abandoned the blood business. Rather, they have concentrated their efforts on the collection of blood plasma. The processing of plasma permits the separation and concentration of a number of elements such as albumin, fibrinogen, and globulin, which are useful in combating disease and treating injury. Albumin, for example, is effective in treating shock, and certain globulins in immunizing against mumps and tetanus. As medical techniques have improved, the demand for all blood products, but especially plasma derivatives, has grown rapidly. Plasma may be obtained from "outdated" whole blood, placentas, or "packed" red-cell production, but in the volume now needed the preferred method of collection is plasmapheresis, a process involving the removal of plasma from a whole-blood donation and the immediate return of the red cells to the donor through transfusion. Pheresis donors may give twice a week double the amount of plasma obtained from a whole-blood donor every three months. (The commercial firms are the main pheresis-collection agents. Each pheresis session requires up to one-and-a-half hours, as opposed to half an hour for a whole-blood donation; few individuals are apparently willing to sacrifice the extra time without payment.) Albumin, globulins, and diagnostic reagents—plasma products whose use is associated with a negligible risk of hepatitis transmission—account for the overwhelming share of blood-derivative sales. Almost all of these products are storable for a period of time much greater than that of whole blood, and most do not need the cross-matching required for whole blood and red cells.

If there is a major shortage in blood, it is in the production of plasma fractions—and it occurs in the European countries, not in the United States. Plasma fractionation in the United States is largely considered a separate undertaking from the collection and distribution of whole blood. The field is dominated by several large pharmaceutical manufacturing firms who obtain the largest part of their plasma materials from commercial pheresis centers, with most of the remainder from blood purchased from nonprofit blood banks. Under this arrangement, the United States is self-sufficient in the production of plasma. In Europe, plasma fractionation is most often an integral part of the whole-blood procurement system, with government agencies assuming responsibility for the collection and processing of the plasma. Supply problems occur there both because government health officials have not invested sufficient resources in manufacturing facilities to keep up with demand (believing apparently that other health needs deserve higher budgeting priorities), and because plasma is usually obtained from whole-blood donations, resulting in either a shortage of donors or in the collection of excess red cells. In Britain, for example, there has been a shortage of production capacity for plasma factors used in the treatment of hemophiliacs.

The prime market for plasma products is in the developed countries, since they are the countries that have the sophisticated medical facilities that generate the greatest demand for such products. Because many of these countries are not self-sufficient, an international trade has arisen in plasma and plasma products, with American and European pharmaceutical firms obtaining plasma through pheresis collections (some call it "plasma farming") in the underdeveloped countries of Latin America, Africa, and Asia, and processing it there or in Europe. The existence of this trade, which creates a population of professional donors in the world's poorest lands for the profit (medically and financially) of the world's richest lands, has been a source of some international anguish. An effort is being made to ban the trade, but this is likely to occur only when the prime consuming nations, including the European countries, are self-sufficient in the production of plasma derivatives, which several are now striving to be, though only a few have succeeded.

Titmuss notwithstanding, the American blood system, as presently structured, appears to function quite well. There are no widespread shortages of whole blood in the United States. The nation's needs for plasma derivatives are being met without major complications, and the blood system is considered among the most progressive in the world, in terms of its technology and medical practice. . . .

● ● ●

POSTSCRIPT

SHOULD BLOOD BE A GIFT?

The most serious threat to the voluntary blood donation system in America has come not from commercial sources but from the public's recent fear of contracting acquired immune deficiency syndrome (AIDS) from blood transfusions. In March 1983 the blood banking community reacted to the news that some hemophiliacs had apparently contracted AIDS from blood transfusions by requesting high-risk groups (primarily homosexual and bisexual men with multiple partners) to refrain from selling or donating blood. Many regular blood donors stopped giving blood, fearing (incorrectly) that they could contract the disease. More seriously, many patients who needed blood requested that it come from a designated donor—that is, a specific person rather than from a blood bank. Some physicians and hospitals have acceded to this request; others have refused, claiming that such a policy will eventually destroy the blood banking system. The blood supply is safe, they say, and asking for designated donations may actually be riskier than blood from a bank because homosexual men may lie about their activities rather than be revealed to their relatives or friends.

Ronald Bayer's article, "Gays and the Stigma of Bad Blood," *Hastings Center Report* (April 1983) describes the decision to ban blood from groups at high risk for AIDS. For a fuller critique of Titmuss's views, see Alvin W. Drake, Stan N. Finkelstein, and Harvey M. Sapolsky, *The American Blood Supply* (MIT Press, 1982). Also see *Blood: Gift or Merchandise* by Piet J. Hagen (Liss, 1982) for a view of the international blood supply system.

ISSUE 16

SHOULD ORGANS BE HARVESTED FROM THE DEAD?

YES: Willard Gaylin, from "Harvesting the Dead," *Harper's* 249 (September 1974)

NO: William May, "Attitudes Toward the Newly Dead," *Hastings Center Studies* 1 (No. 1 for 1973)

ISSUE SUMMARY

YES: Psychiatrist Willard Gaylin describes how the continuing march of technology has made it possible to sustain vital life processes, thus creating the potential for recycling human bodies.

NO: Professor of Christian ethics William May warns that long-standing attitudes and rituals concerning the newly dead must be taken into account before organs are routinely salvaged.

Not so long ago organ transplants were the stuff of science fiction. Although the first successful cornea transplant took place in 1905, the first kidney transplant (between identical twins) did not take place until 1954. The first liver transplant was performed in 1966, and the first heart transplant in 1967. Today—with the aid of better surgical techniques, better tissue-matching capabilities, and most important, new drugs that suppress the body's natural tendency to reject a transplanted organ—kidneys, hearts, pancreases, livers, lungs, spleens, and bone marrow can all be transplanted. And people are living longer with the transplanted organs than ever before. At Stanford University, for example, about eighty percent of the people who receive heart transplants now live two years or longer, while a decade or so ago only twenty percent survived as long as a year.

In the 1960s and 1970s the question was: Are these admittedly experimental operations too risky? Today the question is: Where are we going to get all the transplantable organs to fill the ever-expanding demand? A person can donate one of the body's two kidneys to a relative (assuming there is a tissue match) without endangering his or her own health, but the other organs must come from cadavers. Many people, of course, have no suitable live kidney donor in their families, and nationwide about six thousand to ten thousand people are waiting for cadaver kidneys. Some cardiologists estimate that the lives of as many as fifty thousand to 100 thousand people could be saved each year if heart transplants were more readily available.

If medical technology has created the demand, it has also created a means to obtain the supply. For in the same period in which organ transplantation moved from experiment to therapy, medical technology also perfected techniques of maintaining heart and respiratory function in people whose brains had stopped functioning. In many states the definition of death has been changed from one that describes the cessation of heart and lung function as legal death, to one that includes the cessation of all functions of the entire brain, often called a "brain death" criterion. In effect, dead bodies can be made to breathe, blood to circulate, hearts to beat. And from these dead bodies can come organs to serve the living. About twenty thousand people die each year from accidents or from other causes, and they are potential organ donors—that is, they are young enough, healthy enough (except of course for the fatal injury) that their organs are suitable for transplantation.

The Uniform Anatomical Gift Act, adopted in 1968, was intended to eliminate unnecessary formalities and to make available human organs for transplantation while protecting the rights and interests of the families of the deceased. It stressed the need for informed consent before any organs or tissue were removed from a dead body. But voluntary donations, either from people who have signed organ donor cards or from families who have been approached by transplant teams when a relative has died, have not kept pace with the need. Last year only about two thousand to twenty-five hundred of the twenty thousand potential donors actually provided organs. The main reason, it appears, is not that families are reluctant to donate (although that does occur) but that physicians and other medical personnel are reluctant to ask a grieving family.

The selections that follow were written a decade ago, but they foresaw the shortage of organs that now exists because of advances in medicine. They recognized both the tremendous potential and the grave threat to human values that are posed by the possibility of "harvesting the dead." Willard Gaylin predicted that "neomorts" (his term for newly dead bodies) could be used not only for organ harvesting but also for training medical students and for experimentation. They could even, he said, be used to manufacture blood and bone marrow. At the end of his persuasive listing of the benefits, however, Gaylin wondered whether the costs would be too great. Would such a practice violate some fundamental human qualities that make life worth sustaining in the first place? William May concluded that, in the long run, routine salvaging of organs would corrode the basic trust between physicians and patients and would make the hospital a place where people are devoured rather than healed.

YES

Willard Gaylin

HARVESTING THE DEAD

REDEFINING DEATH

Nothing in life is simple anymore, not even the leaving of it. At one time there was no medical need for the physician to consider the concept of death; the fact of death was sufficient. The difference between life and death was an infinite chasm breached in an infinitesimal moment. Life and death were ultimate, self-evident opposites.

With the advent of new techniques in medicine, those opposites have begun to converge. We are now capable of maintaining visceral functions without any semblance of the higher functions that define a person. We are, therefore, faced with the task of deciding whether that which we have kept alive is still a human being, or, to put it another way, whether that human being that we are maintaining should be considered "alive."

Until now we have avoided the problems of definition and reached the solutions in silence and secret. When the life sustained was unrewarding—by the standards of the physician in charge—it was discontinued. Over the years, physicians have practiced euthanasia on an ad hoc, casual, and perhaps irresponsible basis. They have withheld antibiotics or other simple treatments when it was felt that a life did not warrant sustaining, or pulled the plug on the respirator when they were convinced that what was being sustained no longer warranted the definition of life. Some of these acts are illegal and, if one wished to prosecute, could constitute a form of manslaughter, even though it is unlikely that any jury would convict. We prefer to handle all problems connected with death by denying their existence. But death and its dilemmas persist.

New urgencies for recognition of the problem arise from two conditions: the continuing march of technology, making the sustaining of vital processes possible for longer periods of time; and the increasing use of parts of the newly dead to sustain life for the truly living. The problem is well on its way to being resolved by what must have seemed a relatively simple and ingenious method. As it turned out, the difficult issues of euthanasia could be evaded by redefining death.

In an earlier time, death was defined as the cessation of breathing. Any movie buff recalls at least one scene in which a mirror is held to the mouth of a dying man. The lack of fogging indicated that indeed he was dead. The spirit of man resided in his *spiritus* (breath). With increased knowledge of human physiology and the potential for reviving a nonbreathing man, the circulation, the pulsating heart, became the focus of the definition of life. This is the tradition with which most of us have been raised.

There is of course a relationship between circulation and respiration, and the linkage, not irrelevantly, is the brain. All body parts require the nourishment, including oxygen, carried by the circulating blood. Lack of blood supply leads to the death of an organ; the higher functions of the brain are particularly vulnerable. But if there is no respiration, there is no adequate exchange of oxygen, and this essential ingredient of the blood is no longer available for distribution. If a part of the heart loses its vascular supply, we may lose that part and still survive. If a part of the brain is deprived of oxygen, we may, depending on its location, lose it and survive. But here we pay a special price, for the functions lost are those we identify with the self, the soul, or humanness, i.e., memory, knowledge, feeling, thinking, perceiving, sensing, knowing, learning, and loving.

Most people are prepared to say that when all of the brain is destroyed the "person" no longer exists; with all due respect for the complexities of the mind/brain debate, the "person" (and personhood) is generally associated with the functioning part of the head—the brain. The higher functions of the brain that have been described are placed, for the most part, in the cortex. The brain stem (in many ways more closely allied to the spinal cord) controls primarily visceral functions. When the total brain is damaged, death in all forms will ensue because the lower brain centers that control the circulation and respiration are destroyed. With the development of modern respirators, however, it is possible to artificially maintain respiration and with it, often, the circulation with which it is linked. It is this situation that has allowed for the redefinition of death—a redefinition that is being precipitously embraced by both scientific and theological groups.

The movement toward redefining death received considerable impetus with the publication of a report sponsored by the Ad Hoc Committee of the Harvard Medical School in 1968. The committee offered an alternative definition of death based on the functioning of the brain. Its criteria stated that if an individual is unreceptive and unresponsive, i.e., in a state of irreversible coma; if he has no movements or breathing when the mechanical respirator is turned off; if he demonstrates no reflexes; and if he has a flat electroencephalogram for at least twenty-four hours, indicating no electrical brain activity (assuming that he has not been subjected to hypothermia or central nervous system depressants), he may then be declared dead.

What was originally offered as an optional definition of death is, however, progressively becoming *the* definition of death. In most states there is no specific legislation defining death;* the ultimate responsibility here is assumed to reside in the general medical community. Recently, however, there has been a series of legal cases which seem to be establishing brain death as a judicial standard. In California in May of this year an ingenious lawyer, John Cruikshank, offered as a defense of his client, Andrew D. Lyons, who had shot a man in the head, the argument that the cause of death was not the bullet but the removal of his heart by a transplant surgeon, Dr. Norman Shumway. Cruikshank's argument notwithstanding, the jury found his client guilty of voluntary manslaughter. In the course of that trial, Dr. Shumway said: "The brain in the 1970s and in the light of modern day medical technology is the sine qua non—the criterion for death. I'm saying anyone whose brain is dead is dead. It is the one determinant that would be universally applicable, because the brain is the one organ that can't be transplanted."

This new definition, independent of the desire for transplant, now permits the physician to "pull the plug" without even committing an act of passive euthanasia. The patient will first be defined as dead; pulling the plug will merely be the harmless act of halting useless treatment on a cadaver. But while the new definition of death avoids one complex problem, euthanasia, it may create others equally difficult which have never been fully defined or visualized. For if it grants the right to pull the plug, it also implicitly grants the privilege *not* to pull the plug, and the potential and meaning of this has not at all been adequately examined.

*Kansas and Maryland have recently legislated approval for a brain definition of death.

These cadavers would have the legal status of the dead with none of the qualities one now associates with death. They would be warm, respiring, pulsating, evacuating, and excreting bodies requiring nursing, dietary, and general grooming attention—*and could probably be maintained so for a period of years.* If we chose to, we could, with the technology already at hand, legally avail ourselves of these new cadavers to serve science and mankind in dramatically useful ways. The autopsy, that most respectable of medical traditions, that last gift of the dying person to the living future, could be extended in principle beyond our current recognition. To save lives and relieve suffering—traditional motives for violating tradition—we could develop hospitals (an inappropriate word because it suggests the presence of living human beings), banks, or farms of cadavers which require feeding and maintenance, in order to be harvested. To the uninitiated the "new cadavers" in their rows of respirators would seem indistinguishable from comatose patients now residing in wards of chronic neurological hospitals.

PRECEDENTS

The idea of wholesale and systematic salvage of useful body parts may seem startling, but it is not without precedent. It is simply magnified by the technology of modern medicine. Within the confines of one individual, we have always felt free to transfer body parts to places where they are needed more urgently, felt free to reorder the priorities of the naturally endowed structure. We will borrow skin from the less visible parts of the body to salvage a face. If a muscle is paralyzed, we will often substitute a muscle that subserves a ess crucial function. This was common surgery at the time that paralytic polio was more prevalent.

It soon becomes apparent, however, that there is a limitation to this procedure. The person in want does not always have a second-best substitute. He may then be forced to borrow from a person with a surplus. The prototype, of course, is blood donation. Blood may be seen as a regeneratable organ, and we have a long-standing tradition of blood donation. What may be more important, and perhaps dangerous, we have established the precedent in blood of commercialization—not only are we free to borrow, we are forced to buy and, indeed, in our country at least, permitted to sell. Similarly, we allow the buying or selling of sperm for artificial insemination. It is most likely that in the near future we will allow the buying and selling of ripened ova so that a sterile woman may conceive her baby if she has a unctioning uterus. Of course, once *in vitro* ertilization becomes a reality (an imminent possibility), we may even permit the rental of womb space for gestation for a woman who does manufacture her own ova but has no uterus.

Getting closer to our current problem, here is the relatively long-standing tradiion of banking body parts (arteries, eyes, skin) for short periods of time for future ransplants. Controversy has arisen with ecent progress in the transplanting of major organs. Kidney transplants from a near relative or distant donor are becoming more common. As heart transplants become more successful, the issue will certainly be heightened, for while the heart may have been reduced by the new defintion of death to merely another organ, it will always have a core position in the popular thinking about life and death. It has the capacity to generate the passion that transforms medical decisions into political issues.

The ability to use organs from cadavers has been severely limited in the past by the reluctance of heirs to donate the body of an individual for distribution. One might well have willed one's body for scientific purposes, but such legacies had no legal standing. Until recently, the individual lost control over his body once he died. This has been changed by the Uniform Anatomical Gift Act. This model piece of legislation, adopted by all fifty states in an incredibly short period of time, grants anyone over eighteen (twenty-one in some states) the right to donate en masse all "necessary organs and tissues" simply by filling out and mailing a small card.

Beyond the postmortem, there has been a longer-range use of human bodies that is accepted procedure—the exploitation of cadavers as teaching material in medical schools. This is a long step removed from the rationale of the transplant—a dramatic gift of life from the dying to the near-dead; while it is true that medical education will inevitably save lives, the clear and immediate purpose of the donation is to facilitate training.

It is not unnatural for a person facing death to want his usefulness to extend beyond his mortality; the same biases and values that influence our life persist in our leaving of it. It has been reported that the Harvard Medical School has no difficulty in receiving as many donations of cadavers as they need, while Tufts and Boston Universities are usually in short supply. In Boston, evidently, the cachet of getting into Harvard extends even to the dissecting table.

The way is now clear for an ever-increasing pool of usable body parts, but the current practice minimizes efficiency and maximizes waste. Only a short period exists between the time of death of the patient and the time of death of his major parts.

USES OF THE NEOMORT

In the ensuing discussion, the word *cadaver* will retain its usual meaning, as opposed to the new cadaver, which will be referred to as a *neomort.* The "ward" or "hospital" in which it is maintained will be called a *bioemporium* (purists may prefer *bioemporion*).

Whatever is possible with the old embalmed cadaver is extended to an incredible degree with the neomort. What follows, therefore, is not a definitive list but merely the briefest of suggestions as to the spectrum of possibilities.

Training

Uneasy medical students could practice routine physical examinations—auscultation, percussion of the chest, examination of the retina, rectal and vaginal examinations, etcetera—indeed, everything except neurological examinations, since the neomort by definition has no functioning central nervous system.

Both the student and his patient could be spared the pain, fumbling, and embarrassment of the "first time."

Interns also could practice standard and more difficult diagnostic procedures, from spinal taps to pneumoencephalography and the making of arteriograms, and residents could practice almost all of their surgical skills—in other words, most of the procedures that are now normally taught with the indigent in wards of major city hospitals could be taught with neomorts. Further, students could practice more exotic procedures often not available in a typical residency—eye operations, skin grafts, plastic facial surgery, amputation of useless limbs, coronary surgery, etc.; they could also practice the actual removal of organs, whether they be kidneys, testicles, or what have you, for delivery to the transplant teams.

Testing

The neomort could be used for much of the testing of drugs and surgical procedures that we now normally perform on prisoners, mentally retarded children, and volunteers. The efficacy of a drug as well as its toxicity could be determined beyond limits we might not have dared approach when we were concerned about permanent damage to the testing vehicle, a living person. For example, operations for increased vascularization of the heart could be tested to determine whether they truly do reduce the incidence of future heart attack before we perform them on patients. Experimental procedures that proved useless or harmful could be avoided; those that succeed could be available years before they might otherwise have been. Similarly, we could avoid the massive delays that keep some drugs from the marketplace while the dying clamor for them.

Neomorts would give us access to other forms of testing that are inconceivable with the living human being. We might test diagnostic instruments such as sophisticated electrocardiography by selectively damaging various parts of the heart to see how or whether the instrument could detect the damage.

Experimentation

Every new medical procedure demands a leap of faith. It is often referred to as an "act of courage," which seems to me an inappropriate terminology now that organized medicine rarely uses itself as the experimental body. Whenever a surgeon attempts a procedure for the first time, he is at best generalizing from experimentation with lower animals. Now we can protect the patient from too large a leap by using the neomort as an experimental bridge.

Obvious forms of experimentation would be cures for illnesses which would first be induced in the neomort. We could test antidotes by injecting poison, induce cancer or virus infections to validate and compare developing therapies.

Because they have an active hematopoietic system, neomorts would be particularly valuable for studying diseases of the blood. Many of the examples that I draw from that field were offered to me by Dr. John F. Bertles, a hematologist at St. Luke's Hospital Center in New York. One which interests him is the utilization of marrow transplants. Few human-to-human marrow transplants have been successful, since the kind of immunosuppression techniques that require research could most safely be performed on neomorts. Even such research as the recent experimentation at Willowbrook—where mentally retarded children were infected with hepatitis virus (which was not yet culturable outside of the human body) in an attempt to find a cure for this pernicious disease—could be done without risking the health of the subjects.

Banking

While certain essential blood antigens are readily storable (e.g., red cells can now be preserved in a frozen state), others are not, and there is increasing need for potential means of storage. Research on storage of platelets to be used in transfusion requires human recipients, and the data are only slowly and tediously gathered at great expense. Use of neomorts would permit intensive testing of platelet survival and probably would lead to a rapid development of a better storage technique. The same would be true for white cells.

As has been suggested, there is great wastage in the present system of using kidney donors from cadavers. Major organs are difficult to store. A population of neomorts maintained with body parts computerized and catalogued for compatability would yield a much more efficient system. Just as we now have blood banks, we could have banks for all the major organs that may someday be transplantable—lungs, kidney, heart, ovaries. Beyond the obvious storage uses of the neomort, there are others not previously thought of because there was no adequate storage facility. Dr. Marc Lappe of the Hastings Center has suggested that a neomort whose own immunity system had first been severely repressed might be an ideal "culture" for growing and storing our lymphoid components. When we are threatened by malignancy or viral disease, we can go to the "bank" and withdraw our stored white cells to help defend us.

Harvesting

Obviously, a sizable population of neomorts will provide a steady supply of blood, since they can be drained periodically. When we consider the cost-benefit analysis of this system, we would have to evaluate it in the same way as the lumber industry evaluates sawdust—a product which in itself is not commercially feasible but which supplies a profitable dividend as a waste from a more useful harvest.

The blood would be a simultaneous source of platelets, leukocytes, and red cells. By attaching a neomort to an IBM cell separator, we could isolate cell types at relatively low cost. The neomort could also be tested for the presence of hepatitis in a way that would be impossible with commercial donors. Hepatitis as a transfusion scourge would be virtually eliminated.

Beyond the blood are rarer harvests. Neomorts offer a great potential source of bone marrow for transplant procedures, and I am assured that a bioemporium of modest size could be assembled to fit most transplantation antigen requirements. And skin would, of course, be harvested—similarly bone, corneas, cartilage, and so on.

Manufacturing

In addition to supplying components of the human body, some of which will be continually regenerated, the neomort can also serve as a manufacturing unit. Hormones are one obvious product, but there are others. By the injection of toxins, we have a source of antitoxin that does not have the complication of coming from another animal form. Antibodies for most of the major diseases can be manufactured merely by injecting the neomort with the viral or bacterial offenders.

Perhaps the most encouraging extension of the manufacturing process emerges from the new cancer research, in which immunology is coming to the fore. With certain blood cancers, great hope attaches to the use of antibodies. To take just one example, it is conceivable that leukemia could be generated in individual neomorts—not just to provide for *in vivo* (so to speak) testing of anti-leukemic modes of therapy but also to generate antibody immunity responses which could then be used in the living.

COST-BENEFIT ANALYSIS

If seen only as the harvesting of products, the entire feasibility of such research would depend on intelligent cost-benefit analysis. Although certain products would not warrant the expense of maintaining a community of neomorts, the enormous expense of other products, such as red cells with unusual antigens, would certainly warrant it. Then, of course, the equation is shifted. As soon as one economically sound reason is found for the maintenance of the community, all of the other ingredients become gratuitous by-products, a familiar problem in manufacturing. There is no current research to indicate the maintenance cost of a bioemporium or even the potential duration of an average neomort. Since we do not at this point encourage sustaining life in the brain-dead, we do not know the limits to which it could be extended. This is the kind of technology, however, in which we have previously been quite successful.

Meantime, a further refinement of death might be proposed. At present we use total brain function to define brain death. The source of electroencephalogram activity is not known and cannot be used to distinguish between the activity of higher and lower brain centers. If, however, we are prepared to separate the concept of "aliveness" from "personhood" in the adult, as we have in the fetus, a good argument can be made that death should be defined not as cessation of total brain function but merely as cessation of cortical function. New tests may soon determine when cortical function is dead. With this proposed extension, one could then maintain neomorts without even the complication and expense of respirators. The entire population of decorticates residing in chronic hospitals and now classified among the incurably ill could be redefined as dead.

But even if we maintain the more rigid limitations of total brain death it would seem that a reasonable population could be maintained if the purposes warranted it. It is difficult to assess how many new neomorts would be available each year to satisfy the demand. There are roughly 2 million deaths a year in the United States. The most likely sources of intact bodies with destroyed brains would be accidents (about 113,000 per year), suicides (around 24,000 per year), homicides (18,000), and cerebrovascular accidents (some 210,000 per year). Obviously, in each of these categories a great many of the individuals would be useless—their bodies either shattered or scattered beyond value or repair.

And yet, after all the benefits are outlined, with the lifesaving potential clear, the humanitarian purposes obvious, the technology ready, the motives pure, and the material costs justified—how are we to reconcile our emotions? Where in this debit-credit ledger of limbs and livers and kidneys and costs are we to weigh and enter the repugnance generated by the entire philanthropic endeavor?

Cost-benefit analysis is always least satisfactory when the costs must be measured in one realm and the benefits in another. The analysis is particularly skewed when the benefits are specific, material, apparent, and immediate, and the price to be paid is general, spiritual, abstract, and of the future. It is that which induces people to abandon freedom for security, pride for comfort, dignity for dollars.

William May, in a perceptive article,* defended the careful distinctions that have traditionally been drawn between the newly dead and the long dead. "While the body retains its recognizable form, even in death, it commands a certain respect. No longer a human presence, it still reminds us of that presence which once was utterly inseparable from it." But those distinctions become obscured when, years later, a neomort will retain the appearance of the newly dead, indeed, more the appearance of that which was formerly described as living.

Philosophers tend to be particularly sensitive to the abstract needs of civilized man; it is they who have often been the guardians of values whose abandonment produces pains that are real, if not always quantifiable. Hans Jonas, in his *Philosophical Essays*, anticipated some of the possibilities outlined here, and defended what he felt to be the sanctity of the human body and the unknowability of the borderline between life and death when he insisted that "Nothing less than the maximum definition of death will do—brain death plus heart death plus any other indication that may be pertinent—before final violence is allowed to be done." And even then Jonas was only contemplating *temporary* maintenance of life for the collection of organs.

The argument can be made on both sides. The unquestionable benefits to be gained are the promise of cures for leukemia and other diseases, the reduction of suffering, and the maintenance of life. The proponents of this view will be mobilized with a force that may seem irresistible.

They will interpret our revulsion at the thought of a bioemporium as a bias of our education and experience, just as earlier societies were probably revolted by the startling notion of abdominal surgery, which we now take for granted. The proponents will argue that the revulsion, not the technology, is inappropriate.

Still there will be those, like May, who will defend that revulsion as a quintessentially human factor whose removal would diminish us all, and extract a price we

*"Attitudes Toward the Newly Dead," *The Hastings Center Studies*, volume 1, number 1, 1973.

cannot anticipate in ways yet unknown and times not yet determined. May feels that there is "a tinge of the inhuman in the humanitarianism of those who believe that the perception of social need easily overrides all other considerations and reduces the acts of implementation to the everyday, routine, and casual."

This is the kind of weighing of values for which the computer offers little help. Is the revulsion to the new technology simply the fear and horror of the ignorant in the face of the new, or is it one of those components of humanness that barely sustain us at the limited level of civility and decency that now exists, and whose removal is one more step in erasing the distinction between man and the lesser creatures—beyond that, the distinction between man and matter?

Sustaining life is an urgent argument for any measure, but not if that measure destroys those very qualities that make life worth sustaining.

• • •

NO

William May

ATTITUDES TOWARD THE NEWLY DEAD

Maigret suddenly realized that there was one character in the drama about whom almost nothing was known, the dead man himself. From the outset, he had been to all of them merely a dismembered corpse. It was an odd fact that the Chief Superintendent had often noticed before, that people did not respond in the same way to parts of a body found scattered about as to a whole corpse. They did not feel pity in the same degree, or even revulsion. It was as though the dead person were somehow dehumanized, almost an object of ridicule.

Georges Simenon,
Maigret and the Headless Corpse

Just one aspect of the problem of organ transplants surfaces in this passage from Simenon's novel. To extract organs from a corpse is, in a sense, to dismember it. And, if Simenon is to be believed, dismemberment is an act of violence; it dehumanizes; it reduces the body to an object of ridicule.

While living, a person is identified with his body in such a way as to render the dignity of the two inseparable. A man not only *has* a body, he *is* his body; it is the medium of his self-revelation. His behavior betrays the bond between the two: pride expresses itself in his carriage; humiliation leaves his body striken with shame. Thus, when a man is subject to embarrassment, he wishes that the earth would swallow him up; he averts his face, turns on his heels, or blushes and perspires as though he wished to fabricate for himself a veil.

Apparently this association of self and body does not terminate abruptly with death. Admittedly the corpse is no longer a man. The cadaver is a kind of shroud that now masks rather than expresses the soul that once animated it. And yet—while the body retains its recognizable form, even in death, it commands a certain respect. No longer a human presence, it still reminds us of that presence which once was utterly inseparable from it.

Such is not the case, however, argues Simenon, when the body loses its integrity. The detached organ or member becomes, in a sense, a fit object for ridicule. It has lost its *raison d'etre* and therefore its centeredness. It has become an eccentricity, an embarrassment, an obscenity. It seems to have committed the indecency of refusing to vanish along with the self, while simultaneously failing effectively to remind us of what has vanished. The severance of death has been crazily compounded by a different order of severance that leaves the community charged with picking up leftovers rather than laying to rest remains.

Proposals, then, for the dismemberment of the body, even if that dismemberment is justified as serving important social purposes, such as organ transplants, awaken certain deep-going reservations that ought not to be ignored. If even in a very preliminary way, we ought to bring them into view and interpret them.

These reservations, of course, may vary considerably according to the specific proposal for salvaging organs; therefore we should keep in mind the several options in their variety:

1. A system of routine salvaging of organs from which exemption may be granted only at the special initiative of the pre-deceased or his family;
2. A program of organized giving of organs which is dependent upon the consent of the donor or his family;
3. Provision for the sale of organs by the pre-deceased or his family; and
4. Provision for the crediting of a family account against the day that some member (of the family) may require an organ.

Advocates of routine salvaging argue that it maximizes the number of organs made available for social purposes and spares citizens the awkwardness of wearing donor cards, or physicians the necessity of making ghoulish overtures to the bereaved at the time of death.[1] Proponents of organized giving argue that the system will provide some (maybe not so many) organs, while protecting the perceived rights of citizens and their families concerning burial and encouraging a pattern of *giving* that will have positive moral consequences for the society at large.[2] In matters so fundamental as the exchange of human organs, it is argued, "giving and receiving" is better than "taking and getting" and certainly to be preferred to "selling and buying." If any bartering is admitted into the process of transplanting organs, a system of family credits for donated organs is to be preferred to the debasing effects of their public sale.

Whether a system of automatic salvaging *alone* will provide a sufficient supply of organs to meet social needs, I would not attempt to resolve. The question of adequate supply cannot be answered until a program of organized giving has been given a fair trial. As advocates of the latter point out, such a trial has not been possible until the recent passage of the Uniform Anatomical Gifts Act in over forty-four states, which, for the first time, removes the legal obstacles in the way of organ donations.[3] More restrictedly, I would argue that human attitudes toward death (and the newly dead) are such that a system of organized giving must be granted a serious test before entertaining the alternative of routine salvaging. In the course of this argument, it will be necessary to examine certain primordial attitudes and basic symbols for death, some further specific convictions about the newly dead as reflected in the funeral practices of both traditional and Christian societies, and, finally, certain resources in belief and practice that give moral warrant for sustaining a program of organized giving.

ATTITUDES AND SYMBOLS

Drawing his evidence from both traditional societies and dreams, Edgar Herzog argues in *Death and Psyche*[4] that the most primitive response to a corpse is flight. This phenomenon is more than a matter of the aversion of an individual to a cadaver. Entire villages have been known to move to another location to avoid any further traffic with a corpse. If flight is a primary human response to death, then the development of funeral rites must be interpreted as a secondary response on the part of the community to force itself to be present to death. This presence, of course, does not wholly eliminate the original aversion. The community becomes present, after all, for the purpose of removal. It burns or buries the corpse. The community no longer journeys away from the dead, but it sends the dead on a journey, as it were, away from its presence. Thus, the element of aversion and horror persists even within the form of funeral practice.

The modern humanitarian, of course, will grow impatient with this kind of analysis. What does a rather primitive, almost subhuman emotion, like horror, have to do with the resolution of modern policy issues? Surely civilized men should not be distracted by such matters. A discussion of organ transplants should focus on the question of the most efficient way of supplying the needs of those dying for the want of vital organs. Let atavistic emotions give way to the central human issue.

Yet the fact of horror may be more germane to the subject of humane procedures for transplants than first appears. It is not advisable in the pursuit of worthy social goals to sidestep or repress the element of aversion with respect to means.

The Grimm Brothers included in their collection of folk tales the intriguing story of a young man who is incapable of horror. He does not shrink back from the dead—neither a hanged man he encounters nor a corpse with which he attempts to play. From one point of view, his behavior seems pleasantly childish, but, from another angle, inhuman. His father is ashamed of him, and so the young man is sent away "to learn how to shudder." Not until he has learned to shudder will he be brought out of his nameless, undifferentiated state and become human. Ingmar Bergman plays with (and complicates) the same theme in his movie *The Magician,* in which the hero—sometime artist, actor, charlatan, magician—contrives to make an apparently detached scientist acknowledge his human capacity for horror. When the magician succeeds in lifting the hair off the head of the scientist, the latter, with an irrecoverable loss of dignity, denies that he has had the experience. At a somewhat more comic level, the modern undertaker has trouble in securing respect for his person and work—because of his overfamiliar association with death. Our laughter and contempt testify to our deep-going sense of the connection between human dignity and a capacity for horror.

A policy that institutes the routine cutting up of corpses, even for high-minded social purposes, may fail precisely at this point; its refusal to acknowledge the fact of human horror. There is a tinge of the inhuman in the humanitarianism of those who believe that the perception of social need easily overrides all other considerations and reduces the acts of implementation to the everyday, routine, and casual. Even the proponents of routine salvaging have to concede indirectly the awkward fact of human revulsion. A system requiring consent, they argue, has two defects. It will fail to produce as many organs as categorical salvaging and it forces upon staff the necessity of making "ghoulish" overtures to the pre-deceased or his relatives. The question remains whether a system that overrides rather than faces up to profound reservations, is not, in the long run, more ghoulish in its consequences for the social order.

Human horror before death does not remain a formless, unspecified emotion. The object of horror is associated with certain images and symbols. Specifically, death is identified in language and imagery with the acts of hiding and devouring. An analysis of these two images is required for further appraisal of a system of routine salvaging. . . .

HIDER-GODDESS AND DEVOURER

Basic images for death have a way of associating with the institution which deals most with the dying. Traditionally, the hospital was a place of healing and recuperation for the sick and wounded. More recently the hospital, along with homes for the chronically ill and the aged, penal institutions, and mental hospitals, has acquired certain subliminal associations with the Hider-Goddess. Prisoners call themselves the forgotten men. The mentally disturbed and the chronically ill are hidden away from the society at large in preparation for their final disappearance. This process of hiding goes on for all the understandable reasons that pertain in a highly differentiated society and its specialization of functions and services. One would hate to do without these technical services, but they have exacted a high price by imposing upon inmates a kind of premature burial. The institutionalized have forced upon them a loss of name, identity, companionship, and acclaim—an extremity of deprivation of which the ordinary citizen has a foretaste in his complaints about the anonymous and impersonal conditions of modern life. The society at large, of which the hospital is destination and symbol, functions as a kind of Hider-goddess, depriving its citizens of significance.

The development of a system of routine salvaging of organs would tend to fix on the hospital a second association with death—as devourer. In the course of life, a breakdown in health is often accompanied by a sense that one has been exhausted and burned out by a world that has consumed all one's resources. The hospital traditionally offered a respite from a devouring world and the possibility of restoration. The healing mission of the hospital is obscured, however, if the hospital itself becomes the arch-symbol of a world that devours. Categorical salvaging of organs suggests that eventually and ultimately the process of consumption that dominates the outer world must now be consummated in the hospital. One's very vitals must be inventoried, extracted and distributed by the state on behalf of the social order. What is left over is utterly unusable husk.

While the procedure of routine salvaging may, in the short run, furnish more organs for transplants, in the long run, its systemic effect on the institutions of medical care would seem to be depressing and corrosive of that trust upon which the arts of healing depend.

FUNERALS, AND DONOR-CONSENT

A system of salvaging that requires the consent of the donor and/or his family, respects, for want of a better phrase, the "principle of extra-territoriality" in the relations of the person to the social order. This principle of extra-territoriality is already embedded in traditional legal rights concerning burial.

Society traditionally located "quasi-property rights" to the corpse in the family of the deceased. The rights were quasi—in the sense that the cadaver could not be put up for commercial use or sale. But rights they were in the sense that no other party could normally interpose claims upon the corpse that would interfere with the family's right and obligation to provide for a fitting disposition of the remains. In other words, whatever use and abuse, conflicts and tragedies, a person has been subjected to in the course of his public life, at the deepest level he cannot be reduced to them without remainder. He was a human presence that transcended the world into which he was apparently absorbed. . . .

From one perspective, the funeral service (which includes fitting disposition of the corpse) presupposes and reinforces a certain continuity between the person, his mortal remains, and the family unit. This continuity is particularly prominent while the newly dead body has its recognizable form; it attenuates when the body returns to particles. Thus funeral rites are an expression of the continuity of the soul with its body and with the gathered community of friends, colleagues, and family. From this perspective, the principle of extra-territoriality applies to the family group. The corpse, the deceased, and the family belong, as it were, to a continuum which should enjoy a certain sanctuary against the larger society and the state. Within this context, if one wants to proceed beyond traditional funeral rites to a justification for donating organs, then one will have to interpret the donation as a further and different expression of continuity between the generations. Something like Robert Jay Lifton's—or preceding him, Unamuno's, Soloviev's, or Bulgakov's—concept of symbolic or surrogate immortality is at work in this interpretation of the funeral service and the donation of organs.

From another perspective, the function of the funeral service is not so much to maintain continuity with the deceased as to provide public occasion for the acknowledgment that continuity has been broken by death. The acknowledgment of this separation is a particularly acute problem for those intimates whose lives have been so inextricably intertwined with the deceased. The family therefore has a special need for rites through which it acknowledges and participates in the process of surrender. "Dust thou art and unto dust thou shall return." There is nothing like the rigidity of death and the finality of cremation or burial to force the community to acknowledge that the process of separation has begun. Viewed from this second perspective, if one wants to proceed beyond traditional funeral practice and donate organs to the living, this action will be construed not as a way of achieving symbolic immortality but rather as a finite act in which one mortal human being assists another.

In any event, this second perspective also argues intensively against a system of routine salvaging of organs because the system places the burden of proof on the family if it seeks exemption from the state's right of emminent domain. What is wrong, indecorous, and enraging about placing the burden of proof on the family is that it forces the family to *claim the body as its possession,* only in order to proceed with rites in the course of which it must acknowledge the process of surrender and separation. . . .

"Quasi-property rights," directed to decent burial, were wisely vested in the family because the family, most of all, has used up and consumed the person in the course of his life, and the family, most of all, must acknowledge that he has moved beyond its effective control. By way of redaction, the rites tacitly acknowledge that the deceased is now, what he has always been, a human presence whose extra-territoriality must be honored.

In summary, the provision of organs for transplants should preferably be based on a system of consent. If the state is granted the categorical authority to dispose of the corpse, package it as it pleases, then it goes a long way toward establishing its total and unlimited claim over the person living or dead. Funeral rites, at the center of which are the "remains" attended to by the family and intimates, help establish the principle of a remainder above and beyond the claims of the family and the state. It establishes the principle of extra-territoriality. The person does not belong without limit to his society.

This needs to be acknowledged precisely by those who have most consumed the person in the course of the living—his family, colleagues, and friends—those who have most eaten him alive, who are most torn by guilt and remorse. . . .

NOTES

1 Jesse Dukeminier and David Sanders, "Organ Transplantation: A Proposal for Routine Salvaging of Cadaver Organs," *New England Journal of Medicine,* 279:413-419, 1968.

2 Alfred M. Sadler and Blair L. Sadler, "Transplantation and the Law: the Need for Organized Sensitivity," *The Georgetown Law Journal,* 57:5; Alfred M. Sadler *et al.,* "Transplantation—A Case for Consent," *The New England Journal of Medicine,* 280:862-867, 1969; Alfred M. Sadler, Blair L. Sadler, and E. Blythe Stason, "Transplantation and the Law: Progress Toward Uniformity," *New England Journal of Medicine,* 282:717-723, 1970; and Paul Ramsey, *The Patient as Person* (London and New Haven: Yale University Press, 1970), Ch. 5.

3 There are additional, non-legal obstacles to organ transplants (such as organ rejection, high costs, logistics, and limits on available medical manpower) that legislation for automatic salvaging alone would not solve. Alfred M. Sadler and Blair L. Sadler deal with these in "Providing Cadaver Organs for Transplantation: Three Legal Alternatives," an unpublished paper written for the Freedom and Coercion project of the Institute of Society, Ethics and the Life Sciences.

4 Edgar Herzog, *Psyche and Death, Archaic Myths and Modern Dreams in Analytical Psychology* (London: Hodder and Stroughton, 1966).

• • •

POSTSCRIPT

SHOULD ORGANS BE HARVESTED FROM THE DEAD?

Not all the possibilities outlined in Willard Gaylin's article have been implemented, but we are moving in that direction. Several studies have been reported in which bodies maintained on respirators were used as research subjects, including one in which a blood substitute was circulated through the body. The voluntary system of organ donation established in the 1970s is being re-examined. One alternative, favored by Arthur Caplan of The Hastings Center, would be a system of "presumed consent." That is, unless the person had legally specified that he or she did not wish to donate organs, or unless the family specifically objected, physicians could presume that the organs could be used. Such a system exists in France and several other countries. Another idea, proposed by Harry Schwartz, a medical writer, is to provide financial incentives for families to agree to organ donations. Critics of such proposals argue that they are coercive and disregard the rights and sensibilities of families.

Two classic articles from the allocation of scarce medical resources, such as organ transplants, are James F. Childress's "Who Shall Live When Not All Can Live?" *Soundings,* (Winter 1970); and Nicholas Rescher, "The Allocation of Exotic Medical Lifesaving Therapy," *Ethics* (April 1969). A good summary of the current status of organ shortages is John K. Iglehart, "Transplantation: The Problem of Limited Resources," *New England Journal of Medicine* (July 14, 1983). The problem of coercing a potential donor is discussed in "Mrs. X and the Bone Marrow Transplant," *Hastings Center Report* (June 1983). Also see Renee C. Fox and Judith P. Swazey, *The Courage to Fail: A Social View of Organ Transplants and Dialysis,* Second edition (Chicago, 1979).

ISSUE 17

IS GENETIC ENGINEERING A THREAT TO FUTURE GENERATIONS?

YES: Foundation on Economic Trends, from "The Theological Letter Concerning the Moral Arguments Against Genetic Engineering of the Human Germline Cells," June 8, 1983.

NO: President's Commission for the Study of Ethical Problems in Medicine and Biomedical and Behavioral Research, from *Splicing Life: The Social and Ethical Issues of Genetic Engineering with Human Beings* (Washington, D.C.: Government Printing Office, 1982)

ISSUE SUMMARY

YES: A group of theological leaders urges a ban on efforts to engineer specific genetic traits into the germline of the human species because no individual, group, or institution can legitimately claim the right or authority to make such decisions on behalf of the rest of the species—either today or in the future.

NO: The President's Commission concludes that genetic engineering is not intrinsically wrong for human use and sees no fundamental danger to world safety or human values in any current or planned forms of the technology.

In 1953, James Watson and Francis Crick made one of the major scientific discoveries of our time: The structure of deoxyribonucleic acid (DNA), the basic building block of all living things, is a double helix. In a masterpiece of understatement, they wrote in a letter to *Nature*: "It has not escaped our notice that the specific pairing we have postulated suggests a possible copying mechanism for the genetic material." What they recognized, and what has become a reality in the past decade, is that pieces of DNA can be broken and relinked in different combinations (the technique of recombinant DNA or "gene splicing"). A new life form can be created by inserting the DNA of one species into the DNA of another. The new molecule then forms a genetic replica of itself and continues to reproduce. This process occurs in nature but now scientists can direct it to achieve particular goals.

Much of the potential application of genetic engineering lies in industry and agriculture—the creation of bacteria that will consume oil spills at sea, for example, or bacteria that will fix nitrogen and thereby increase crop harvests. The possibilities in the medical field are enormous as well: Products that are now scarce and expensive—such as hormones, enzymes, and vaccines—can be produced in large quantities. Cancer diagnosis and treatment can be improved by the use of targeted monoclonal antibodies, which will attack only the malignant cells. In the future genetic defects might be detected earlier, and some genetic disorders, such as Tay-Sachs disease, a fatal disorder, might be treated by replacing or altering the defective gene.

When recombinant DNA techniques first became possible, in the early 1970s, most concern centered around their safety. Scientists themselves called a moratorium on DNA experiments until they felt sure that the creation of new life forms (mainly bacteria) would not pose any hazards either to themselves or to the public should a laboratory product escape into the environment. The general public became alarmed and a debate about how to regulate the technology raged for several years. Now, however, concern about safety has largely (although not entirely) disappeared; working with DNA appears to be no more hazardous than with any other material. Today the issue is: In what direction will this impressive technology move, and who will control it? Will it be used for good or evil?

The social and ethical issues of genetic engineering were not on the original agenda of the President's Commission for the Study of Ethical Problems in Medicine and Biomedical and Behavioral Research when Congress established it in 1978. However, the general secretaries of three Jewish, Catholic, and Protestant church associations urged the commission, in a July 1980 letter, to explore the questions raised by the creation of new life forms. "Control of such life forms by any individual or group poses a potential threat to all of humanity," they warned. "Those who would play God will be tempted as never before." These fears are expressed even more dramatically in the "theological letter" reproduced in this section. It sees "humanity at a crossroads," technologically able to engineer and produce human beings as we do machines. If diabetes, sickle cell anemia, and cancer can be cured by altering the genetic makeup of an individual, the theologians ask, what is to stop society from deciding that a certain skin color or a certain kind of thought process is a "disorder" to be altered genetically?

Against this apocalyptic view of genetic engineering, the President's Commission concluded that no such sweeping plans to alter human nature have been proposed (or could be implemented at present) and that the benefits to medical therapy and diagnosis outweigh the risks. However, mindful of the deeply felt objections of many people, it stressed that great powers entail great responsibility.

YES

Foundation on Economic Trends

THE THEOLOGICAL LETTER CONCERNING THE MORAL ARGUMENTS AGAINST GENETIC ENGINEERING OF THE HUMAN GERMLINE CELLS

While the nation has begun to turn its attention to the dangers of nuclear war, little or no debate has taken place over the emergence of an entirely new technology which in time could very well pose as serious a threat to the existence of the human species as the bomb itself. We are referring to human genetic engineering. On July 22, 1982 the *New York Times* published a major editorial entitled "Whether to Make Perfect Humans." It will soon be possible, says the *Times*, to fundamentally alter the human species by engineering the genetic traits of the sex cells—the sperm and egg. Humanity's new found ability to engineer genetic traits could well lead to the creation of a new species, as different from homo-sapiens as we are to the higher apes. So grave is the threat of human genetic engineering that the *Times* suggests that we consider "the question of whether the human germline should be declared inviolable."

Programming genetic traits into human sex cells subjects the human species to the art of technological manipulation and architectural design.

With the arrival of human genetic engineering, humanity approaches a crossroads in its own technological history. It will soon be possible to engineer and produce human beings by the same technological design principles as we now employ in our industrial processes.

The wholesale design of human life, in accordance with technological prerequisites, design specifications, and quality controls, raises a fundamental question. Nobel laureate biologist Dr. Salvador Lauria puts the question in its most succinct context when he asks "When does a repaired or manufactured man stop being a man... and become a robot, an object, an industrial product?"

From "The Theological Letter Concerning the Moral Arguments Against Genetic Engineering of the Human Germline Cells," circulated by Jeremy Rifkin of the Council on Economic Trends, June 8, 1983.

The debate over genetic engineering is similar to the debate over nuclear power. For years the nuclear proponents argued that the potential benefits of nuclear power outweighed the potential harm. Today an increasingly skeptical public has begun to seriously question this basic presumption.

In a similar vein, proponents of human genetic engineering argue that the benefits outweigh the risks and that it would be irresponsible not to use this powerful new technology to eliminate serious "genetic disorders." The *New York Times* editorial board correctly addressed this conventional scientific argument by concluding in its editorial that once the scientists are able to repair genetic defects "it will become much harder to argue against adding genes that confer desired qualities, like better health, looks or brains." According to the *Times*, "There is no discernible line to be drawn between making inheritable repairs of genetic defects, and improving the species."

Once we decide to begin the process of human genetic engineering, there is really no logical place to stop. If diabetes, sickle cell anemia, and cancer are to be cured by altering the genetic make-up of an individual, why not proceed to other "disorders:" myopia, color blindness, left-handedness. Indeed, what is to preclude a society from deciding that a certain skin color is a disorder?

As knowledge about the genes increases, the bio-engineers will inevitably gain new insights into the functioning of more complex characteristics, such as those associated with behavior and thoughts. Many scientists are already contending that schizophrenia and other "abnormal" psychological states result from genetic disorders or defects. Others now argue that "antisocial" behavior, such as criminality and social protest, are also examples of malfunctioning genetic information. One prominent neurophysiologist has gone so far as to say "there can be no twisted thought without a twisted molecule." Many sociobiologists contend that virtually all human activity is in some way determined by our genetic make-up and that if we wish to change this situation, we must change our genes.

Whenever we begin to discuss the idea of genetic defects there is no way to limit the discussion to one or two or even a dozen so-called disorders because of a hidden assumption that lies behind the very notion of "defective." Ethicist Daniel Callahan penetrates to the core of the problem when he observes that "behind the human horror at genetic defectiveness lurks . . . an image of the perfect human being. The very language of 'defect,' 'abnormality,' 'disease,' and 'risk,' presupposes such an image, a kind of proto-type of perfection."

The question, then, is whether or not humanity should "begin" the process of engineering future generations of human beings by technological design in the laboratory.

What is the price we pay for embarking on a course whose final goal is the "perfection" of the human species?

First there is the ecological price to consider. It is very likely that in attempting to "perfect" the human species we will succeed in engineering our own extinction. Eliminating so-called "bad genes" will lead to a dangerous narrowing of diversity in the gene pool. Since part of the strength of our gene pool consists in its very diversity, including defective genes, tampering with it might ultimately lead to extinction of the human race. It should be recalled that in the 1950's genetic modifications were made in wheat strains to create bumper crops of "super wheat." When a new strain of disease hit the fields, farmers found that their wheat was too delicate to resist. Within two years, virtually the entire crop was destroyed.

We have no doubt that a similar effort to "perfect" the human species by eliminating the so-called bad genes would prove equally destructive. This simple biological fact is so patently obvious that one begins to wonder why it is so conveniently ignored by so many of the "experts" in the scientific community. Even Dr. Thomas Wagner, the scientist at Ohio University who is responsible for the first successful transfer of a gene trait from one mammalian species to the embryo of another mammalian species, has gone on record as being opposed to genetic engineering of the human germline cells because of the potentially devastating effect that such narrowing of genetic diversity might have on the ability of the human species to survive in the future. Dr. Wagner says,

> It is a terrible mistake to make a permanent, heritable change, even if it appears to be for the better, in a human being's genetic make-up. We don't know what the future brings, and we don't understand fully the process of evolution. Any species of animal needs a certain degree of diversity, some of which appears negative, in order for it to survive into the future. I don't think we should be manipulating the genetic material beyond the individual generation of the human involved.

Then there is the question of eugenics to carefully consider. Eugenics is the inseparable ethical wing of the Age of Biotechnology. First coined by Charles Darwin's cousin, Sir Francis Galton, eugenics is generally categorized into two types, negative and positive. Negative eugenics involves the systematic elimination of so-called biologically undesirable characteristics. Positive eugenics is concerned with the use of genetic manipulation to "improve" the characteristics of an organism or species.

Eugenics is not a new phenomenon. At the turn of the century the U.S. sported a massive eugenics movement. Politicians, celebrities, academicians and prominent business leaders joined together in support of a eugenic's program for the country. The frenzy over eugenics reached a fever pitch with many states passing sterilization statutes and the U.S. Congress passing a new emigration law in the 1920's based on eugenics considerations. As a consequence of the new legislation, thousands of American citizens were sterilized so they could not pass on their "inferior" traits and the federal government locked its doors to certain emigrant groups deemed biologically unfit by then existing eugenics standards.

While the Americans flirted with eugenics for the first thirty years of the twentieth century, their escapades were of minor historical account when compared with the eugenics program orchestrated by the Nazis in the 1930's and 40's. Millions of Jews and other religious and ethnic groups were gassed in the German crematoriums to advance the Third Reich's dream of eliminating all but the "Aryan" race from the globe. The Nazis also embarked on a "positive" eugenics program in which thousands of S.S. officers and German women were carefully selected for their "superior" genes and mated under the auspices of the state. Impregnated women were cared for in state facilities and their offspring were donated to the Third Reich as the vanguard for the new super race that would rule the world for the next millenium.

Eugenics lay dormant for nearly a quarter of a century after World War II. Then the spectacular breakthroughs in molecular biology in the 1960's raised the spectre of a eugenics revival once again. By the mid 1970's, many scientists were beginning to worry out loud that the potential for genetic engineering might lead to a return to the kind of eugenics hysteria that swept over America and Europe earlier in the century. Speaking at a National Academy of Science forum on recombinant DNA, Ethan Signer, a biologist at MIT, warned his colleagues that

> this research is going to bring us one more step closer to genetic engineering of people. That's where they figure out how to have us produce children with ideal characteristics... Last time around, the ideal children had blonde hair, blue eyes and Aryan genes.

The concern over a re-emergence of eugenics is well-founded but misplaced. While professional ethicists watch out the front door for telltale signs of a resurrection of the Nazi nightmare, eugenics doctrine has quietly slipped in the back door. The new eugenics is commercial not social. In place of the shrill eugenic cries for racial purity, the new commercial eugenics talks in pragmatic terms of medical benefits and improvement in the quality of life. The old eugenics was steeped in political ideology and motivated by fear and hate. The new eugenics is grounded in medical advance and the spectre of extending the human life span.

Genetic engineering, then, is coming to us not as a threat, but as a promise; not as a punishment but as a gift. And here is where the danger lies. If the Brave New World comes, it will not be forced on us by an evil cabal of self-serving scientists and Machiavellian politicians. On the contrary, what makes opposition to the Brave New World so difficult is the seductive path that leads to it. Every new advance in human genetic engineering is likely to be heralded as a great stride forward, a boon for humankind. Every one of the breakthroughs in genetic engineering will be of benefit to someone, under some circumstance, somewhere in society. And step by step, advance by advance, we human beings might well choose to trade away the spontaneity of natural life for the predictability of technological design until the human species as we know it is transformed into a product of our own creation; a product that bears only a faint resemblance to the original.

How important is it that we eliminate all the imperfections, all the defects? What price are we willing to pay to extend our lives, to insure our own health, to do away with all of the inconveniences, the irritations, the nuisances, the infirmities, the suffering, that are so much a part of the human experience? Are we so enamored with the idea of physical perpetuation at all costs that we are even willing to subject the human species to rigid architectural design? Is guaranteeing our health worth trading away our humanity?

What is the price we pay for medical advance, for securing our own physical well being? If it means accepting the idea of reducing the human species to a technologically designed product, then it is too dear a price.

Ultimately, there is no security to be found in engineering the human species, just as we have now learned that there is no security to be found in building bigger, more sophisticated nuclear bombs.

Perhaps, if we had taken the time to look at the long-range implications of our work in nuclear physics forty years ago, we might well have decided to restrict or prohibit the research and development of nuclear weaponry. Today we have the opportunity to look ahead and envision the final logical consequences of our work in genetic engineering. The question is whether we will choose to do so.

It is our hope that this resolution will represent a watershed in our thinking concerning science and technology. For the first time, it affirms the right of humanity to say no to the application of its own scientific knowledge. Just because something can be done is no longer an adequate justification for assuming it should be done or that it can't be stopped from being done.

We believe we have a sacred obligation to say no when the pursuit of a specific technological path threatens the very existence of life itself.

It is with this thought in mind that we now turn to you for support of this resolution.

Human genetic engineering presents the human race with the most important political question it has ever had to contend with. Who do we entrust with the ultimate authority to decide which are the good genes that should be engineered into the human gene pool and which are the bad genes that should be eliminated?

Today the ultimate exercise of political power is within our grasp; the ability to control the future lives of human beings by engineering their characteristics in advance; making them a hostage of their own architecturally designed blueprints. Genetic engineering represents the power of authorship. Never before in history has such complete power over life been a possibility. The idea of imprisoning the life span of a human being by simply engineering its genetic blueprint at conception is truly awesome.

Aldous Huxley's spectre of a biologically designed caste system with its alphas, betas, gammas and deltas looms on the horizon. Our society must now ponder whether to give sanction to this fundamental departure in how human life is formed. In examining this issue, we would ask everyone to consider one simple question. Would we trust the Congress of the U.S. with the ultimate authority to decide which genes should be engineered into the human gene pool and which should be eliminated? Would we entrust the executive or judicial branch with such authority? Or the corporations and the marketplace? Or the scientists and the medical community?

Who do we designate to play God? The fact is, no individual, group, or set of institutions can legitimately claim the right or authority to make such decisions on behalf of the rest of the species alive today or for future generations.

Genetic engineering of the human germline cells represents a fundamental threat to the preservation of the human species as we know it, and should be opposed with the same courage and conviction as we now oppose the threat of nuclear extinction.

We would like your support for this proposed resolution to prohibit the engineering of genetic traits into the germline of the human species.

RESOLUTION

To express the conviction that engineering specific genetic traits into the human germline not be attempted.

Whereas molecular biologists have recently succeeded in altering the sex cells of a mammalian species through genetic engineering technology;

Whereas the new advances in genetic engineering technology now raise the possibility of altering the human species;

Whereas the ability to design and program specific physiological characteristics by engineering specific genetic traits into the sperm, egg, or embryo of a human being represents a fundamental alteration in the way a human being may be formed;

Whereas programming genetic traits directly into human sex cells subjects the human species to the art of technological manipulation and architectural design;

Whereas the redesign of the human species by genetic engineering technology irreversibly alters the composition of the gene pool for all future generations of human life;

Whereas engineering fundamental changes of human sex cells necessitates that decisions be made as to which genetic traits should be programmed into the human gene pool and which should be eliminated; and

Whereas no individual, group of individuals, or institutions can legitimately claim the right or authority to make such decisions on behalf of the rest of the species alive today or for future generations: Now, therefore, be it

Resolved, That efforts to engineer specific genetic traits into the germline of the human species should not be attempted.

• • •

NO

President's Commission for the Study of Ethical Problems in Research

SPLICING LIFE

CONCERNS ABOUT "PLAYING GOD"

. . . Hardly a popular article has been written about the social and ethical implications of genetic engineering that does not suggest a link between "God-like powers" and the ability to manipulate the basic material of life. Indeed, a popular book about gene splicing is entitled *Who Should Play God?* , and in their June 1980 letter to the President, three religious leaders sounded a tocsin against the lack of a governmental policy concerning "[t]hose who would play God" through genetic engineering.

Religious Viewpoints

The Commission asked the General Secretaries of the three religious organizations* to elaborate on any uniquely theological considerations underlying their concern about gene splicing in humans. . . .

In the view of the theologians, contemporary developments in molecular biology raise issues of responsibility rather than being matters to be prohibited because they usurp powers that human beings should not possess. The Biblical religions teach that human beings are, in some sense, co-creators with the Supreme Creator. Thus, as interpreted for the Commission by their representatives, these major religious faiths respect and encourage the enhancement of knowledge about nature as well as responsible use of that knowledge. Endorsement of genetic engineering, which is praised for its potential to improve the human estate, is linked with the recognition that the misuse of human freedom creates evil and that human knowledge and power can result in harm.

While religious leaders present theological bases for their concerns, essentially the same concerns have been raised—sometimes in slightly different words—by many thoughtful secular observers of contemporary science and technology. Concerns over unintended effects, over the morality of genetic manipulation in all its forms, and over the social and political consequences of new technologies are shared by religious and secular commentators. The examination of the various specific concerns need not be limited, therefore, to the religious format in which some of the issues have been raised.

From *Splicing Life*, President's Commission for the Study of Ethical Problems in Medicine and Biomedical and Behavioral Research, 1983.

Fully Understanding the Machinery of Life

Although it does not have a specific religious meaning, the objection to scientists "playing God" is assumed to be self-explanatory. On closer examination, however, it appears to the Commission that it conveys several rather different ideas, some describing the power of gene splicing itself and some relating merely to its consequences.

At its heart, the term represents a reaction to the realization that human beings are on the threshold of understanding how the fundamental machinery of life works. A full understanding of what are now great mysteries, and the powers inherent in that understanding, would be so awesome as to justify the description "God-like." In this view, playing God is not actually an objection to the research but an expression of a sense of awe—and concern.

Since the Enlightenment, Western societies have exalted the search for greater knowledge, while recognizing its awesome implications. Some scientific discoveries reverberate with particular force because they not only open new avenues of research but also challenge people's entire understanding of the world and their place in it. Current discoveries in gene splicing—like the new knowledge associated with Copernicus and Darwin—further dethrone human beings as the unique center of the universe. By identifying DNA and learning how to manipulate it, science seems to have reduced people to a set of malleable molecules that can be interchanged with those of species that people regard as inferior. Yet unlike the earlier revolutionary discoveries, those in molecular biology are not merely descriptions; they give scientists vast powers for action.

Arrogant Interference with Nature

By what standards are people to guide the exercise of this awesome new freedom if they want to act responsibly? In this context, the charge that human beings are playing God can mean that in "creating new life forms" scientists are abusing their learning by interfering with nature.

But in one sense *all* human activity that produces changes that otherwise would not have occurred interferes with nature. Medical activities as routine as the prescription of eyeglasses for myopia or as dramatic as the repair or replacement of a damaged heart are in this sense "unnatural." In another sense, human activity cannot interfere with nature—in the sense of contravening it—since all human activities, including some gene splicing, proceed according to the scientific laws that describe natural processes. Ironically, to believe that "playing God" in this sense is even possible would itself be hubris according to some religious thought, which maintains that only God can interfere with the descriptive laws of nature (that is, perform miracles).

If, instead, what is meant is that gene splicing technology interferes with nature in the sense that it violates God's prescriptive natural law or goes against God's purposes as they are manifested in the natural order, then some reason must be given for this judgment. None of the scholars appointed to report their views by the three religious bodies that urged the Commission to undertake this study suggested that either natural reason or revelation imply that gene splicing technology as such is "unnatural" in this prescriptive sense. Although each scholar expressed concern over particular applications of gene splicing technology, they all also emphasized that human beings have not merely the right but the duty to employ their God-given powers to harness nature for human benefit. To turn away from gene splicing, which may provide a means of curing hereditary diseases, would itself raise serious ethical problems.

Creating New Life Forms

If "creating new life forms" is simply producing organisms with novel characteristics, then human beings create new life forms frequently and have done so since they first learned to cultivate new characteristics in plants and breed new traits in animals. Presumably the idea is that gene splicing creates new life forms, rather than merely modifying old ones, because it "breaches species barriers" by combining DNA from different species—groups of organisms that cannot mate to produce fertile offspring.

Genetic engineering is not the first exercise of humanity's ability to create new life forms through nonsexual reproduction. The creation of hybrid plants seems no more or no less natural than the development of a new strain of *E. coli* bacteria through gene splicing. Further, genetic engineering cannot accurately be called unique in that it involves the creation of new life forms through processes that do not occur in nature without human intervention. . . . [S]cientists have found that the transfer of DNA between organisms of different species occurs in nature without human intervention. Yet, as one eminent scientist in the field has pointed out, it would be unwarranted to assume that a dramatic increase in the frequency of such transfers through human intervention is not problematic simply because DNA transfer sometimes occurs naturally.

In the absence of specific religious prohibitions, either revealed or derived by rational argument from religous premises, it is difficult to see why "breaching species barriers" as such is irreligious or otherwise objectionable. In fact, the very notion that there are barriers that must be breached prejudges the issue. The question is simply whether there is something intrinsically wrong with intentionally crossing species lines. Once the question is posed in this way the answer must be negative—unless one is willing to condemn the production of tangelos by hybridizing tangerines and grapefruits or the production of mules by the mating of asses with horses.

There may nonetheless be two distinct sources of concern about crossing species lines that deserve serious consideration. First, gene splicing affords the possibility of creating hybrids that can reproduce themselves (unlike mules, which are sterile). So the possibility of self-perpetuating "mistakes" adds a new dimension of concern, although here again, the point is not that crossing species lines is inherently wrong, but that it may have undesirable consequences and that these consequences may multiply beyond human control. As noted, the Commission's focus on the human applications of gene splicing has meant that it does not here address this important set of concerns, which lay behind the original self-imposed moratorium on certain categories of gene splicing research and which have been, and continue to be, addressed through various scientific and public mechanisms, such as RAC [Recombinant Advisory Committee].

Second, there is the issue of whether particular crossings of species—especially the mixing of human and nonhuman genes—might not be illicit. The moral revulsion at the creation of human-animal hybrids may be traced in part to the prohibition against sexual relations between human beings and lower animals. Sexual relations with lower animals are thought to degrade human beings and insult their God-given dignity as the highest of God's creatures. But unease at the prospect of human-animal hybrids goes beyond sexual prohibitions.

The possibility of creating such hybrids calls into question basic assumptions about the relationship of human beings to other living things. For example, those who believe that the current treatment of animals—in experimentation, food production, and sport—is morally suspect would not be alone in being troubled by the prospect of exploitive or insensitive treatment of creatures that possess even more human-like qualities than chimpanzees or porpoises do. Could genetic engineering be used to develop a group of virtual slaves—partly human, partly lower animal—to do people's bidding? Paradoxically, the very characteristics that would make such creatures more valuable than any existing animals (that is, their heightened cognitive powers and sensibilities) would also make the moral propriety of their subservient role more problematic. Dispassionate appraisal of the long history of gratuitous destruction and suffering that humanity has visited upon the other inhabitants of the earth indicates that such concerns should not be dismissed as fanciful.

Accordingly, the objection to the creation of new life forms by crossing species lines (whether through gene splicing or otherwise) reflects the concern that human beings lack the God-like knowledge and wisdom required for the exercise of these God-like powers. Specifically, people worry that interspecific hybrids that are partially human in their genetic makeup will be like Dr. Frankenstein's monster. A striking lesson of the Frankenstein story is the uncontrollability and uncertainty of the consequences of human interferences with the natural order. Like the tale of the Sorcerer's apprentice or the myth of the golem created from lifeless dust by the 16th century rabbi, Loew of Prague, the story of Dr. Frankenstein's monster serves as a reminder of the difficulty of restoring order if a creation intended to be helpful proves harmful instead. Indeed, each of these tales conveys a painful irony: in seeking to extend their control over the world, people may lessen it. The artifices they create to do their bidding may rebound destructively against them—the slave may become the master.

Suggesting that someone lacks sufficient knowledge or wisdom to engage in an activity the person knows how to perform thus means that the individual has insufficient knowledge of the consequences of that activity or insufficient wisdom to cope with those consequences. But if this is the rational kernel of the admonition against playing God, then the use of gene splicing technology is not claimed to be wrong as such but wrong because of its potential consequences. Understood in this way, the slogan that crossing species barriers is playing God does not end the debate, but it does make a point of fundamental importance. It emphasizes that any realistic assessment of the potential consequences of the new technology must be founded upon a sober recognition of human fallibility and ignorance. At bottom, the warning not to play God is closely related to the Socratic injunction "know thyself"; in this case, acknowledge the limits of understanding and prediction, rather than assuming that people can foresee all the consequences of their actions or plan adequately for every eventuality.

Any further examination of the notion that the hybridization of species, at least when one of the species is human, is intrinsically wrong (and not merely wrong as a consequence of what is done with the hybrids) involves elaboration of two points. First, what characteristics are uniquely human, setting humanity apart from all other species? And second, does the wrong lie in bestowing some but not all of these characteristics on the new creation or does it stem from depriving the being that might otherwise have arisen from the human genetic material of the opportunity to have a totally human makeup? The Commission believes that these are important issues deserving of serious study.

It should be kept in mind, however, that the information available to the Commission suggests that the ability to create interspecific hybrids of the sort that would present intrinsic moral and religious concerns will not be available in the foreseeable future. The research currently being done on experimentation with recombinant DNA techniques through the use of single human genes (for example, the insertion of a particular human hemoglobin gene into mouse cells at the embryonic stage) or the study of cellular development through the combining of human genetic material with that of other species in a way that does not result in a mature organism (for example, *in vitro* fusion of human and mouse cells) does not, in the Commission's view, raise problems of an improper "breaching of the barriers." . . .

Evolutionary Impact on Human Beings

Some critics warn against the dangers of attempting to control or interfere with the "wisdom of evolution" in order to satisfy scientific curiosity. Those who hold this view object in particular to crossing species lines by gene splicing because they believe that the pervasive inability of different species to produce fertile offspring by sexual reproduction must be an adaptive feature, that is, it must confer some significant survival advantage. Thus they view species lines as natural protective barriers that human beings may circumvent only at their peril, although the harm such barriers are supposed to shield people from remains unspecified.

Most proponents of genetic engineering argue that the benefits it will bring are more tangible and important and will affect more people than those objecting suggest. Further, the notion of the "wisdom of evolution" that apparently underlies this consequentialist version of the objection to crossing species lines is not well founded. As the scientific theory of evolution does not postulate a plan that the process of evolution is to achieve, evolutionary changes cannot be said to promote such a plan, wisely or unwisely. Moreover, evolutionary theory recognizes (and natural history confirms) that a "wise" adaptation at one time or place can become a lethal flaw when circumstances change. So even if it could be shown that species barriers have thus far played an important adaptive role, it would not follow that this will continue. An evolutionary explanation of any inherited characteristic can at most show that having that characteristic gave an organism's ancestors some advantage in enabling them to live long enough to reproduce and that the characteristic has not yet prove maladaptive for the offspring.

Furthermore, as a philosopher concerned with assessing the risks of genetic engineering has recently noted, the ability to manipulate genes, both within and across species lines, may become a crucial asset for survival.

> There may . . . come a time when, because of natural or man-induced climatic change, the capacity to alter quickly the genetic composition of agricultural plants will be required to forestall catastrophic famine.

The consequentialist version of the warning against crossing species lines seems, then, to be no more a conclusive argument against genetic engineering than the admonition that to cross species lines is wrong because it is playing God. But it does serve the vital purpose of urging that, so far as this is possible, the evolutionary effects of any interventions are taken into account. . . .

Changing the Meaning of Being Human

Some geneticists have seen in their field the possibility of benefit through improving human traits. Human beings have the chance to "rise above (their) nature" for "the first time in all time," as one leader in the field has observed:

> It has long been apparent that you and I do not enter this world as unformed clay compliant to any mold. Rather, we have in our beginnings some bent of mind, some shade of character. The origin of this structure—of the fiber in this clay—was for centuries mysterious.... Today... we know to look within. We seek not in the stars but in our genes for the herald of our fate.

Will gene splicing actually make possible such changes in "human nature" for the first time? In some ways this question is unanswerable since there is great disagreement about which particular characteristics make up "human nature." For some people, the concept encompasses those characteristics that are uniquely human. Yet most human genes are actually found in other mammals as well; moreover, recent work by ethologists and other biologists on animal behavior and capacities is demonstrating that many characteristics once regarded as unique to human beings are actually shared by other animals, particularly by the higher primates, although an ability to record and study the past and to plan beyond the immediate future appears to be a singularly human trait.

Other people regard the critical qualities as those natural characteristics that are common to all human beings, or at least all who fall within a certain "normal range." "Natural" here means characteristics that people are born with as opposed to those that result from social convention, education, or acculturation.

To consider whether gene splicing would allow the changing of human nature thus breaks down into two questions. Which characteristics found in all human beings are inborn or have a large inborn basis? And will gene splicing techniques be able to alter or replace some of the genetic bases of those characteristics? As to the first, the history of religious, philosophical, and scientific thought abounds with fundamental disputes over human nature. Without a consensus on that issue the second question could only be answered affirmatively if it were clear that gene splicing will eventually allow the alteration of all natural characteristics of human beings.

As it is by no means certain that it will ever be possible to change the genetic basis of all natural characteristics, it seems premature to assume that gene splicing will enable changes in human nature. At most, it can perhaps be said that this technology may eventually allow some aspects of what it means to be human to be changed. Yet even that possibility rightly evokes profound concern and burdens everyone with an awesome and inescapable responsibility—either to develop and employ this capability for the good of humanity or to reject it in order to avoid potential undesirable consequences.

The possibility of changing human nature must, however, be kept in perspective. First, within the limits imposed by human beings' genetic endowment, there is already considerable scope by means other than gene splicing for changing some acquired characteristics that are distinctively human. For example, people's desires, values, and the way they live can be changed significantly through alterations in social and economic institutions and through mass education, indoctrination, and various forms of behavior control. Thus, even if gene splicing had the power that some people are concerned about, it would not be unique in its ability to produce major changes in what it means to be human—although it would be unusual in acting on the inheritable foundation of thoughts and actions. If the technology can ever be used in this way, the heritability of the changes ought probably to be regarded as significantly different from any changes now possible.

Second, according to the theory of evolution, the genetic basis of what is distinctively human continually changes through the interplay of random mutation and natural selection. The concern, then, is that gene splicing will for the first time allow deliberate, selective, and rapid alterations to be made in the human genetic constitution.

Finally, concern about changing human nature may at bottom be still more narrowly focused upon those characteristics of human beings—whether unique to the species or not—that are especially valued or cherished. Here, too, there may be disagreement as to which characteristics are most valuable and the value of a given characteristic may depend upon the social or natural environment in which it is manifested.

In sum, the question of whether gene splicing will enable changes in human nature—and the ethical, social, and philosophical significance of such changes—cannot be determined until much more is known about human genetics, specifically the exact contribution of heredity to many human physical and, more important, behavioral traits. Indeed, one of the most important contributions genetic engineering could make to the science of behavioral genetics may be that it will help resolve the age-old controversy of nature versus nurture. If designed changes were possible, society would have to confront whether such changes should be made, and, if they should, which ones. The problems created by uncertainty are particularly notable here since any decision about what characteristics are "desirable" would depend on the world that people will be living in, which is itself unknowable in advance. . . .

CONTINUING CONCERNS

A distinction has been drawn in this Report between two views: (1) that gene splicing technology is intrinsically wrong or contrary to important values and (2) that, while the technology is not inherently wrong, certain of its applications or consequences are undesirable. Regarding the latter, it has also been noted that genetic engineering involves an array of uncertainties beyond those usually found in technological developments. Not only is the occurrence of specific desirable or undesirable consequences impossible to predict but the application of gene splicing could have far-reaching consequences that could alter basic individual and social values.

The Commission could find no ground for concluding that any current or planned forms of genetic engineering, whether using human or nonhuman material, are intrinsically wrong or irreligious per se. The Commission does not see in the rapid development of gene splicing the "fundamental danger" to world safety or to human values that concerned the leaders of the three religious organizations. Rather, the issue that deserves careful thought is: by what standards, and toward what objectives, should the great new powers of genetic engineering be guided? . . .

• • •

POSTSCRIPT

IS GENETIC ENGINEERING A THREAT TO FUTURE GENERATIONS?

Shortly after the "theological letter" was announced, some of the original signers withdrew their support. They felt that the overall tone of the letter did not convey their willingness to approve scientific genetic engineering techniques designed to treat persons suffering from genetic disease.

When the President's Commission ended its work in the spring of 1983, it urged that an appropriate overseeing body be established to continue to monitor developments in genetic engineering. Such a body, the commission recommended, should be broadly based and not dominated by geneticists and other scientists. Several possible successors to the President's Commission are being considered.

Meanwhile, the technology is proceeding rapidly. Genetic defects have been corrected in fruit flies, and artificially-inserted genes have functioned in succeeding generations of mammals. Investigators have also succeeded in isolating and studying the gene underlying the Lesch-Nyhan syndrome in humans, a severe disorder resulting in retardation and compulsive self-mutilation. The way has been opened to correct the deficiency in the cells.

A comprehensive history of recombinant DNA techniques and the political and social debates about safety is Sheldon Krimsky, *Genetic Alchemy* (MIT Press, 1982). Jeremy Rifkin's book *Algeny* (Viking, 1983) expands on the ideas expressed in the "theological letter." An earlier and influential book with the same point of view is Ted Howard and Jeremy Rifkin, *Who Should Play God?* (Dell, 1977). A positive view of the prospects of genetic engineering is Zsolt Harsanyi, with Richard Hutton, *Genetic Prophecy: Beyond the Double Helix* (Rawson, Wade, 1981).

CONTRIBUTORS TO THIS VOLUME

EDITOR

CAROL LEVINE is the editor of the *Hastings Center Report* and the managing editor of *IRB: A Review of Human Subjects Research*, periodicals published by the Hastings Center in Hastings-on-Hudson, New York.

Ms. Levine received her BA in history from Cornell and an MA in public law and government from Columbia University. She is the co-author of *Comparative Government and Politics, 2nd Edition* (Harper and Row, 1981) and is a frequent contributor of articles on genetic engineering and related subjects.

AUTHORS

MARY ROSE BARRINGTON is a solicitor of the Supreme Court of Judicature of England and an administrator of alms houses for the aged.

TOM L. BEAUCHAMP teaches in the Philosophy Department and in the Kennedy Institute of Ethics at Georgetown University.

SISSELA BOK is a philosopher and author of several books, including *Secrets: On the Ethics of Concealment and Revelation* (Pantheon, 1982).

RICHARD J. BONNIE is professor of law and director of the Institute of Law, Psychiatry and Public Policy at the University of Virginia.

A.G.M. CAMPBELL is a professor of child health at the University of Aberdeen, Scotland.

JAMES F. CHILDRESS is a professor of religious studies and medical education at the University of Virginia.

PAUL CHODOFF is an M.D. and clinical professor of psychiatry at George Washington University.

WILLIAM P. CLARK was an associate justice of the California Supreme Court. He now serves as the assistant to President Reagan for national security affairs.

CARL COHEN is a professor in the Department of Philosophy, Residential College, University of Michigan.

STEPHEN COHEN teaches at the Georgetown University Law Center.

The late JOSEPH COLLINS was an eminent neurologist who wrote a number of books.

RAYMOND S. DUFF is at the Department of Pediatrics, Yale University School of Medicine.

STAN N. FINKELSTEIN is a physician interested in medical innovations and is on the faculty of MIT.

WILLARD GAYLIN is a psychiatrist who is president of the Hastings Center and the author of *The Killing of Bonnie Garland* (Simon and Schuster 1982).

CLIFFORD GROBSTEIN is professor of biological science and public policy at the University of California, San Diego.

BEVERLY WILDUNG HARRISON is a professor of Christian ethics at Union Theological Seminary in New York.

HERBERT HENDIN is a psychiatrist and author.

C. EVERETT KOOP is the Surgeon General of the United States. Formerly he was professor of pediatrics and pediatric surgery, University of Pennsylvania School of Medicine.

HERBERT T. KRIMMEL is professor of law, Southwestern University, School of Law, Los Angeles, California.

WILLIAM MAY is Joseph P. Kennedy Sr. Professor of Christian Ethics at the Kennedy Institute of Ethics at Georgetown University.

STANLEY MILGRAM is professor of psychology at the Graduate School and University Center of the City University of New York. He is the author of *Obedience to Authority: An Experimental View* (Harper and Row, 1975).

THOMAS H. MURRAY is an associate in behavioral studies at the Hastings Center.

ROBERT NEVILLE is professor of philosophy and religion at the State University of New York at Stony Brook.

JOHN T. NOONAN is professor of law at the University of California, Berkeley Law School and author of several books, including three works on contraception and abortion.

ROGER PEELE is an M.D. and chairman of the Department of Psychiatry, Overholser Division of Training, St. Elizabeth's Hospital, Washington, DC.

ROSALIND POLLACK PETCHESKY is assistant professor of political and social theory at Ramapo College.

JAMES RACHELS is a philosopher who is also the Dean of the School of Humanities at the University of Alabama, Birmingham.

JOHN A. ROBERTSON is Mars McLean Professor of Law at the University of Texas, Austin.

HARVEY M. SAPOLSKY is a political scientist on the faculty of MIT.

PETER SINGER teaches in the Department of Philosophy at Monash University in Australia. He is also the director of the Monash Centre for Human Bio-Ethics.

THOMAS S. SZASZ is a psychiatrist, writer and educator affiliated with the Upstate Medical Center, State University of New York, Syracuse. He is the author of many controversial books and articles on psychiatry.

HANS O TIEFEL teaches in the Department of Religion at the University of Virginia.

The late RICHARD M. TITMUSS was a professor of public administration at the London School of Economics.

MATHEW O. TOBRINER is an associate justice of the Supreme Court of California.

The late MAURICE B. VISSCHER was a physiologist who taught at the University of Minnesota school of medicine.

INDEX